PÉ

D1271739

MUNICIPAL MANAGEMENT SERIES

Community
Health Services

THE MUNICIPAL MANAGEMENT SERIES

Harold Herman
Mary Elisabeth McKay

Public Health Service
U.S. Department of Health,
Education, and Welfare

Community Health Services

Prepared in consultation with the
Committee on Public Health Administration
American Public Health Association
PAUL Q. PETERSON, M.D., M.P.H., Chairman
and a special advisory committee:
HOLLIS S. INGRAHAM, M.D., M.P.H., Chairman
DAVID S. ARNOLD, M.Sc.
HAROLD HERMAN, Ph.D.
THOMAS R. HOOD, M.D., M.P.H.
JAMES D. WHARTON, M.D., M.P.H.

Published for the
Institute for Training in
Municipal Administration
by the
International City
Managers' Association

MUNICIPAL MANAGEMENT SERIES

The Technique of Municipal Administration

Principles and Practice of Urban Planning

Municipal Finance Administration

Municipal Personnel Administration

Municipal Police Administration

Municipal Fire Administration

Municipal Public Works Administration

Municipal Recreation Administration

Supervisory Methods in Municipal Administration

Management Practices for Smaller Cities

Community Health Services

Local Public Library Administration

Case Problems in City Management

Effective Supervisory Practices

Municipal Public Relations

Foreword

COMMUNITY HEALTH SERVICES is intended for local government administrators to provide information on comprehensive health services, governmental and nongovernmental organization for health services, community responsibilities in environmental health and other areas, current and emerging health service programs, and measurement, evaluation, planning, staffing, and other aspects of health service management. The theme of the book is better understanding of total health services within the total community environment.

This is the second edition of a book that has been widely used by health officers and other local government administrators in all parts of the United States as a continuing resource for training and reference. Known as ADMINISTRATION OF COMMUNITY HEALTH SERVICES in the first edition, the change in title to COMMUNITY HEALTH SERVICES is deliberate. The change was made in recognition of the need for recasting the book to cover the total range of health services in the newer community setting of increasing relationships between public and private action.

This book has been published by the International City Managers' Association as part of its Municipal Management Series. Like others in the series, this book has drawn on the first-hand experience of administrators, consultants, and teachers.

The fifteen titles in the Municipal Management Series have been prepared especially for the Institute for Training in Municipal Administration. The Institute offers in-service training courses designed specifically for local government officials whose jobs are to plan, direct, and coordinate the work of others. The Institute has been sponsored since 1934 by the International City Managers' Association and is an accredited member of the National Home Study Council.

A special advisory committee was organized to help in the planning and development of COMMUNITY HEALTH SERVICES. This committee included Hollis R. Ingraham, M.D., M.P.H., Commissioner, New York State Department of Health, Chairman; David S. Arnold, M.Sc., Assistant Director, Publications, International City Managers' Association; Harold Herman, Ph.D., then Chief, Metropolitan Health Section, Division of Community Health Services, and now Chief, Health Planning Branch, Office of Comprehensive Health Planning, Public Health Service, U.S. Department of Health, Education, and Welfare; Thomas R. Hood, M.D., M.P.H., Deputy Executive Director, American Public Health Association; and James D. Wharton, M.D., M.P.H., then Chief, Public Health Administration Branch, Division of Community Health Services, Public Health Service, and now Commissioner of Health, City of Cincinnati.

Dr. Herman and Mary Elisabeth McKay, Public Health Analyst, then in the Division of Community Health Services, and now in the Health Planning Branch, Office of Comprehensive Health Planning, Public Health Service, wrote this book and worked closely with the special advisory committee at all stages in development, review, and final preparation of the manuscript. They also received technical counsel from many members of the staff of the Public Health Service and other constituents of the Department of Health, Education, and Welfare.

Special thanks are due to four persons who provided comprehensive review of the manuscript at various stages of preparation. The first 15 chapters were reviewed in early draft form by Thomas W. Fletcher, then City Manager of San Diego, California, and now Deputy Commissioner, District of Columbia; Charles T. Henry, City Manager, University City, Missouri; and D. G. Weiford, then City Manager of Eau Claire, Wisconsin, and now Secretary, Wisconsin Department of Local Affairs and Development. The entire book was reviewed in draft by Jerome W. Lubin, Chief, California Health Information for Planning Service, California State Department of Public Health.

Our special thanks go to the Public Health Service for making it possible for Harold Herman and Mary Elisabeth McKay to write this book. Dr. Herman has an extensive background in political science, public administration, and public health and was on the faculty of the Fels Institute of Local and State Government, University of Pennsylvania, before joining the Public Health Service. Miss McKay has held positions in several programs of the Public Health Service and with both public and voluntary health agencies outside the federal government.

A special acknowledgment is due to Eugene A. Confrey, Chief, Division of Research Grants, National Institutes of Health, Public Health Service, who served as editor for the first edition which was published in 1961. This volume, as with others in the Municipal Management Series, has been prepared under the general supervision of David S. Arnold, Assistant Director, Publications, ICMA.

MARK E. KEANE
Executive Director

International City
Managers' Association

Washington
July, 1968

Preface

IN THE SEVEN YEARS since the first edition in this book was published, perspectives on community health services have changed in ways that have special significance for local governments. In 1961, the local government executive's responsibilities with regard to health were seen as related almost exclusively to governmental health activities—services provided primarily by local health departments and local public hospitals. Even these responsibilities were defined most often as dealing with fiscal aspects, and leadership in health matters was expected to come from the health professions rather than from local government executives. Relationships with the private sector were primarily in terms of routine licensing and other regulatory functions.

Today, increasingly, community health services are becoming a central issue in community life. They are no longer regarded as the business of health professionals alone. The community itself, its citizens, and its government, are involved more and more in decision-making about health services.

The source of these changes is a new public attitude about health. Growing appreciation of the potential of the health sciences to improve the quality of life brings with it growing demand for services to realize that potential. Indeed, health services are seen by most as a right, similar to the right to education. Furthermore, the citizens, the consumers of health services, are making it quite clear that they want and expect to have a voice in what health services will be provided in their communities, and how

their collective dollars for health, both public and private, will be spent. They do not expect to make the professional decisions—to diagnose their own ailments or prescribe their own remedies—but they quite rightly intend to make their wishes known about the manner in which health services will be delivered to them.

Response to public demand on the part of government at every level has taken the form of increased involvement in the financing and organization of health services. During the past five years, more than 30 major federal health bills have been enacted into law by the Congress, and health legislation by state and local governments has been increased at the same time.

Measures which affect the financing of medical care—for example Medicare and Medicaid—do not thereby increase governments' activities in the direct provision of health services. As a matter of fact, they may lessen government's role as a provider of health care, and reduce, if not eliminate, the separation of public and private health services. At the same time, they require sharpened governmental interest in the effective organization of health care services by all providers, private and public.

The comprehensive health planning legislation enacted in 1966 and 1967 is addressed to the matter of organization and coordination of health service. Planning conducted by states and areas under the grants this legislation provides will be truly comprehensive, concerned with physical, mental, and environmental health and with all health facilities, services, and manpower under both public and private auspices.

In this program that has come to be known as the Partnership for Health, government is an important partner. Planning at the state level, which will be broad policy planning, will be conducted by agencies of state government with close and continuing participation of the private partners. At the areawide level, comprehensive health planning under these grants may be conducted by local governments or councils of governments, and when it is not, the law requires that there be appropriate representation of the interests of local government. We trust that this will mean that local government will be one of the active partners in all areawide comprehensive health planning, where deliberations and recommendations will deal with specific health activities, institutions, and resources in the area, for the purpose of encouraging their greatest effectiveness.

The International City Managers' Association deserves high praise for its continuing work of informing its members and others of the major issues, problems, and developing potentials facing communities and the nation. The Public Health Service is gratified to have had the opportunity to participate with ICMA and the American Public Health Association in preparation of this volume. We see the book as a description of community health services at a given time—a time when change is coming about rapidly. It is fair to predict that an edition produced after another seven years will differ as greatly from this one as this does from the first edition. We predict that it will reflect the salutary effect upon community health services of their emergence into the arena of total community decision-making.

WILLIAM H. STEWART
Surgeon General

Public Health Service
U.S. Department of Health,
Education, and Welfare

Table of Contents

Figures

Tables

Community Health Services

Part One

The Scope of
Community Health Services

1

The Goal of Comprehensive
Health Services

Health, or the state of physical and mental well-being, is almost universally valued by man. Concern for health and for prevention and treatment of illness has been a part of all cultures through human history.

Concepts of Health and Health Services

In American society today, general concern about health is evident in the amount of television time and newspaper and magazine space devoted to health subjects. Personal health appears to be esteemed not necessarily for itself, as it was by the ancient Greeks, but for the freedom it provides from illness or disability that would interfere with "living a normal life"; and a normal life in our society involves not only work but social and recreational activity as well. America is made up of many different cultural groups having different attitudes and values, and individuals within those groups differ from one another in their feelings about various aspects of life, including health. Those whose attitudes are dominant in our society take pride in playing active roles in the social scheme and in being able to "pull their weight." They also prize their independence, viewing health, or the absence of illness, as one of the necessary qualifications for the desired role.

The idea, once quite common, that illness is a punishment for sin is infrequent in this country now, and our culture does not credit the no- tion that health is influenced by forces of evil or magic. Disease and illness are considered misfortunes, visited upon their victims impersonally, through no fault of their own.[1] Although persons in the health professions recognize that individuals can often substantially influence their own health and feel that this point should have more attention, they do not look upon illness as punishment, even when it results from unhealthy behavior.

Even when they think of ill health as a piece of hard luck, most Americans are not fatalistic about it. They believe in the ability of science to cure illness and alleviate its symptoms, as well as to prevent it. As a matter of fact, Hsu points out that Americans' typical faith in science makes some of them prey to quacks dealing in pseudoscience.[2] On the other hand, the conviction that science can influence health leads to individual and community action on its behalf.

The enormous growth of knowledge in the health and medical sciences in the past 50 years has coincided with the emergence in this country of an informed and vocal public, concerned with all circumstances affecting the well-being of the community or its members. As facts be-

[1] See Talcott Parsons, "Social Change and Medical Organization in the United States: A Sociological Perspective," ANNALS OF THE AMERICAN ACADEMY OF POLITICAL AND SOCIAL SCIENCE, March, 1963.

[2] Francis L. K. Hsu, "A Cholera Epidemic in a Chinese Town," in Benjamin D. Paul (ed.), HEALTH, CULTURE, AND COMMUNITY (New York: Russell Sage Foundation, 1955), pp. 147–48.

came generally known about the germ theory of disease and the potentials for prevention of communicable disease, people demanded that communities act to apply the new knowledge for the common benefit. The evolution of public health and preventive medicine, and indeed of all the social institutions that contribute to providing the community's health services, has resulted from the insistence of the informed public.

The accomplishments of health and medicine in controlling communicable diseases in this country have been remarkable. Tuberculosis, which killed one person in every 500 in the population in 1900, now kills only five in 100,000 each year. Of course, the fact that most of the 50,000 new cases of TB reported annually occur in the lower socioeconomic groups suggests that better living standards are additional factors contributing to the reduction of diseases. But some dramatic changes can, in all fairness, be almost solely attributed to the effect of health and medical services—changes such as the reduction in diphtheria death rates from 40 per 100,000 population in 1900 to almost none in 1964, and in typhoid fever death rates from 31 to almost none. Malaria is becoming rare in this country; and smallpox, cholera, and yellow-fever do not occur indigenously. The outstanding recent example, of course, is the reduction in cases of paralytic polio from over 18,000 in 1954 to 61 in 1965.

The hazards of childbirth and early infancy have also been dramatically reduced. Since 1915, maternal death rates have gone down from 61 to 3.2 per 10,000 live births in 1965. In 1915, one child in every 10 failed to survive until his first birthday; today all but about one in 40 live through the first year. Here, too, social and economic conditions, as well as science, have had an effect. In economically deprived neighborhoods today, maternal and infant mortality rates, which are considered indexes of public health status, are several times higher than in higher income areas. The reasons probably are that high quality health services are not always available to these people or they do not always use them when they are, and that their substandard living conditions influence this aspect of their total health status.

Realization that health services can influence man's well-being has created an expectation that such services will be available. Some health services have thus come to be regarded as a right, in the same manner as public education. Many services that an earlier generation worked hard to establish are now generally taken for granted, such as pure tap water, protection from communicable diseases, and the immediate availability of medical and hospital services. When these expectations are not fulfilled, the public reacts with indignation.

In recent decades, the focus of enlightened public concern about health has changed. Since communicable diseases causing high mortality rates in young people have declined and the survival chances of mothers and infants have increased, new health problems have emerged that had been overshadowed in the past. Chronic diseases assumed major importance as a cause of death and disability, accidents came to be recognized as a serious problem, attention was drawn to the thousands of hospital beds occupied by people suffering mental illness. As awareness of these problems grew, public demand brought about multiplication of national research efforts to find ways to prevent and treat, for instance, cardiovascular diseases, cancer, diabetes, mental illness, accidents, and many other causes of human misery. As a result of this research, much new information has been uncovered that provides the technical means to reduce significantly the human and economic losses due to such diseases.

Public pressure for application of new knowledge has brought about the initiation in many communities of a number of programs aimed at preventing or mitigating the consequences of ills once considered irremediable. The procedures involved in such programs are usually more complex than those against communicable diseases, and often require long-term medical care. However, the general opinion among middle-class people whose influence is felt in the community is that if means are known to prevent or cure a disease, they should be available to those who need them.

Today most cities have a wide range of resources for the promotion of health and treatment of illness, but a new problem has arisen as resources have increased. The potential for fulfilling the promise of current knowledge is diminished by the number and complexity of such health resources.

For instance, the great extension of medical knowledge has necessitated professional specialization to such a degree that if a young family needs care for mother after the birth of a baby, health supervision for the baby, corrective treatment for a five-year-old's speech defect, orthodontia for an older child, and tests to find out the cause of what father calls his allergy, the family may have to seek these services in five different places. Even if the family can afford to pay for or has health insurance covering all or part of the services, some services may be neglected because of the sheer difficulty of getting them and the pressure of other family concerns. And if the parents and children do manage to receive the various kinds of specific services necessary, they still may fail to have continuing health service for each family member.

Even the well-informed person usually recognizes the importance of health services only for special conditions, such as pregnancy, or for special age groups, such as infants or the elderly.

The person who does not concern himself in his daily life with maintaining good health will not even get treated for his symptomatic ailments. An elderly person, for example, who discovers through a screening program that he has heart disease will probably get treated for this condition. However, his other, less crucial ailments such as arthritis or ill-fitting dentures, while lessening his capacity for normal living, will not be treated. Although his health insurance may cover such care, he is discouraged by the prospect of separate admissions procedures and long waits for service. Sometimes, of course, the services are not available. Dr. George

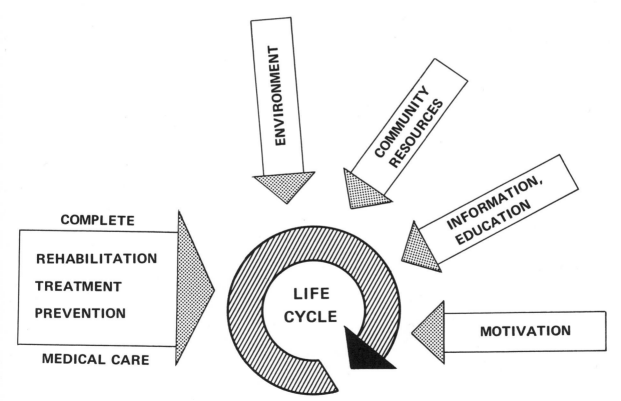

FIGURE 1. *An almost complete circle signifies the life cycle of an individual with prevention, treatment, and other aspects of health services impinging on the life cycle*

James, formerly Commissioner of Health of New York City, once said that in lower Manhattan there were three places where the medically indigent could have open heart surgery and not one where they could have their teeth fixed.[3] However, services that do exist are far from fully used, both because their usefulness is not fully understood or accepted and because they are not convenient.

A related problem is the splitting of service for one disease or condition, with one agency carrying on screening functions, another providing certain diagnostic procedures, and a third offering rehabilitation service. At every successive referral, a certain number of people drop out, and sometimes the division of labor omits an essential component, so that no one service is truly effective. In most communities some services are duplicated and others are lacking, as Dr. James' example illustrated. Health programs or procedures are often maintained after they are no longer needed, sometimes at the expense of programs to meet new needs.

There has been a growing awareness of the aforementioned problems on the part of members of health professions, as well as the public.[4] As a result, the concept of comprehensive health services meeting all the requirements of health for individuals and the community, readily available and used by those who need them, is becoming the goal of community health action. The means of achieving the goal are to a great extent in administration, rather than in medicine or science. The major tasks are to coordinate all community health resources, under whatever auspices, so that they operate as a unified system providing uninterrupted health services for the community and its members and to develop in the public, knowledge and attitudes that will lead them to use the services. These purposes lie behind the present move toward comprehensive health planning discussed in Chapter 18.

Necessary Health Services

In the language and literature of the health professions, discussion of many varieties of health needs is a recurring theme. Needs of particular groups of people, such as mothers and children, the chronically ill, or the tuberculous, have received much attention. Recently, however, there has been a growing trend toward the idea that a person's health needs are continuous and inclusive. Thus, each person is assumed to need such skills and services as can be brought to bear at any time in behalf of his physical and mental well-being. This interpretation implies what has been called a continuum[5] of service for each individual. It includes complete medical care in and out of hospital; before, during, and after birth; and throughout life. Complete medical care in this context means not only treatment for illness and injury but all the protective procedures that can prevent disease or reduce disability. It includes therapeutic, educational, and prosthetic rehabilitative measures that can make possible the fullest use of the individual's capacities. It goes beyond what has been normally included in medical care, taking in such things as dentistry and dentures, hearing aids, and eyeglasses. Individual health needs in these broad terms include a healthful environment, free of unnecessary hazards to physical well-being, and conducive to mental and emotional health. The formula also includes the information necessary for each person to know what steps he can take to insure his own and his family's health and to motivate him to take indicated action.

Individuals would not necessarily define their health needs in this way. A great many people undoubtedly think of meeting each health crisis as it arises, having drugs when they are sick and using a hospital only if they are very sick, or have had an accident, or have a

[3] George James, "Public Health Program Planning for the Future," Delta Omega Lecture, School of Public Health, University of Michigan, Ann Arbor, March 24, 1964. Mimeographed.

[4] *Ibid.*; also Howard Ennes, "Toward a Constructive Appraisal of Community Health Services," AMERICAN JOURNAL OF PUBLIC HEALTH, November, 1957, Part 2, pp. 3–6; and Luther L. Terry, "The Complex World of Modern Public Health," AMERICAN JOURNAL OF PUBLIC HEALTH, February, 1964, pp. 189–95.

[5] U.S. Department of Health, Education, and Welfare, GOALS FOR COMMUNITY SERVICES (Washington: Government Printing Office, 1963), p. 13.

baby. Therefore, the community concept of comprehensive health service includes help for individuals to perceive their health needs accurately.

In the United States, where the health of the public is considered a positive value to society and the ability of science to protect health and cure disease is generally acknowledged by leaders, health needs of communities are interpreted in terms of the community's role in furthering the application of scientific knowledge for the benefit of the community as a whole and for each of its members. Inasmuch as American culture also places a high value on personal independence and financial responsibility, the community's responsibility is usually limited to matters with which the individual cannot cope.

Historically, the first health concern of communities was the change in the physical environment that results when large numbers of people live in a relatively small area. For example, systems to provide clean water and dispose of waste have long been accepted as community health needs in American cities. The broader present-day concept of community health needs and responsibilities has grown out of both social change and vast extension of health knowledge and skill.[6] Although American cities vary considerably in their ideas about how health needs of the community should be met, there is general recognition that the individual citizen, left to his own devices, derives only limited benefit from the wonders of medical science and that communities must organize themselves to help him do so. The public, as well as the individuals who make it up, has a growing interest in health and in the manner in which health services are provided.[7]

The Health Action System

Health services are provided in American communities by various combinations of commercial enterprises, private practitioners, voluntary nonprofit organizations, and governmental agencies.

Some hospitals and a large proportion of nursing homes are run for profit, and the usual sources of drugs and other medical supplies are commercial. A number of private insurance companies write policies covering some costs of medical and hospital care, and some industries carry on a variety of employee health activities. Medical and dental practice is carried on chiefly as private enterprise, in which fees are charged according to services rendered, sometimes adjusted according to the patient's ability to pay. Otherwise, health services are provided through various patterns of community organization, either voluntary or governmental.

The majority of general hospitals are operated without profit by voluntary organizations, but many communities have such hospitals operated by government agencies as well. Other voluntary organizations provide various direct personal services, some general, such as home nursing, and others for specific diseases or conditions. Voluntary health agencies also support and conduct research, carry on health education programs, and work toward community organization for health purposes. Hospital and health insurance is available under voluntary auspices in most areas.

The health functions of government agencies vary with the agency and the locality. Environmental sanitation is almost always a government responsibility. Other responsibilities are the control of communicable disease; maternal and child health services; health education; recording of vital statistics; medical and/or hospital care for various special groups such as the indigent, the mentally ill, or people with tuberculosis; and certain rehabilitation services. In a growing number of communities, government agencies also carry on control or research activities aimed at the problems of chronic disease, accidents, or mental health. Licensing of members of health professions, hospitals, nursing homes, and various other health facilities and setting standards of care in these facilities are also accepted governmental functions. Legal procedures connected with health, such as the regulation of drugs, are also government responsibilities.

---

[6] See Part II.

[7] Edward A. Suchman, SOCIOLOGY AND THE FIELD OF PUBLIC HEALTH (New York: Russell Sage Foundation, 1955), pp. 44–45.

In addition to local governments, both state and federal governments participate in community health services. A state may support in part or totally some of the aforementioned functions; or a state agency may actually carry them out. The federal government makes grants in support of certain health services and provides consultation and other forms of assistance. It contributes significantly to financing medical care for the indigent and administers, under Social Security, the health insurance program for the elderly initiated in 1965.

Classification of health services by type of sponsorship is difficult, because the division of function and responsibility is not clear-cut. "Private medical care," for instance, is usually assumed to include hospitalization, but most hospitals are under some type of community sponsorship. For this reason, definitions of commonly used terms referring to health services are somewhat indistinct and vary considerably according to different points of view.

Public health may be viewed as a set of activities or a set of conditions. It is frequently equated with the activities of health departments and other governmental agencies, but Freeman and Holmes address both activities and conditions when they say that:

Public health may be considered as the state of well being of the community. This embraces not only the additive health of the individuals who constitute the community, but the condition of those structures, facilities and patterns of action that the community uses to conserve its collective health.[8]

As a set of activities the key concept in public health is organized community action—the "patterns of action" in the Freeman and Holmes definition. The American Medical Association more specifically describes public health activity as:

The art and science of maintaining, protecting, and improving the health of the people through organized community efforts. It includes those arrangements whereby the community provides medical services for special groups of persons and is concerned with prevention and control of disease, with persons requiring hospitalization to protect the community and with the medically indigent.

Thus public health is seen as encompassing all the agencies, both voluntary and official, concerned with health.

Confusion sometimes arises between the meanings of public health and *preventive medicine*. Public health does involve the practice of preventive medicine, and many physicians in public health practice are diplomates of the American Board of Preventive Medicine. However, the scope of public health is much larger than that of preventive medicine and includes the work of professions, such as engineering, that are far removed from medical practice. On the other hand, although the main concern of most private physicians' practice is treatment, many perform preventive procedures too, and in so doing act to protect the public health. As this is becoming increasingly the case, the term *comprehensive medical care* has come to be used, meaning both therapeutic and preventive care.[9] The concept of comprehensive medical care also focuses on the patient's general health, rather than on immediate illness.

Personal health services are those that individuals receive directly as opposed to those affecting them through the environment or other indirect means, such as sanitation measures. The private practice of medicine or dentistry is a personal health service, as is hospital care. Many community agencies, including health departments, provide a variety of personal health services. Those provided by physicians are called *clinical* whether they are given in a clinic, the private physician's office, or a hospital, the determining factor being actual contact with the patient.

The techniques of disseminating information about health, encouraging its acceptance, and fostering relationships with groups of the population that will promote positive attitudes about health services are grouped by professional health people under the heading of *health education*. Insights from the social sciences have added greatly in recent years to

---

[8] Ruth B. Freeman and Edward M. Holmes, ADMINISTRATION OF PUBLIC HEALTH SERVICES (Philadelphia: W. B. Saunders Company, 1960), p. 6.

[9] John J. Hanlon, PRINCIPLES OF PUBLIC HEALTH PRACTICE (St. Louis: The C. V. Mosby Company, 4th ed., 1964), p. 25.

skills in this area, and almost all health workers consider education an important responsibility in their own work. It is the primary activity of health educators, who are on the staff of many health agencies, both public and voluntary.

Incorporation of all health resources into a system of services for the total health of the community and its citizens is the objective of comprehensive health services. Such an association, if well planned and efficiently operated, can significantly increase the benefits derived from the modern medical and health sciences and increase the effectiveness of the persons and organizations involved.

Outlook for Achievement

Since the knowledge, attitudes, and feelings of groups and individuals in the community determine the success of any social undertaking that affects them, health professionals must be aware that knowledge about health is not very comprehensive in much of the population; that many cultural attitudes toward health are inconsistent with the scientific approach; and that health and illness are matters that easily arouse negative emotions. On the positive side, however, growing knowledge about health has been responsible for increasing public concern. The universal desire to avoid illness, even though its influence is diluted by certain cultural and personal ideas and patterns of behavior, is a feeling that can be useful. The fears, doubts, and anxieties that people have about health and sickness can usually be dealt with if they are recognized and understood. Indeed, professional skill can sometimes channel them into productive action.

Another obstacle to the achievement of community health services that are used by all who need them is the pressure of other personal matters in people's lives. Both use and provision of services must compete with many other necessary or desirable demands upon the family's and the community's money, time, and effort. Persons in the lower socioeconomic groups, who are most in need of health services, are preoccupied with immediate wants and desires; and they understand poorly and often accept reluctantly procedures intended to deal with possible future trouble, especially when these interfere with what they see as their daily needs. But even middle-class people, who more commonly place value on providing for the future and as a rule have greater knowledge and motivation about health, often neglect it because other affairs of their lives intervene.

Communities also make numerous demands upon their leaders, and even though public health affects many aspects of the community's existence, matters of more immediate appeal frequently are given precedence over health activities. Sometimes it is difficult for health workers to understand this behavior on the part of persons who they know value health and on the part of leaders who seem sincerely to accept responsibility for community health services. However, the health professions are increasingly recognizing that their responsibilities include development of interest and motivation about health appropriate to its potential for the well-being of individuals and society.

The total system that is the goal of comprehensive health services must be built upon the structure already existing. Community health services in this country have evolved under various auspices at separate times and for different purposes. In most urban communities, in addition to the health department and other official agencies, there are now many independent voluntary health organizations, each determining its own program. Their long separate existence tends to dispose them toward separate rather than united action.

Independent agencies dealing with certain diseases represent special interests. The identification of such an agency with the cause of better community health is focused on prevention or cure of the particular disease the organization was formed to combat. Many citizens who participate in voluntary health activities and who are influential in such health agencies have strong personal and emotional motivations for doing so, often related to experience with the disease. They may find it difficult to see the community's needs as a whole. From their point of view, the total needs and resources of the community may seem irrelevant in considering the cause they have espoused. This idea is not universal in categorical health agencies and is not unique to them. Many people unaffiliated with organizations have extreme partisan feelings about health matters. But an organization provides a means of expressing such feelings and therefore attracts people who are dedicated to its special interest. The concept of comprehensive health services poses to many agencies the problem of evaluating their activities in terms broader than their own reason for being.

Health agencies do not, of course, work in complete isolation from each other. Voluntary agencies usually cooperate to some extent with health departments in certain aspects of their work, and interagency committees, often involving local professional organizations, are an accepted method of approaching specific problems. Health councils contribute importantly to mutual understanding, especially when they are widely representative of all community forces concerned with health. Cooperation among health agencies, although it is incomplete, is an established practice in the American system, and it is a basis upon which a more active and effective partnership can be built.

In general, industry and business are impartially interested in community health, and leadership is often drawn from the business community for projects that cut across agency lines. Occasionally, of course, the aims of health activities, in environmental health for instance, conflict with industrial practices, such as waste disposal that pollutes streams. Unless there is unusual mutual respect for the importance of both industry and health, the situation can be destructive to community relationships, as well as to the health of the public.

Another situation that serves to fragment health services is jurisdictional complexity in metropolitan areas, where population growth has crossed geographic boundaries of cities, counties, or states. If the air of one town is polluted by smoke from a factory in another, the first may have no authority to act against the offender. Suburbs that grow up outside city limits frequently do not have sewer systems, and the multiplication of individual septic tanks may soon constitute a public health hazard that extends into the city. If a jurisdictional line cuts through the middle of a neighborhood, the contacts of a tuberculosis case on one side may not be examined if they live on the other side; on one side strict regulations about mosquito control may be enforced, but mosquitoes bred in standing water in the backyards across the line will find their way to the regulated side. Regional planning and intergovernmental cooperation are needed to solve such problems and prevent their occurring in the future.

Members of the health professions, concerned about the segmentation of services, are likely to see the community's health only from the point of view of their own professional activity. Thus, the clinician sees it in terms of hospital care. The health department at the executive level usually, but not always, perceives health needs in broad terms. However, in the staff as a whole, perceptions are often narrower, confined within agency, program, or professional lines. The specialization demanded by the prodigious body of modern health knowledge does not foster breadth of vision. If communities are to obtain full value from the specialized health services available, they must also have what Detlev Bronk has called "specialists in synthesis"[10] who can bring together and integrate diverse fields and points of view.

The shortage of health manpower has serious implications for community health services. Although the deficiency is not as great in most cities as it is in rural areas, few communities of any size have enough adequately trained people in all the health professions who are organized in such a way as to provide comprehensive health services to the entire population. The situation calls not only for recruitment and training of new candidates, but also for efficient use of existing professional skill. The shortage of trained and talented manpower is common to most fields of endeavor in our society, but this fact does not justify delay while remedies are sought.

Achievement of comprehensive health services means translating the discoveries of science into acceptable social institutions. The proportion of health services that can be useful to

---

[10] Detlev Bronk, "The Changing American Scene," in HIGHLIGHTS OF THE 1954 NATIONAL HEALTH FORUM (New York: The National Council, 1954), p. 22.

communities with only minimum participation by individuals is relatively small. Success of most services depends upon how readily the community responds to health programs. Support of community leaders is also essential, as it is for all community activities. Intimate understanding of the community and its social and economic structure is as necessary as scientific knowledge to the accomplishment of health aims.

Leadership in Community Health

Because community health services are carried on under a variety of auspices, public and private, leadership for them is also dispersed among various areas. Thus medical leadership is manifested through medical societies and hospital staffs. Voluntary health organizations provide leadership in their respective fields of interest through both volunteer members and professional staff. Other community organizations, such as women's clubs and service clubs not primarily concerned with health, frequently take leadership in special campaigns or on special issues.

The health department, because it serves the whole community in a range of programs and activities and has been given legal responsibility in many community health areas, is perhaps the most suitable source of community leadership for comprehensive health services. Essential qualifications for such leadership include the following: a detailed knowledge of the community as a social and physical environment, its patterns of disease, its health organizational structure, its cultural composition; and the ability to work successfully with many different people of diverse backgrounds and interests and to persuade and negotiate skillfully for establishment, maintenance, coordination, and use of community health programs. Leadership in comprehensive health services also requires a

commitment beyond the limits of traditional public health to the broader concept of complete services, what Dr. Luther Terry, former Surgeon General of the U.S. Public Health Service, has called "the conviction that no single element or uncoordinated group of elements in our national health resource can match performance with potential—can close the gap between what is known and what is applied."[11]

Continuous productive communication with the people of the community is basic to the accomplishment of public health objectives. The health department is looked to for accurate information and guidance on health subjects. However, communication goes beyond dissemination of information; it includes listening and discussion as well, both with groups and individuals, and is the chief business of health educators on the health department staff. While the health department is only one of many organizations conducting health communications activities, it may be unique in its breadth of subject matter and in the size and diversity of the population it deals with.

In some communities, the health department cannot take a position of leadership for comprehensive health services. The rather unusual combination of qualities needed may not be present with sufficient strength in the health department, or the community's perception of the health department's role may limit it to traditional public health activities. Sometimes a history of conflict or failure may have damaged the health department's prestige and reduced its effectiveness. These situations present serious obstacles to the accomplishment of comprehensive health services. Such obstacles can be removed only when community leaders recognize that the health department has a key role and that progress depends upon strengthening it.

---

[11] Terry, *op. cit.*, p. 195.

2

Nongovernmental Organization for Health Services

IN 1964, more than $35 billion was spent for health and medical purposes in the United States, and almost three-quarters of it represented private expenditures; only 26 per cent of the total came from tax sources.[1] Private expenditures for health and medical care indicate the extent of nongovernmental organization for these purposes. Some form of organized activity is involved in the provision of almost all privately financed health services, including hospitals and many other institutions, health insurance plans, and services provided by voluntary health agencies or through commercial enterprise. Although most physicians and dentists provide their services directly rather than through an organization, positions taken by their professional organizations strongly influence the pattern of their practice.

The Medical Society

In the United States, private practice by a physician in an office that he establishes and maintains himself is the most common form of medical practice. Although many private physicians see patients as part of a teaching responsibility, or on time that they make available to public or voluntary clinics, the bulk of their practice consists of patients who have selected them. Those in organized medicine generally take the position that the patient's right to select his physician is essential to the doctor-patient relationship. One medical educator has pointed out that, as an indication of approval, the patient's selection of him is important to the physician's confidence in filling his role.[2]

Safeguarding medical ethics and promoting and improving the quality of professional competence are the stated purposes of the organizations representing the medical profession at national, state, and local levels. Such organizations do not always confine themselves to matters of internal professional management. As community and governmental concern with medical care increases, the line between professional and political or economic affairs becomes less distinct. For example, most laymen do not consider issues such as prepayment of medical expenses to be a matter of professional ethics, but medical societies have long been active opponents of many types of prepayment.

As with any professional organization, the local and state medical societies and their national association cannot speak for every practicing physician. However, most physicians feel that the positions taken by their organizations promote and sustain the standards of the pro-

---

[1] Louis S. Reed and Ruth S. Hanft, "National Health Expenditures, 1950–64," SOCIAL SECURITY BULLETIN, January, 1966, p. 3. Data for later years, not yet available, will show the effect of Medicare.

[2] Richard M. McGraw, FERMENT IN MEDICINE, A STUDY OF THE ESSENCE OF MEDICAL PRACTICE AND OF ITS NEW DILEMMAS (Philadelphia and London: W. B. Saunders Company, 1966), Chapter 7.

fession. Most important, the majority of them recognize the need for organizations to represent their interests and believe that the present system serves this purpose.

Membership in any of the nearly 2,000 county or multicounty medical societies in this country is open to almost all licensed physicians who conform to the individual society's code of ethics, and the majority of eligible physicians are members. In past years most county medical societies in southern states and some in other areas did not accept Negroes for membership. Although this situation has greatly improved, definitive results are not yet available. The National Medical Association, composed primarily of Negro physicians, was organized as a means of affiliation for Negro physicians who were not members of the American Medical Association (AMA). Local societies elect their own officers and delegates to the governing body of the state society, which, in turn, elects state representatives to the House of Delegates of the American Medical Association. Although belonging to a local society qualifies a physician for membership in the state society and in the AMA on payment of dues, a number of doctors belong to county or district societies rather than to the AMA, whose membership includes "more than 206,000 physicians, approximately 71 per cent of the nation's 291,000 doctors of medicine."[3] Thus the building block of organized medicine is the local society; and although the AMA has national influence, it is the local society that carries weight on a community level.

Organized medicine's professional educational function is formalized in publications (monthly journals of some state or regional societies, the weekly *Journal of the American Medical Association*, a number of specialty journals, and a large number of annual or occasional publications); in state, regional, and national medical conventions; and in periodic local society meetings. Some local medical societies maintain medical libraries.

Other services to members of medical societies may be sponsorship of group insurance

—life, health and accident, malpractice, retirement, hospitalization—or prevention and review of liability claims. A few societies own or sponsor collection services. Public relations activities of some type are nearly always a part of the medical society program.[4]

Through committees, the medical society represents its members in dealings with outside groups in the community such as government, labor, or voluntary health agencies, on matters of mutual interest. Most large societies have grievance committees and other "mechanisms to assist in resolving complaints" from the public.[5] Many have fee schedule committees to suggest maximum fees for families with limited income or for the elderly, or to determine usual and customary charges. A majority of societies with 300 or more members have formal arrangements for handling emergency medical calls. Organized liaison with Blue Shield and Blue Cross groups and with private insurance carriers is often established, and some societies make formal provisions to supply medical witnesses.[6]

The American Medical Association, representing the membership of all county and district societies, states its purpose as furthering the interest of both the public and the profession. Its campaign against medical quacks and unscientific remedies has been aggressive for many years. The AMA's Council on Medical Education has improved standards in American medical colleges and helped to do away with "diploma mills." It accredits medical schools and evaluates internship and residency programs, as well as training programs for allied professions. The AMA participates with the American College of Surgeons, the American College of Physicians, and the American Hospital Association in the Joint Commission on Accreditation of Hospitals, a service aimed at evaluating and raising the standards of hospital care through a system of survey in which hospitals are voluntarily measured against certain

---

[3] AMERICAN MEDICAL ASSOCIATION, ... PROMOTING THE SCIENCE AND ART OF MEDICINE AND THE BETTERMENT OF PUBLIC HEALTH (Chicago: The Association, undated).

[4] American Medical Association, NATIONWIDE SURVEY ON COUNTY MEDICAL SOCIETY ACTIVITIES (Chicago: The Association, 1963), p. 21.

[5] *Ibid.*, p. 8.

[6] *Ibid.*

Table 1

Nongovernmental Organization for Health Services

Organization	Membership	Purposes	Activities
Medical societies.........	Open to almost all licensed physicians conforming to the society's code of ethics	Safeguarding medical ethics Promoting and improving the quality of professional competence	Publications State, regional, and national conventions Local meetings Medical libraries Sponsorship of group insurance Prevention and review of liability claims Collection services Public relations Grievance committees and representation of members in community relations Health education
Voluntary health agencies.............	Primarily laymen; participation by physicians either on the board or advisory committee Health officers and other official agency people	Educating people concerning their own health and motivating them to take necessary action Creating favorable public opinion about community activities in specific fields Some agencies organized to provide certain types of service rather than deal with certain health problems	Health education Support of local research in health department, hospital, or medical school Sponsor continuing education for physicians, nurses, other health workers Demonstrate new programs and techniques Temporary payment of professional salaries until other funds are available Screening for unrecognized diseases Direct services to individuals: referral and information, public health nursing, purchase of drugs, transportation, volunteer clerical or aide service in hospitals and clinics, friendly visiting
Hospitals			
Voluntary............	Administered by trustees either appointed by the sponsoring agency or elected by a self-perpetuating group of incorporators; serve without pay, represent the hospital in the community. Trustees	Founded by church or religious order, group of citizens, or individual philanthropist State charters permit them to solicit funds under guarantee they will not pay a profit in operating the hospital	

Table 1 (cont.)

Organization	Membership	Purposes	Activities
	name an administrator who increasingly is a layman with professional training in hospital administration Members of medical staff are practicing physicians from the community who treat patients in the hospital and are appointed by the board on the basis of qualifications established by the hospital and on recommendation of a committee of existing medical staff		
Proprietary...........	Administered by owners or persons appointed by owners Members of medical staff selected by owners; sometimes owners are members of medical staff	Operated as business enterprises	6% of beds used for short-term general care
Coordinating Organizations..............	Voluntary and governmental health and welfare agencies Citizens representing community forces and the public	To coordinate health and welfare services To encourage cooperative community planning for health and welfare services	Programs aimed at specific community problems Provide consultation and guidance to agencies in administering their programs Information services Educational activities

standards and those meeting the standards are accredited.

The AMA also engages in a variety of health education programs, often with other agencies, and in efforts to influence legislation on matters relating to health and medical practice.

Local medical societies have established codes of ethics and professional behavior for their members. Such codes are accepted not only by the profession, but to a considerable extent outside the profession as well. Membership in a medical society is essential to eligibility for specialty board examinations and ratings, and for membership on most hospital staffs. Some of the AMA standards are included in state medical practice laws, and in a few states medical so-

cieties have been given the function of licensing physicians to practice. A nonmember who is eligible for membership can usually practice in the community, but one who has been denied membership or has been expelled from a society, even though he may still be licensed to practice, carries a stigma that excludes him from association with colleagues and other services essential to the care of his patients.[7]

The codes of medical ethics issued by the AMA and state and local societies are concerned with standards of practice and also con-

[7] "The American Medical Association: Power, Purpose, and Politics in Organized Medicine," THE YALE LAW JOURNAL, May, 1954, pp. 938–1022.

tain several strictures on the circumstances of practice. For instance, the Principles of Medical Ethics approved by the House of Delegates of the AMA contain the following sections:

Section 6.—A physician should not dispose of his services under terms or conditions which tend to interfere with or impair the free and complete exercise of his medical judgment and skill or tend to cause a deterioration of the quality of medical care.

Section 7.—In the practice of medicine a physician should limit the source of his professional income to medical services actually rendered by him, or under his supervision, to his patients. His fee should be commensurate with the services rendered and the patient's ability to pay. He should neither pay nor receive a commission for referral of patients. Drugs, remedies or appliances may be dispensed or supplied by the physician provided it is in the best interests of the patient.

These sections are often interpreted as opposing the practice of medicine for a salary or even for fees for service in medical care plans under auspices such as lay corporations or governments.

Membership in the medical society does not necessarily mean regular attendance at meetings[8] or active participation in the affairs of the medical society. However, organized medicine reflects the point of view of most private practitioners and with infrequent exceptions fulfills its role as spokesman for them. Community groups and forces that find themselves differing with the medical society can reasonably assume the difference is with many doctors in the community. As a matter of fact, organizations planning to engage in activities that require medical participation often make it a practice to obtain official approval from the medical society. Such approval helps to ensure needed medical cooperation.

The professional training of physicians and the circumstances and pressures of most medical practice are such that contacts with peers outside the profession may be limited. Physicians spend long years of training during which they learn to assume the doctor's role.[9] In the

usual pattern, a physician's working time is spent with medical colleagues, with other professional people, and with patients. Most practicing physicians have little free time, and, like people in other occupational groups, they tend to spend it with professional associates. It is not surprising that their personal identification with the medical profession is very strong and that their point of view about matters of public concern is influenced by it.

The physician working outside the usual pattern—in public health or industry, for instance —and whose responsibility is therefore to the public or to a corporation, loses some of his strong identification with the profession. Private physicians may look upon this loss as a kind of defection or feel that it results from such colleagues' inadequacy as private practitioners. Although it is true that in the early days of public health many health officers took up the work to supplement or compensate for an inadequate income from private practice, standards of public health practice today call for competence equal to that required for specialized clinical practice. In 1949 a specialty board on preventive medicine was established, sponsored partly by the AMA, and over 1,500 physicians have its certification. However, private physicians' image of colleagues in public practice persists, especially among the great number of doctors who have no continuing contacts outside the usual pattern of medical practice.

The attitude of private medicine is of utmost importance in organizing and administering community health programs because participation of private doctors as the principal providers of medical care is essential to success. Organized medicine has often opposed community action taken to reorient or change the methods of distributing health services. Nevertheless, there are always physicians of high professional standing whose comprehension of community needs, and of the fact that their own individual patients share those needs, leads them to use their influence in the medical profession to further community programs.

Health department activities in the control of communicable disease, for instance, once looked upon by physicians as interfering in

_____

[8] NATIONWIDE SURVEY ON MEDICAL SOCIETY ACTIVITIES, *op. cit.,* p. 5.

[9] See E. Gartly Jaco (ed.), "Patients, Physicians and Illness," SOURCEBOOK IN BEHAVIORAL SCIENCE AND MEDICINE (Glencoe, Illinois: The Free Press, 1958), Part V.

their relationships with patients, are now officially supported by many medical societies and largely taken for granted by private practitioners. Voluntary health agencies, once viewed with suspicion, as a rule now have amiable and cooperative relationships with medical societies. Group practice, which not long ago was frowned upon by the AMA, now has its official acceptance. Even "closed panel" group health insurance plans, in which comprehensive medical care is provided to the membership by a panel of physicians paid by the group, in a recommendation adopted by the AMA House of Delegates in 1959 received tentative acceptance on the basis that the individual's privilege of selecting his own physician includes also the right to choose the system of medical care he prefers.[10]

Other Professional Organizations

Most professional groups involved in community health services are organized to improve their competence and interests. The American Public Health Association (APHA), established to protect and promote public and personal health, provides a common forum for physicians, nurses, civic leaders, engineers, and other specialists in community health. Most of the 18,000 members affiliate themselves with one of the 15 speciality sections such as epidemiology, health officers, maternal and child health, or public health education.

The APHA takes responsibility for accrediting schools of public health, establishes qualifications for practice of various public health professions, sponsors programs of continuing education in public health, and through its Professional Examination Service develops examinations for evaluating professional public health personnel. It also develops community health and appraisal processes and publishes methods, guides, and manuals in areas such as public health law, air pollution control, accident prevention, and control of communicable diseases in man.

The national organization has 52 affiliated state, regional, and local organizations; and a large proportion of professional public health workers in many categories are active members.

The American Dental Association has constituent organizations in the states, and there are district dental societies in local areas. These organizations promote the improvement of dentistry and also take an active part in community programs. They have given strong and vocal support to water fluoridation to prevent dental caries.

In nursing, two major national organizations have state and local chapters. The American Nurses' Association (ANA) is open to all graduate nurses and is concerned with all their interests, including licensure and economic security. The National League for Nursing (NLN) is basically an educational organization and has lay as well as professional membership. It is the recognized accrediting body for schools of nursing. Both organizations carry on recruitment activities. Local chapters of either the ANA or the NLN determine their own activities to a considerable extent but also participate in national programs.

All the aforementioned organizations and a great many others formed by a large number of professional groups contribute in various ways to community health services and may be important sources of support and counsel. However, none of them represents its constituents as strongly as the county medical society represents private physicians.

Voluntary Health Agencies

Voluntary health organizations have been called "the largest social movement in the United States"[11] and have played an important part in the growth of public health and community health services. Most of the organizations were founded by groups of laymen and physicians who recognized the need for community action to combat a particular disease or health problem or to better the situation of a

---

[10] Herman Miles Somers and Anne Ramsay Somers, DOCTORS, PATIENTS AND HEALTH INSURANCE (Washington: The Brookings Institution, 1961), p. 341.

[11] Richard Carter, THE GENTLE LEGIONS (Garden City, N.Y.: Doubleday & Company, Inc., 1961), p. 19.

specific group of people. From the beginning such organizations have accepted responsibility for health education of the public in their various areas of concern.

Health education, as it is practiced now by both public and voluntary health agencies, covers a wide range of activities, using the skills of educators, community organizers, group workers, writers, artists, public media specialists, and behavioral scientists. Its purpose is usually twofold: first, to educate people on matters concerning their own health and motivate them to take necessary action; second, to create a favorable public opinion about community activities in specific fields. For either purpose, broad public participation is essential, and many voluntary agencies have developed great talent in enlisting it.

Voluntary health agencies have recognized that by themselves they cannot solve the problems they were organized to deal with, and they have been influential in bringing about public action for this purpose. In many parts of the United States, local health departments owe their existence to a voluntary agency's vigorous efforts in educating the body politic about the need, and many categorical health programs came into being through similar influence. These organizations at the local, state, and national levels have had great success in backing legislation that provides for or finances public health, institutional, and medical research activities.

The typical local voluntary health agency is basically an organization of laymen, with participation by physicians either on its board or on advisory committees. Health officers and other official agency people are often active in the organization, but most of the membership is drawn from the nonprofessional public. The paid staff of voluntary agencies at one time had no specific training but is now recognized as requiring special competence; the American Public Health Association has established standards for qualifications of the executives of these agencies.[12]

[12] American Public Health Association, "Educational Qualifications of Executives of Voluntary Health Organizations and Health Councils," AMERICAN JOURNAL OF PUBLIC HEALTH, May, 1959.

Many influential local health agencies are affiliated with state and national organizations. Tuberculosis associations, the first to be organized both locally (in 1892) and nationally (in 1904), have a great deal of state and local autonomy. The National Tuberculosis Association (NTA) is governed by a board made up of representatives from each of 59 constituent organizations (54 state or territory, 5 large city) with which it has contracts allowing the sale of Christmas seals in return for certain guarantees about program and procedures. Of the proceeds from the sale of the seals, the NTA receives not more than 10 per cent for national office activities and research, and the remainder stays in the state. State associations also have contracts with local associations, to whom they provide leadership, consultation, and service.

Tuberculosis associations were founded at a time when local official public health organization was almost nonexistent, and the national plan purposely allowed for local initiative and for a large local share of the funds collected. In more recent times, advantages of somewhat greater centralization have become apparent, and some state tuberculosis associations are taking steps to reduce the number of locals in order to ensure their effective size.

Other national agencies, organized later than the NTA, have a much greater proportion of their resources centered in a national organization. The American Cancer Society, for instance, receives 40 per cent of the total contributions to local Society divisions. This money is used for research (25 per cent), medical fellowships (3 per cent), and national office programs (12 per cent).

In addition to health education of the public, which is a function of all voluntary health agencies concerned with the control of diseases or disabilities, such agencies conduct a variety of other activities. Some support local research efforts in the health department or in a hospital or medical school. Many of them sponsor continuing education for physicians, nurses, and other health workers. In what has been accepted as an appropriate role for nonofficial organizations, some undertake demonstrations of new programs or techniques. They may, temporarily, pay salaries of professional or clerical staff members in health departments, clinics, hospitals or other institutions, until other funds are available. Screening for unrecognized disease may be undertaken either independently or in cooperation with the health department. Direct services to individuals may include information and referral; public health nursing service; purchase of drugs, appliances, or items for the personal comfort of patients; transportation; volunteer clerical or aide service in hospitals and clinics; or friendly visiting.

Under the best circumstances, a local voluntary agency can be an important resource in the total health program, providing enlightenment to the public and the professions, giving help and support to the health department and to medical care institutions as well as interpreting their needs to the public and to governing bodies. The agency can also offer opportunities for establishment of common ground for the medical profession, the health department, and others involved in controlling the conditions with which they are concerned. Busy professional people sometimes protest the number of meetings held by voluntary agencies, but their value as an avenue for communication on many levels is unquestionable.

Voluntary agencies are not without their critics. They are frequently accused of a thirst for publicity that goes beyond a sincere wish to tell their story. In reporting to the public about their own activities they sometimes, perhaps unconsciously, leave the impression that they have carried out singlehandedly all the community programs in their area of concern, thus minimizing what may be a major activity of health departments and other agencies. In their eagerness to promote programs in their own field, voluntary groups may overlook needs in other areas and press for increases that would only result in unbalanced programs. When they perceive their role as watchdog over the health department and other community institutions, they occasionally indulge in destructive criticism, rather than constructive stimulation. Some of their fund-raising practices have come under extensive censure in recent years. In spite of these faults, voluntary agencies have been characterized as "a principal means for raising the level of society's well-being,"[13] and it is in the public interest that their potential should be developed fully.

Some voluntary health agencies differ from those just described in being organized to provide certain types of service, rather than to deal with certain health problems. The American Red Cross is a quasi-official national voluntary organization, chartered but not financed by Congress, having close relationships with the federal government. Its services to the military and to victims of disaster are based on legal responsibilities stipulated in its charter. However, many of its chapters also provide important local services such as blood banks; instruction in lifesaving, first aid, and home nursing; and volunteer assistance in hospitals. Some public health nursing service is provided, chiefly in rural areas, as a means of promoting the establishment of health department services.

The visiting nurse society is another type of service agency found in many cities. Unlike the Red Cross, it is purely a local organization. As the name implies, it provides nursing service in the home. The major source of support of visiting nurse societies is voluntary contributions from the public (often through the Community Chest or United Fund), but many of them charge modest fees to those able to pay. They also may give service to certain patients under contract with categorical health agencies such as cancer and heart associations, an arrangement much preferred to independent home nursing services by several organizations. In most communities, the visiting nurse society has a working relationship with the health department in which responsibilities for field nursing are shared or even delegated to the society by the health department.

Alcoholics Anonymous differs from most health agencies in being sponsored, organized, and operated entirely by those whom it serves. Although there are a few other groups formed with similar purposes to deal with other addictions, only AA has national stature. Local asso-

---

[13] Robert H. Hamlin, VOLUNTARY HEALTH AND WELFARE AGENCIES IN THE UNITED STATES, an Exploratory study by an Ad Hoc Citizens Committee (New York: The Schoolmasters, Press, 1961).

ciations of persons who have or have had certain diseases or conditions and have joined together for mutual help in adapting to their situation fill a special need with which other agencies or individuals can only sympathize.

Hospitals

Long-term hospitals, such as those for mental illness, tuberculosis, and other chronic conditions, are most often under government auspices, and many cities and counties also run general hospitals. However, about 70 per cent of the nonfederal hospital beds for short-term general care in the United States are in voluntary nonprofit hospitals. Over two-thirds of admissions to all hospitals are to the nonprofit establishments, and their annual expenses are about $6.6 billion, almost half the nation's total hospital expenditure.[14]

Voluntary hospitals are usually founded by a church or religious order, a group of citizens, or an individual philanthropist and have state charters that permit them to solicit funds under the guarantee that they will not make a profit in operating the hospital. Their trustees, who may be appointed by the sponsoring agency or elected by a self-perpetuating group of incorporators, serve without pay and have the responsibility for directing hospital work. Hospital board members also represent the hospital in the community, and their own interest and status determine to a large extent the financial support the hospital receives.[15] The hospital administrator is the agent of the board of trustees. In the past the administrator was usually either a physician or a nurse; but now, in an increasing number of instances, he is a layman with professional training in hospital administration.

The medical staff of the hospital is made up of practicing physicians from the community who have been given the privilege of treating patients in the hospital. (Some hospitals provide courtesy privileges for physicians not on the regular staff so that they may have their patients admitted and may care for them in the hospital under certain circumstances.) Members of the medical staff are appointed by the hospital board on the basis of qualifications established by the hospital and usually on the recommendation of a committee of the existing medical staff. Inasmuch as the members of the medical staff are responsible to their patients and to the board for the quality of medical care provided in the hospital, their effective organization for self-government and smooth working relationships with the hospital administration is of utmost importance.

In most hospitals, physicians are not salaried employees; as a matter of fact, the practice in some hospitals of paying the radiologists, anesthetists, or pathologists a fixed stipend instead of fees for service actually rendered has been vigorously protested by the American Medical Association. On the other hand, the physician cannot have complete control of his patient's situation in the hospital and cannot be totally responsible for him. Such matters as food and nursing service, for example, are responsibilities of the hospital rather than of the medical staff. In these circumstances friction can be avoided only through clever management by the administrator, unbiased interest on the part of the board, and wise leadership in the medical staff. Organized medicine has concerned itself with this problem and has set down many of the ground rules that encourage smooth relationships.[16]

Proprietary hospitals are operated as business enterprises and constitute about 6 per cent of the beds for short-term general care throughout the country. Such hospitals do not usually have boards of trustees and are administered either by owners or by persons appointed by the owners. Members of the medical staff are also selected by the owners; sometimes the owners themselves are members of the medical staff.

[14] HOSPITALS, JOURNAL OF THE AMERICAN HOSPITAL ASSOCIATION, August 1, 1966, Part II, Table 1.

[15] Ivan Belknap and John G. Steinle, THE COMMUNITY AND ITS HOSPITALS (Syracuse, N.Y.: The Syracuse University Press, 1963).

[16] Laura G. Jackson, HOSPITAL AND COMMUNITY (New York: The Macmillan Company, 1964), pp. 19–20. See also publications of Joint Commission on Hospital Accreditation.

HOSPITAL COUNCILS

Most voluntary hospitals are independently operated, and in the past their relationships with each other tended to be competitive, rather than cooperative. In recent years, partly at the urging of organizations such as the American Hospital Association and its affiliated state associations, many communities have organized hospital councils so that hospitals can act in concert on their mutual problems. Such councils do more than protect the hospitals' interests if they are associated with or are a part of larger agencies such as health or health and welfare councils.

ORGANIZATION FOR MEDICAL CARE INSURANCE

The functions of hospitals as a part of comprehensive community health services and aspects of hospital administration are discussed at length in Chapter 8. Another type of agency that profoundly affects hospital financing, however, deserves mention in the context of the community's voluntary organization for health services. This is the Blue Cross, Blue Shield, or other voluntary, nonprofit hospital or medical care prepayment plan.

There are more than 75 affiliated but independent Blue Cross plans in the United States, all of which cover hospitalization and some surgical-medical services as well. The major purpose of Blue Shield plans, of which there are also about 75, is surgical-medical coverage, but some also include hospitalization. A number of other very similar plans are not affiliated with Blue Cross or Blue Shield. All of these organizations undertake to pay hospitals or physicians for services covered. Although individuals may belong to most of them under certain conditions, enrollment is predominantly of groups, many of whose members have the fee deducted from their paychecks, with or without employer contributions. It is obvious, therefore, that such plans have extensive relationships with hospitals and the medical profession, as well as with industry and organized labor.[17] (Health insur-

ance written by commercial companies is discussed later in this chapter.)

Other Health Institutions

Because of the number of older people in the population, the frequent occurrence of chronic diseases among them, and changes in their pattern of family living, the need for nursing-home care has increased significantly in recent years.[18] Many nursing homes that provide skilled nursing care are proprietary, but some of these are affiliated with voluntary hospitals. Voluntary nonprofit nursing homes are often a part of or administered by a hospital. To be eligible to provide service under Medicare, a nursing home must have an agreement with a hospital so that patients can be transferred if necessary.

Most communities have a number of other institutions under philanthropic, religious, or other voluntary auspices, such as rehabilitation centers, halfway houses for posthospital care of mental illness, facilities for handicapped children (sometimes supported in part by the Easter Seal Society), or clinics or hospitals for special purposes.

Health-related Voluntary Organizations

The concept of community health services as a comprehensive whole tends to blur the difference between health agencies and other social agencies. The counseling and casework provided by family service associations, for instance, can help prevent ill health as well as provide help when illness does occur. Such agencies frequently refer people to health care, encourage them to accept it, or provide the financial means for it. The health implications of child guidance centers, clubs or centers for the elderly, agencies that give emergency financial aid, and day care centers are obvious, as are those of youth organizations, such as boys' and girls' clubs, boy scouts, and girl scouts.

Parent-teachers' associations contribute to

---

[17] See Chapter 14 for detailed discussion of health insurance.

[18] See Chapters 8 and 10 for discussions of nursing homes.

community health through their interest in the health of children. The League of Women Voters studies health needs and provides effective nonpartisan support through community action to meet such needs. The various fraternal organizations and service clubs found in American communities not only offer a forum for discussion of health matters, but frequently make contributions of equipment and supplies or offer certain kinds of health care.

Foundations are another source of financial help for research, building, and service and also of objective consultation. Churches not only help individual members in need of health services, but often operate health institutions or agencies, and their support for health projects and programs is exceedingly useful.

In most areas, there are philanthropic private citizens interested in health. Their financial contributions to such things as capital funds for building hospitals or establishing other institutions are often substantial, and their influence in the community is considerable.

The informal organization of influence affects many aspects of community life. Although the influence is frequently not obvious, it is ignored at the peril of any coordinated community activity.

Coordinating Organizations

The multiplicity of organizations for health in American communities would result in overall disorganization if they were all completely detached from each other. Most agencies establish relationships with others having common interests, sometimes formalized through interagency committees, but these are limited to specific areas of endeavor. Over 40 years ago, the first councils of social agencies were formed; they were aimed at exchange of information among a larger group of agencies to eliminate duplication of effort. Today more than 2,000 health and welfare councils in the United States and Canada (often known by other names, such as community council, citizens' council, and so on) are members of the United Community Funds and Councils of America. Their purpose

is to coordinate health and welfare services and to move toward cooperative community planning for such services.[19] Some of them have programs aimed at specific community problems or give consultation and guidance to agencies in administering their programs. Many have information services, such as directories of agencies or referral service, and carry on such educational activities as forums to discuss controversial issues.[20]

Membership of effective councils includes not only voluntary and governmental health and welfare agencies, but citizens representing community forces and the public as well. The origin of many councils was based on federated fund raising, but recommended membership is far broader than the agencies that participate in the Community Chest or United Givers Fund. Indeed, the trend is away from "structure dominated by agencies to one in which major responsibility rests in the hands of leading lay citizens, many of whom, of course, have had experience as members of boards of functional welfare agencies."[21] This type of organization is perhaps more favorable to the development of community leadership than one in which all members represent individual agencies or interests, but it may not be as satisfactory to the separate agencies.

The internal organization of a council may include divisions of health, family and child welfare, group work, and recreation, or even more specialized fields. But some councils are organized around projects rather than fields of work, and in such a case they may have a committee structure to allow for communication among agencies working in similar areas.

Some health councils are divisions of health and welfare councils; others are independent organizations. Their patterns of organization are similar to those of health and welfare councils. They are most effective in promoting comprehensive health services for the community

[19] United Community Funds and Councils of America, THE ROLE OF COMMUNITY HEALTH AND WELFARE COUNCILS (New York: UCFCA, 1965).

[20] Wayne McMillen, "Urban and Regional Welfare Planning," in Harry L. Lurie (ed.), ENCYCLOPEDIA OF SOCIAL WORK (New York: National Association of Social Workers, 1965), p. 802.

[21] Ibid., p. 804.

when they are broadly representative of all the agencies under whatever auspices that provide or finance health services, of professional organizations, and of the lay community's leadership in business, labor, and various cultural and religious groups. The National Health Council's guide for health agencies emphasizes the importance of broad representation, of avoiding the dominance of any agency or interest, and of coordinating health planning with other community planning.[22]

Activties of health councils cover a considerable range of subjects and include meetings, workshops, and conferences; surveys, studies, and research; and negotiation to effect recommendations growing out of studies. Some councils actually operate service programs themselves.[23]

The financing of councils, whether they are concerned with health and welfare or only health, varies in different areas. Some are affiliated with community chests and are financed partly by the chest and partly by membership dues. The National Health Council recommends that health councils should be financed as far as possible by contributions from the participating agencies. Funds may be awarded by foundations or by governmental agencies for special purposes. The method by which a council is financed is reflected in the emphasis of its activities.

The nature of a council's staff depends upon its size, strength, and objectives. Some have large staffs from a number of professional disciplines, competent to determine changing problems in the community and to plan for effective solutions.

Councils have a great potential for serving the community through leadership and coordination. Even an association of agencies for the purpose of exchanging information has a valuable function, but it is limited unless the exchange results in positive action. Such councils do not have authority over other agencies, and

they can bring about positive action only by persuasion. A council that represents the community as a whole may be able to effect improvement as a result of public demand.

In about 70 areas of the United States, area-wide health facility planning agencies have been established, most of them since 1960. Although the majority of them have received some financial support from the federal government, they are local voluntary agencies with policies determined by boards representing the public and various special interests in the area. Generally stated, their purpose is to plan for the efficient and economical development and utilization of health facilities and related services of high quality, without unnecessary duplication, to meet present and projected future needs of the area.

Although initially geared for the task of hospital coordination, as these planning groups have developed, they have given increasing attention to the relationship of hospitals to other health facilities and to the availability of out-of-hospital services in their areas. When the Comprehensive Health Planning and Public Health Services Amendments of 1967 (Public Law 89–749) repealed the section of federal law under which grants to health facilities planning organizations had been made, many of those who had received such support prepared to broaden their scope in order to be eligible under the new legislation.

Under the recent legislation, areawide comprehensive health planning grants from the PHS can be made to either public or nonprofit private organizations; in the latter case, there must be assurance that the interests of local government are represented. Planning under these grants must encompass all the health needs of the people in the area—physical, mental, and environmental—and must attempt to coordinate all health services under both public and private auspices. Federal policy requires that a majority of members of the policy-making body for areawide comprehensive health planning be consumers and that all segments of the population be represented, including such groups as the poor and ethnic minorities, whose health problems are disproportionate and who have previously had no voice in health plan-

---

[22] National Health Council, TAKING PART IN COMMUNITY HEALTH PLANNING (New York: The Council, undated).

[23] National Health Council, BIENNIAL SURVEY OF ACTIVITIES REPORTED BY HEALTH COUNCILS, STATE–LOCAL, 1962–1963 (New York: The Council, 1963).

ning. Applications for these grants must have the approval of the state comprehensive health planning agency (see Chapter 3) , and the area-wide agencies will be expected to work cooperatively with the state agency.

In order to qualify for a grant for areawide comprehensive health planning, an applicant must establish a recognized position in its area as the organization responsible for the function. Since funds became available on July 1, 1967, many prospective applicants, especially in highly organized metropolitan areas, have found that achieving the necessary consensus takes considerable time and effort. As this book goes to press, nearly all of the grants made to areas have been for the purpose of organizing, rather than conducting, comprehensive health planning. Although the delay has disappointed the expectations of many enthusiastic supporters of areawide planning, the time needed to develop strong community understanding and acceptance is undoubtedly well spent.

Business in the Health Field

Although it would be neither practical nor useful to attempt to cover all the business enterprises related to health, it seems worthwhile to enumerate several types, in addition to proprietary hospitals and other institutions, directly involved in community health services.

Almost a fifth of private expenditures for health purposes are for medicines and appliances,[24] and these are available largely through commercial outlets. Even though drug stores sell a great many other things, their reason for being is the medicines and other health supplies they sell, and a registered pharmacist is essential to their operations. Eyeglasses are provided also by private entrepreneurs, some of whom are trained and licensed optometrists who fit glasses as well as fill prescriptions for them. Other health-supply dealers sell hearing aids and orthopedic appliances. Although most medical laboratory service is provided by health departments and hospitals, private laboratories are run as businesses in many communities.

A number of the services needed to maintain a healthful environment are supplied commercially, at least in part, in many communities. For instance, garbage and other solid waste disposal may be a private business, conducted either through direct negotiation with householders or on contract with municipal government. Most city governments have some programs for pest and vermin control, but private exterminating companies carry on a major part of this work. In some areas all or part of the public water supply is provided under commercial auspices.

The insurance industry covers more people for hospital, surgical, and medical care than do the voluntary groups. Commercial health insurance is usually indemnity insurance rather than direct payment for service like the Blue Cross and Blue Shield plans.[25] The insurance industry also writes policies totaling vast sums for accident coverage. These interests, as well as the life insurance companies' concern with preventing premature death, give the insurance industry a special interest in health and preventive medicine. Insurance men are often active in community health agencies, and many insurance companies provide materials for health education and in other ways support efforts toward health improvement.

Many resources for comprehensive health services are in the nongovernmental organizations of the community. Coordinating these various independent enterprises and relating them to government resources are basic to achieving health services for the community and all its people.

---

[24] Reed and Hanft, *op. cit.*, p. 4.

[25] See Chapter 14.

3

Governmental Organization for Health Services

Although the constitution of the United States does not mention health specifically, it grants powers to the federal government that have allowed for continually increasing activities aimed at improving the nation's health. The authority to regulate commerce with foreign countries and between the states and to govern the armed forces and federal territory includes authority in matters pertaining to health, and the power to tax and spend funds for the general welfare allows for federal participation in many national health efforts. Under these prerogatives Congress annually appropriates several billion dollars of federal funds to various departments of the Executive Branch for health purposes.[1]

The Federal Government

U.S. DEPARTMENT OF HEALTH, EDUCATION, AND WELFARE

When the Social Security Act of 1935 greatly extended the federal government's responsibilities for the nation's health, the agencies concerned were scattered in a number of federal departments. In 1939 the Federal Security Agency was established, bringing such agencies together, and 14 years later, the Agency's functions were transferred to the newly created Department of Health, Education, and Welfare, whose Secretary is a member of the President's Cabinet.

The Department's Regional Offices, in Boston, New York, Charlottesville, Atlanta, Chicago, Kansas City, Dallas, Denver, and San Francisco, represent the Secretary in the field and maintain liaison between the states and the Department. In each Regional Office, staffs representing Social Security Administration, Office of Education, Social and Rehabilitation Service, and Public Health Service conduct the business of those agencies in close working relationship with the states.

All the Department's constituent agencies carry on some health-related activities. The Social Security Administration, which manages the Old Age and Survivor's Insurance program, also has responsibility for administering Medicare, the program of health insurance for the elderly under the 1965 Amendments to the Social Security Act.[2] Over 600 district offices of the SSA in population centers throughout the country provide information, accept applications for insurance benefits, and furnish assistance requested on any social security matter.

The Office of Education provides grants for education and supporting services for handicapped and deprived children, includes information about health and safety in its analyses, studies, and reports about schools in the United States, and has cooperative research funds that

---

[1] For a listing of health work of federal agencies, see John J. Hanlon, PRINCIPLES OF PUBLIC HEALTH PRACTICES (St. Louis: The C. V. Mosby Company, 4th ed., 1964), pp. 351–54.

[2] See Chapter 14.

can be used for research in school health.

Social and Rehabilitation Service. This constituent of the Department was created in a 1967 reorganization, combining the Vocational Rehabilitation Administration and the Welfare Administration, which had been separate constituents, the Mental Retardation Division of the PHS, and the Administration on Aging, which had been in the Office of the Secretary, into the new service. The SRS is now organized in five components: the Rehabilitation Services Administration, the Assistance Payments Administration, the Medical Services Administration, the Children's Bureau, and the Administration on Aging.

The Rehabilitation Services Administration is responsible for programs aiding the handicapped, disabled Social Security applicants, the mentally retarded, the blind, and the permanently and totally disabled. Through grants-in-aid, the Administration supports services provided by the vocational rehabilitation agencies of the states, reaching over 100,000 persons in the United States annually. Grants available to all the states are for services to both the physically and the mentally disabled. Programs may include diagnostic services to determine eligibility and services needed; training, guidance, and placement; and, for persons in financial need, any other services needed to fit them for jobs, including physical restoration or purchase of applicances. Some states also purchase equipment and initial stocks for small businesses like vending stands, operated by severely handicapped persons and under the supervision of the state agency.

In addition to support for continuing service programs the RSA also makes grants for partial support of extending or improving service programs, for research and demonstration, for the establishment of rehabilitation facilities and research and training centers, and for training of professional personnel in fields related to rehabilitation.

The Assistance Payments Administration is responsible for grants for various categories of public assistance, such as old age assistance, aid to families with dependent children, aid to the blind, and aid to the permanently and totally disabled.

The 1965 Amendments to the Social Security Act, discussed in detail in Chapter 14, greatly extended medical care programs for the needy in all categories of public assistance, and administrative responsibility for such programs rests with the Medical Services Administration of SRS.

The Children's Bureau has two responsibilities under federal law: to investigate and report on all aspects of the welfare of children, and to provide technical and financial assistance to the states for child health and welfare services. In fulfilling these responsibilities, the Bureau engages in and supports research activities, and compiles data on several aspects of child welfare. They issue such data as well as many other publications, including *Infant Care,* long the best seller of the Government Printing Office. Grants to the states administered by the Bureau are for (1) maternal and child health programs, (2) crippled children's services, and (3) child welfare services. Essentially all of the states participate in these programs, and they are operated by state agencies. In 1965, the Bureau was authorized to provide project grants for comprehensive health care and services for children in low-income areas.[3]

The Administration on Aging serves as a clearinghouse for information, provides technical assistance to the states, and administers grants for several purposes.[4]

Public Health Service. The agency which perhaps most clearly reflects the growth of national interest and concern about health is the Public Health Service. From a small unit called the Marine Hospital Service established in 1798 to provide medical care for merchant seamen, the Service grew slowly during the nineteenth century, acquiring responsibilities for foreign quarantine and for investigating epidemic diseases. Under the pressures of expanding technology and social change, the Service has grown rapidly in recent decades to its present position as the largest contributor to medical research in the nation and as the administrator of about $400 million in grants-in-aid for support of state and local programs and professional training.

---

[3] See Chapter 9.
[4] See Chapter 15.

Reorganization measures that became effective as of April and July of 1968, grouped the former components of the Service into two administrations, each comprising several bureaus, and added to the PHS the Food and Drug Administration, previously an independent constituent of the Department. The three components of the Service are now the Health Services and Mental Health Administration, the National Institutes of Health, and the Consumer Protection and Environmental Health Service. The administrators of all three are directly responsible to the Assistant Secretary for Health and Scientific Affairs, whose deputy is the Surgeon General. (As this book goes to press, the detailed reorganization of the PHS is still in process. Throughout the book the names of specific divisions or other units of the Public Health Service may be inaccurate but the programs described continue to be conducted by the PHS.)

The Health Services and Mental Health Administration includes programs that focus on comprehensive health planning and on the development of comprehensive health services, including both prevention and personal care for both physical and mental health. It administers grants to the states and to local recipients for these purposes, and conducts or supports research and demonstrations aimed at improving the quality of all health services and their accessibility to all segments of the population. The Administration administers the grants for Regional Medical Programs to combat heart disease, cancer, and strokes (see Chapter 17). On the basis of vital statistics that it collects and analyzes, and the National Health Survey through which illness and disability is continually analyzed, the Administration provides a means of ongoing evaluation of the nation's health. And continuing the historic role of the PHS, it has responsibility for the personal health care of the Service's legal beneficiaries: merchant seamen, the Coast Guard, inmates of federal prisons, and American Indians.

An important contribution to state and local health services is made in federal grants administered by the Health Services and Mental Health Association. Under the pattern that has grown up since the Social Security Act was passed in 1935, these grants have been made in two forms: (1) formula grants to all the states, determined according to population and economic status, and (2) project grants, made usually to local agencies for special projects. Over the years, both types of grants have been made in specific health areas or categories—venereal disease, tuberculosis, cancer, heart disease, and others. Under the Comprehensive Health Planning and Public Health Services Amendments of 1966 (Public Law 89–749), expanded and extended by the Partnership for Health Amendments of 1967 (Public Law 90–174), this pattern has been altered. The law authorizes grants for five purposes:

1. Formula grants to state agencies designated for the purpose, to enable the states to establish formal provisions for comprehensive state health planning to meet current and future health needs through public and private resources.

2. Project grants to public or nonprofit private agencies (with appropriate representation of the interests of local government) for developing comprehensive regional, metropolitan area, or other local area plans for coordination of health services, facilities, and manpower.

3. Project grants to public or nonprofit private agencies for training, studies, and demonstrations aimed at improved or more effective comprehensive health planning.

4. Formula grants to the states for establishing and maintaining adequate public health and mental health services. These will replace categorical formula grants, and their use will be according to the comprehensive state health plan. Use of seventy per cent of the funds for services in local communities is required.

5. Project grants to public and nonprofit private agencies to help provide services to meet health needs of limited geographic scope or regional or national significance, and to stimulate new programs. These will replace most of the categorical project grants and are required to be consistent with the comprehensive state health plan.

The new legislation will enable states and communities to receive federal assistance for their programs according to their individually determined areas of need, rather than only for the stipulated purposes. It puts upon states and local areas the responsibility of making rational plans, and provides assistance for them in doing so.

Under the 1968 organization, two functional units were added to the National Institutes of Health: (1) the Bureau of Health Manpower, which promotes the development of increased numbers of better trained health workers through grants for training, construction of educational facilities, and student assistance; (2) the National Library of Medicine, which has the largest collection in the world of cataloged publications in the biomedical sciences and is now combining a computerized storage and retrieval system with photoduplication services to make available to medical libraries this great organized store of scientific information.

The National Institutes of Health make up the component of the PHS that is concerned almost entirely with research. They engage in intramural research and support research projects through grants to investigators in universities and other institutions throughout the country. Awards are also made for development of physical resources and for general programs of research related to health.

The Consumer Protection and Environmental Health Service combines the national centers for air pollution control (see Chapter 6), radiological health (see Chapter 6), and urban and industrial health (see Chapters 6 and 9), plus parts of the National Center for Communicable Disease Control, with the Food and Drug Administration.

The Food and Drug Administration enforces the various federal laws designed to protect the public against contamination, impurity, fraud, and hazards in foods, drugs, therapeutic devices, and cosmetics that move in interstate commerce or are imported. Guarding against unsafe or ineffective drugs, the FDA conducts surveillance over those still under investigation, evaluates drugs before they are marketed, and keeps watch for untoward effects of all drugs on the market. Drugs used for animals are also checked for safety and effectiveness and to ensure that food derived from treated animals is safe for human consumption. In food processing plants throughout the country, FDA inspec-

tors make sure of satisfactory sanitation, and imported food is checked for wholesomeness and safety before it can be sold in the United States.

The FDA sets standards for the content of packaged foods and enforces the law requiring honest labeling. Under the 1965 drug abuse control legislation, the FDA works to eliminate illicit traffic in depressant, stimulant, or hallucinogenic drugs. It is also responsible for administering the laws pertaining to labeling of hazardous substances and control of products potentially dangerous to children.

The FDA maintains 18 district offices and nine Drug Abuse Control offices in addition to its central staff. It deals directly with manufacturers and marketers and cooperates with many state and local officials in day-to-day operations of inspection, certification, and examination. Basic and applied research conducted by FDA scientists helps in establishing rules that are current in terms of continual technological development and change. The FDA engages in extensive education and information activities to permit and encourage voluntary compliance with regulations and to invite public interest and understanding.

OTHER FEDERAL AGENCIES

In its medical care and treatment program, the Veteran's Administration operates hospitals, outpatient clinics, and domiciliary facilities for veterans with illness or disability associated with their military service. The VA also gives complete hospital care for other veterans with nonservice illnesses who cannot afford to pay for it. The VA pursues research in the diagnosis and treatment of disease and has developed a number of methods of administering medical care aimed specifically at caring for all of the patient's needs and preventing unnecessary hospitalization.

The Department of Defense furnishes comprehensive medical care for members of the armed forces and their dependents and engages in activities to ensure environmental sanitation in and around military posts. Its Corps of Engineers takes an active part in water supply and pollution control activities. Research in a variety of medical fields is conducted under Armed

Forces auspices, and military medical installations on this continent and throughout the world supply information of great value to the control of epidemic diseases.

The office of Economic Opportunity is concerned with health both directly and indirectly, since poverty contributes to ill health and ill health to poverty. Its Vista and Job Corps programs offer opportunities for improvement in health, and the objectives of many Community Action Programs include meeting health needs.

The programs of the Department of Housing and Urban Development are also pertinent to health matters. For example, the Department administers grants for basic sewer and water facilities, requiring suitable safeguards against pollution of waterways. Grants to neighborhood facilities finance health and recreation projects as well as other community services. Urban renewal activities seek to remedy housing conditions that are unfavorable to health. The Federal Housing Administration, now a component of the Department, has long promoted the healthfulness of federally-supported housing, and it joins with the PHS in planning for health facilities to serve residents of housing projects. The FHA also administers a mortgage insurance program to provide financing of nursing home construction and rehabilitation. Among the concerns of the Model Cities Administration are a variety of health and social services which contribute to improved urban living.

A number of programs of the U.S. Department of Agriculture are related to human health. Programs to eradicate tuberculosis, brucellosis, and other diseases in animals protect the human population, as do activities such as meat inspection that help ensure the purity of food. The Department's long-established program for improving human nutrition has played an important part in reducing the incidence of nutritional deficiency diseases in this country, and the work of its county extension and home demonstration agents has promoted rural health and sanitary measures for many years.

In the U.S. Department of the Interior, the Federal Water Pollution Control Administration, established in 1966, makes grants to com-munities for improved sewage treatment and carries out procedures to enforce federal water pollution law.[5] The Bureau of Mines conducts studies and demonstrations on preventing accidents and protecting the health of miners, and the Fish and Wildlife Service promotes programs for the control of certain animals that carry disease.

The Atomic Energy Commission produces and distributes radioactive materials for medical research as well as conducting and supporting such research itself. A large number of other federal agencies also contribute directly or indirectly to the improvement of health.

Federal agencies have many provisions for coordinating their activities with those of other federal agencies, both through official interdepartmental committees and through less formal arrangements. The Bureau of the Budget also acts to prevent duplication and to encourage cooperation of agencies conducting similar programs.

State Governments

Police power, defined as the power "to enact and enforce laws to protect and promote the health, safety, morals, order, peace, comfort, and general welfare of the people,"[6] is an inherent power of sovereignty that resides initially with state governments. State legislatures may exercise this power through delegation, and most state laws concerning the health of the people provide for delegation of specific authority to the health department and other agencies of the state government, and also to local governments or officials.[7] Agencies created under such laws may be given powers to administer statutory laws: to make rules and regulations on matters that are too detailed, too technical, or too frequently in need of revision to be dealt with by statute; and to make decisions concerning the enforcement of statutes and regulations.

[5] See Chapter 6.

[6] James A. Tobey, PUBLIC HEALTH LAW (New York: The Commonwealth Fund, 1947), p. 40.

[7] Frank P. Grad, PUBLIC HEALTH LAW MANUAL (New York: American Public Health Association, 1965), pp. 8–9.

The extent and nature of powers delegated to local jurisdictions rather than to the state differ among the states. A few states are highly centralized, and state rules and regulations set most requirements throughout the state. Local health departments in such states are under the supervision of state agencies and make only subsidiary rules of their own. In most states, however, state law contains only general requirements, and local governments are empowered to make their own regulations within a broad framework.[8] Usually, states exercise somewhat greater supervisory authority over counties than over cities, although there is a trend in a number of states toward increased local autonomy of counties as well as municipalities. In some states direct services are furnished almost entirely by local agencies; other states have many types of direct-service programs themselves, and most have some.

Every state government has a number of agencies with assigned health functions; some have many such agencies. Activities in a particular health field are often conducted by more than one agency. When five or six separate state government agencies are officially concerned with matters such as mental health services, services for crippled children, or licensure for health reasons, setting and achieving common goals or developing uniform standards may be very difficult.

In considering the problems arising from excessive fragmentation of health functions in state governments, many observers are calling for greater efforts to reorganize activities and to provide for greater concentration of responsibility. The National Commission on Community Health Services recommended that:

States should take steps to effect the consolidation of their official health services (including mental health, school health, mental retardation, the administration of medical care programs for the indigent, and the medical aspects of rehabilitation) in a single state health agency. The state should assign to its health agency responsibility for developing and maintaining all programs necessary to protect people from environmental hazards and from poor quality health services, and it should be specifically charged to initiate action to meet new and changing health needs.[9]

STATE HEALTH DEPARTMENTS

The state health department has the broadest scope of health activities of any state agency. Policy for the department is determined in most states by a board of health (which may be known by another name) whose members are usually appointed by the governor, often with the consent of one or both houses of the legislature. In almost all states, qualifications for membership on the state board of health are stipulated by statute; all but a few require that from one or more members be physicians, and representatives of other health professions (most often dentistry or pharmacy) are usually also required. The law of one state, however, specifies that no more than five of the nine members shall represent health professions; a few states specify that some board members must represent the general public; and in some states the governor is *ex officio* a member. The APHA takes the position that no single profession or group should dominate the board.[10]

The duties of state boards of health, in addition to policy determination, usually include promulgating rules and regulations and drafting or revising public health codes. Some also have executive and enforcement functions.

The state health officer (who may have some other official title) is appointed by the governor in some states and by the board of health or on its recommendation in others, and is frequently *ex officio* a member of the board of health or its secretary. In addition to his function as chief executive of the health department, he usually acts for the board of health when it is not in session, and has authority to put into effect and enforce its rules and regulations, often preparing such rules for the board's approval. He has responsibility for management of funds appropriated to the department, and is the chief advisor to the governor and legislature on health matters.

---

[8] For an explicit discussion of public health law, see *ibid.*

[9] National Commission on Community Health Services, HEALTH IS A COMMUNITY AFFAIR (Cambridge, Mass.: Harvard University Press, 1966), pp. 217–18.

[10] "Policy Statement, The State Public Health Agency," AMERICAN JOURNAL OF PUBLIC HEALTH, December 1965, p. 2017.

The functions of state health departments vary with the governmental organization of states and with the amount and type of responsibilities assigned to departments. In addition, the practices of health departments in using their prerogatives under the state laws differ considerably. Some carry on a much wider range of activities than others within a similar legal framework.

The APHA considers that the state health department has four basic functions: leadership, financial assistance to local health agencies, setting and enforcing health standards, and providing certain health services.[11]

To assume its leadership role, the health department must continually assess the state's health conditions and the quality and adequacy of its health service. On the basis of such an assessment statewide health programs can be planned and promoted. The department must work with other executive departments of the state, and must often negotiate with other states and with the federal government in the interests of health. Local health departments should be able to look to state health department leadership to determine the need for new state legislation and be able to initiate it; to propose and support programs in emerging areas of need or public demand; to provide consultation and guidance for local programs, and on occasion professional assistance; and to enable and encourage regional planning and operations where these are indicated.

Financial aid is given by most states to local governments for public health purposes, often with a requirement for local matching funds, an arrangement considered desirable by the APHA "to stimulate local initiative and to give the local government a greater stake in the expenditure of state funds."[12] Although ideally aid would be given for any suitable local programs, it is sometimes available only for certain specified purposes. The state health department also administers federal funds granted to the state, and reviews many federal grants made directly to local agencies.

The state health department has the legal responsibility in most states for administering public health laws, the sanitary code, some licensing requirements, and other health regulations. Enforcement duties are often delegated at least in part to local health departments.

The health services provided directly by the state health department may be limited to emergency assistance and to service for areas without local health departments. In three states—Hawaii, Rhode Island, and Vermont—all local health services are provided by the state health department, and in New Mexico most of them are. In several other states, state health districts cover areas outside major cities or urban counties. In some sparsely populated states, large areas have no formal provision for local public health services, but these also receive some services from the state. Most states also conduct programs to serve the whole state that are considered impractical for local health departments. For example, they may operate laboratories serving the entire state at least for some procedures, or administer hospitals for tuberculosis or other long-term conditions. Many state health departments have casefinding or clinic teams traveling throughout the state, giving certain special services to areas that may or may not be covered by city or county health departments.

The particular content of any state health department's programs will differ from others according to that state's special health needs, its resources, and the expressed wishes of its citizens. The APHA designates six general program areas with which state health departments are concerned:[13] (1) personal health services; (2) research; (3) environmental health services; (4) public health education; (5) professional education and in-service training; and (6) administrative services.

The staff of state health departments comprises members of many of the health professions—dentists, engineers, health educators, laboratory scientists, nurses, nutritionists, physicians, sanitarians, social workers, statisticians, veterinarians—as well as people concerned with administration and management. The organi-

[11] *Ibid.*, p. 2012–13.
[12] *Ibid.*, p. 2012.
[13] *Ibid.*, pp. 2013–17.

zation of a staff with diverse competences into a working team adapted to growing responsibilities has been an important consideration in recent years. The organizational patterns of state health departments vary considerably, probably in terms of their individual approaches to problems and the personalities involved. The particular form of state health department organization is less important than its provisions for assumption of responsibility and participation in management by members of the staff other than the health officer. The scope of modern health operations is great, and one person cannot be expected to give detailed supervision in all of them and still carry on the many other activities essential to his leadership role.

OTHER STATE AGENCIES

Health functions are assigned to state agencies in many different ways in the 50 states. For example, responsibilities for licensure for health reasons are shared by several agencies in all the states, and of course are also delegated to local governments to some extent. Physicians, nurses, osteopaths, dentists, pharmacists, and members of other health professions are usually licensed by separate and independent boards, but in some states all or some are licensed by the state department of health or education or by a single department of licenses or of professional and occupational standards. Hospitals and other agencies providing treatment or care are usually licensed by the state health department, but sometimes there is a special board or commission for the purpose. The licensing of food-handling and other establishments serving the public is chiefly delegated to local authorities, but some licensing may be done by the state department of health or agriculture or a special commission.

In about 20 states, community activities in mental health and mental retardation under grants from the National Institute of Mental Health are directed by departments of mental health, and in a few, such programs are under the auspices of departments of welfare, or of institutions or other agencies. In the remainder of the states, noninstitutional mental health activities are centered in the health department, but frequently other agencies also conduct programs in the fields of mental health and mental retardation.

Many state hospitals for the mentally ill and for the tuberculous, as well as other state institutions for treatment or custodial care, are directed by agencies other than the health department, such as departments of institutions, special boards or commissions, or welfare departments.

Standards, policies, and procedures for providing medical services for persons receiving public assistance are determined in most states by the welfare department, which also administers state and federal grants to local areas for this purpose. However, the health department in almost all states is responsible for certifying that hospitals and other providers of care meet the federal standards under Medicare.

Certain health services to mothers and children are provided by the state university in a few states; crippled children's services are under a special board in five states, the department of welfare in nine, the state university in four, the state department of education in three, and the state health department in the remaining states. The department of education engages in rehabilitation activities in most states, usually sharing responsibility with the health department, the welfare department, or a special board or commission.

In about half the states, water pollution control is the function of a special agency set up for that purpose, and in addition, there are eight interstate water pollution control agencies. The department of agriculture in a number of states has all or part of the responsibility for regulating the production, processing, packaging and storing of milk and other food products, and departments of labor do a share of the work in occupational health in many states, a major share in a few. Accident prevention activities in almost all states are conducted by several agencies; many states have a special board or commission, and there is also participation by state police, department of mines, department of labor, or others.

STATE COMPREHENSIVE HEALTH
PLANNING AGENCIES

Under federal laws enacted in 1966 and 1967,

known as the Partnership for Health Legislation, grants are available to the states for comprehensive health planning. A single state agency must be designated for this responsibility, and of the 56 eligible jurisdictions, 34 have designated the state health department or department of health and welfare; 16 have placed the function in the Office of the Governor, sometimes as a part of an office of planning; and six have named or constituted interdepartmental commissions for the purpose. The federal law requires that each comprehensive health planning agency have an advisory council that includes "representatives of state and local agencies and nongovernmental organizations and groups concerned with health," but stipulates that a majority of the council members shall be representatives of consumers of health service.

The scope of concern of these agencies is broader than the health concerns of state government agencies. Their planning is to encompass the physical, mental, and environmental health needs of all the people, and to provide the services, facilities, and manpower to meet those needs. The agencies or units now conducting programs under federal grants for the purpose are undertaking an entirely new endeavor, for which neither specially trained manpower nor a body of knowledge has yet been developed. They are using a variety of approaches.

Many agencies, recognizing the need to achieve some sort of common understanding among the various actors in the pluralistic health system, are concentrating on liaison, interpretation, and communication with all those they can reach. Others, in search of hard data they feel are necessary as a basis for planning, are exploring the possibilities of health information systems. The federal law does not specify what activities comprehensive health planning will include, or how these will be conducted, and allows the states, with only a few exceptions, to develop their comprehensive health planning programs in the style they choose and according to their own priorities. The law does require that applications for grants made in their states for areawide comprehensive health planning have their approval, and grants for public health services

must be in accord with such plans as the state agency has made. The 1967 amendments indicated the first specific required function of the state agency: the provision of assistance to health care facilities in the state in their plans for capital expenditures for expansion, modernization, or replacement.

The product of comprehensive health planning is not seen as an eventual blueprint for health services in the state, but rather as a series of recommendations that constitute a plan continually being altered and updated. The actual process of this planning is perhaps as important as its product, and the ultimate success of the enterprise must be measured not in the excellence of a planning document but in the demonstrable effect the process has in improving the health of the people. Unlike much of the planning of agencies or governments or professional groups usually focussed on the services provided, comprehensive health planning is focussed on the people who need health services. The task of such planning is to influence changes in the extent, nature, and manner of provision of all health services that will have the effect, as the legislation states, of "promoting and assuring the highest level of health attainable for every person, in an environment that contributes positively to healthful individual and family living."

Local Governments[14]

Since all local governments exist by permission of the state and under terms specified by the state, their provisions for health services have many different patterns, according to the states' wide variety of practices with regard to their local subdivisions. Generally, however, county health departments (or multi-county local districts) tend to be under somewhat more direct supervision and receive a somewhat higher proportion of their financial support from the state health department than do most city health departments. (The official title of county health officers in Maryland is "deputy state health

[14] For full discussion of local health departments, see Part Five.

officer.") Cities, on the other hand, operate under charters from the state legislature allowing them varying degrees of self-government, in which of course they must be consistent with state laws and regulations. Under most charters, the city may create its own health department, with the state health department acting chiefly in an advisory capacity. Regardless of organizational form, when differences arise between state and local health laws, they are likely to be resolved by the courts in favor of the state.[15]

Cooperation between cities and counties is often of utmost importance to comprehensive community health services, and can be effected in several ways (see Chapter 19) . Failure to use whatever devices are available to give consistency to health programs in neighboring jurisdictions hinders the effectiveness of all.

In many parts of the country, special districts that include geographical areas covered by several local governments have been established for health-related purposes. Special districts are usually for a single purpose, such as air pollution control or sewage disposal, and the ways in which they are established and administered vary widely. Such districts contribute some solutions to the problems presented by artificial boundaries and often allow extension of services into areas where they were previously lacking. On the other hand, they add another jurisdiction to those already existing, possibly increasing costs through duplication of service, and approaching single problems without reference to the community's total needs.[16]

Most cities have separate departments of public works to manage operations closely related to health such as sewer system, refuse disposal, and street cleaning, and they may have responsibility for public markets and slaughterhouses. Public water supply is sometimes included in public works but is more often the function of a separate agency. The health department has certain supervisory and regulatory functions in regard to the health aspects of such public works activities, and it may have

similar responsibilities for parks and recreation facilities.[17]

Municipal hospitals are sometimes under health department auspices, especially in large cities, but may be governed by a special agency or commission set up for the purpose. County hospitals may be administered by the board of county commissioners or a special agency, and either city or county hospitals are sometimes operated by the welfare department. In large cities, public general hospitals tend to give chiefly emergency and indigent care, whereas in smaller cities and counties they are more likely to provide a full range of service to all segments of the community. Large cities often have public hospitals for care of certain conditions such as tuberculosis, chronic disease, or mental illness, and these may be under the direction of the health department, welfare department, or a special board.

Medical care outside the hospital for persons unable to pay for it is usually administered by the welfare department, occasionally by the health department. In some communities, full-time city physicians provide such care, usually in a clinic setting. In others, it is available through outpatient service of a hospital or by arrangement with private physicians; in either of these circumstances, fees for service are paid by the welfare department.

School health programs are administered by the board of education in a great many communities, by health departments in others, and jointly by both agencies in a few. In order to bring together the groups and agencies in the community that can contribute to protecting and promoting the health of school children, some communities have formed school health councils with representation from both education and health departments.

Municipal planning commissions, urban renewal agencies, regional commissions or councils of governments, and other organizations concerned with the growth and changing patterns of communities deal with matters in which health implications are a major factor. In addition to planning and insuring adequate sanitation and a healthful environment, they

---

[15] Grad, op. cit., pp. 21–25.
[16] Charles R. Adrian, GOVERNING URBAN AMERICA (New York: McGraw-Hill Book Company, Inc., 1961) , pp. 279–83.

[17] See Chapter 6.

Table 2

Local Health Units, January 1, 1966

Type of Health Unit	Health Units		Population Served[1] (in thousands)		Counties Served	
	Number	Per Cent	Number	Per Cent	Number	Per Cent
Single County	1,024	59.8	93,471	50.2	1,024	42.0
City Health Department	362	21.2	45,240	24.3	8[2]	0.3
Local Health District	226	13.2	16,837	9.1	661	27.1
State Health District	100	5.8	30,609	16.4	744	30.6
Total[3]	1,712	100.0	186,157	100.0	2,437	100.0

Source: U.S. Public Health Service, Director of Local Health Units, 1966 (Washington, D.C.: Government Printing Office, 1966).

[1] Estimated as of December 31, 1965. Based on estimated populations of local areas as reported in the "Sales Management Survey of Buying Power" dated June 10, 1966.

[2] Eight counties served by seven city health departments, the city and county being coterminous: New Orleans; New York (five counties); Philadelphia; and Boston, Chelsea, Revere, and Winthrop which cover the county of Suffolk.

[3] Data on local health units not reported for 634 counties with a total population of 9,032,300 inhabitants. This represents only 4.6 per cent of the total estimated population of the United States as of January 1, 1966.

must also consider the distribution in changing neighborhoods of health services and facilities. As areawide comprehensive health planning organizations are developed under the Partnership for Health, some will undoubtedly be established under such auspices.[18]

Implications of Governmental Organization

The complexity of governmental organization for health purposes at federal, state, and local levels is as much a handicap to easy accomplishment of comprehensive community health services as the intricacy of nongovernmental organization. The diffusion of responsibility at all three levels reflects not only the pluralism of our society but the political difficulties that have historically attended growth of governmental health programs. The absence of a comprehensive approach to health needs has helped to bring about the present dispersed organization which, in turn, tends to foster continued separation of services.

The social climate that prevailed when most health departments were created was dominated by nineteenth century *laissez faire* philosophy. The government would do what individuals could not do for themselves with the help of private enterprise. The "basic six" of public health[19] are activities serving the whole community and are not easily accomplished under nongovernmental auspices. Even in fulfilling these well-accepted public responsibilities, however, health departments have met opposition, uncooperativeness, and scant community support.

As social concern became directed toward services for special groups of the population, health programs began competing for support in the community and in the nation. Special programs for the aged, the mentally ill or retarded and the medically indigent were proposed, supported, and operated as separate, unrelated services. Federal grants-in-aid, intended to stimulate state and local activity in particular health areas, influenced local programs toward further fragmentation.

Most health department officials have not been satisfied with the limited progress they can make when their activities are restricted to the traditional "basic six." At the same time, many of them have consciously remained aloof from political conflict. In their caution to avoid

[18] See Chapter 2.

[19] Communicable disease control, sanitation, maternal and child health, public health nursing, health education, and vital statistics.

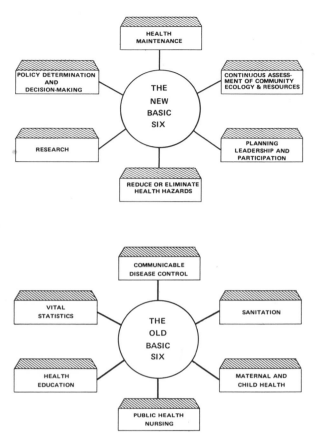

FIGURE 2. *Present-day expectations (top illustration) about health services provided by government go far beyond traditional limitations (bottom illustration)*

involvement with partisan politics, such officials have failed to recognize a responsibility for active effort in the arena of issue politics. As a result, new governmental programs created in response to public demand have often been housed either in existing agencies other than health departments or in new agencies set up for the purpose.

Public health statesmanship is indispensable to achievement of comprehensive community health services, and it demands that health officers have an active part in the community's decisions about health. In making this point, Dr. Luther L. Terry, formerly Surgeon General of the Public Health Service, has said: "He [the health official] can no longer deliver his professional judgment and then leave the arena to other community leaders . . ."[20]

Present-day expectations about health services provided by government go far beyond the traditional limitations, and the area in which health department leadership should be exercised encompasses all comprehensive community health services. Calling for new charters for public health, "new guidelines which are more in tune with the complex world of today than the precepts we have lived by during the developmental stages of our art," Dr. Terry proposed for consideration a new "basic six":

1. Health maintenance activities for the community and the people in it—against diseases or conditions caused by infectious agents, metabolic changes, genetic factors, emotional disorders, or environmental influences.

2. Continuous assessment of the ecology and resources of the community as they relate to health.

3. Leadership in planning for effective community health services, and participation in providing organized patient care services for both episodic and long-term illness.

4. Study of man's environment and appropriate action to reduce or eliminate hazards to health and to provide safe and pleasant surroundings.

5. Support and conduct of research aimed at new health knowledge, and its efficient application to those who can benefit from it.

6. Partnership in policy determination and decision-making so that health is given rightful consideration in all activities of society.[21]

[20] Luther L. Terry, "The Complex World of Modern Public Health," AMERICAN JOURNAL OF PUBLIC HEALTH, February 1964, p. 194.
[21] *Ibid.*, p. 195.

4

Health Professions and Skills

The number of people employed in the health services industry ranges from about 2.4 million to over 3.5 million, depending on such factors as the scope of the job classification and the number and type of ancillary workers included in the total. According to census figures, the public and private health services industry in the United States employed nearly 3 million people in 1965, approximately 4.2 per cent of all persons employed. This amounted to about 14 health employees per 1,000 population in the country as a whole. Among the 71 categories of industry listed in the U.S. Census of Population, 1960, only agriculture and construction employed more workers than did health services. Between 1950 and 1960, employment in health services increased 54 per cent; among the largest nine industries, only government education services had a greater proportionate increase over the same period.

People employed in health services worked in public and private agencies, private offices, laboratories, and other places; but the largest proportion, 1.7 million, or 65 per cent, was employed in hospitals.

As Table 3 shows, health service workers included larger-than-average proportions of persons in professional or technical work, women, and government employees. More of them earned less than $4,000 or more than $10,000 in 1959 than did all workers. Their unemployment rates were low compared with others.

The composite health services industry accounts for public and private expenditures of over $40 billion and is a major employer of the nation's manpower.

Professional and Technical Workers

Rapid extension of scientific knowledge and technology has brought about a proliferation of specialized professions and occupations in the medical and other health fields. The 1965 revision of the *Health Careers Guidebook*[1] identifies some 200 health careers in 32 groups. These groups range from the various specialties of medical practice to occupations requiring a minimum of training, such as animal tending in laboratories. Many occupations are in traditional health fields, but several specialties or groups of occupations have been developed in recent years in response to the demands of developing knowledge. Nuclear medical technology is an example of such specialization, as are computer programming and biomathematics.

The list of health professions in Table 3 is representative rather than inclusive. All professions listed, as well as others in associated fields, require at least some college-level education; in several instances academic requirements extend for as long as eight years beyond high school before practice begins. Specialization or advancement usually depends on further study, and of course constantly growing knowledge in all health fields makes continuing education necessary throughout professional life.

Licensing and Accreditation

In a society based on advancing technology, the pursuit of many occupations entails not only

---

[1] U.S. Department of Labor, Health Careers Guidebook (Washington: Government Printing Office, 1965). This edition replaces a 1955 publication prepared under the auspices of the National Health Council.

Table 3

Characteristics of U.S. Workers in Health Services Industry and in All Industries, 1960

Characteristic	Workers in Health Service Industry %	Workers in All Industries %
Professional-technical workers	45.5	11.8
Service workers	31.2	11.1
Females	69.8	32.8
Employed by government	27.5	12.2
Privately employed	58.4	74.6
Self-employed	13.6	12.2
1959 earnings less than $4,000	70.2	53.6
1959 earnings more than $10,000	8.6	5.0
Unemployed	2.4	4.9

Source: U.S. Department of Health, Education, and Welfare, Public Health Service, HEALTH MANPOWER SOURCE BOOK, SECTION 17, 1960 INDUSTRY AND OCCUPATION DATA (Washington: Government Printing Office, 1963).

sound basic education but frequently special training as well. When the practice of a profession or occupation directly affects the well-being of individuals or communities, as in the health professions; the adequacy of professional knowledge and skill is a matter of public concern, and state laws are enacted stipulating minimum requirements for practice and providing a mechanism for licensing practitioners. Licenses may be mandatory, in which case the statute defines the occupation and forbids its practice by unlicensed persons; or they may be permissive, the statute forbidding only the use of the legal title without a license. Many health occupations are subject to licensure in all the states, others in several states. Requirements for licenses vary with occupations and among states, but fulfillment of certain educational requirements is always necessary. Examinations are usual, varying from routine to detailed and technical, and evidence of good character is a frequent stipulation. A license to practice in one state may or may not be accepted in others.

Although annual registration is sometimes required, it does not usually entail additional training or examinations, in spite of the continual and rapid increase of knowledge in the health fields.

For some professions, whether subject to licensing or not, an organization representing the profession itself sets standards and certifies the qualifications of candidates in voluntary efforts to encourage appropriate competence in practitioners. The 19 medical specialty boards listed in Table 4 are examples of this kind of effort. Each of these boards determines the amount and nature of training and experience needed to prepare a qualified specialist in his given area and also administers examinations to candidates with such training and experience. Upon successful completion of the requirements, candidates become diplomates of the board. Although physicians may specialize in their practice without this accreditation, it carries great weight with the medical profession and is the major factor in advancement in most hospital staffs as well as a basis for referral of patients by colleagues.

In most areas of medical specialty, there is also a professional organization, usually known as a college or academy, that promotes research and undergraduate and postgraduate education in its specialty.

In several professional organizations in health-related fields, such as the American Dietetic Association and the Academy of Certified Social Workers, certain levels of education and experience are conditions of membership. This membership is, in turn, a requirement for advancement to some positions. Statements of recommended qualifications for members of various health professions employed in public health agencies are issued by the American Public Health Association and widely used by both official and voluntary agencies in developing requirements for positions.

Immediate application of constantly growing knowledge in the health and medical sciences requires continuing education of health workers, in addition to their initial professional training. Professional and voluntary organizations, colleges and universities, hospitals, and government agencies at every level provide educational opportunities for practicing health workers. Their efforts include publications, short courses, workshops, and a variety of programs using modern communications media and techniques.

HUMAN RELATIONS SKILLS

Although differences in emphasis and extent of training distinguish the health professions from each other, most are based on the biological sciences. In recent years, however, the utility of biological science has been recognized as contingent on human behavior. Medical knowledge of the control of diabetes, for instance, is useless unless patients follow prescribed regimens; screening techniques for cancer find no cases if people do not submit to the tests; and a city's most refined efforts to clean up its river cannot succeed if the people living upstream continue to dispose sewage into it. Practice in the health fields has therefore been found to require skills in the behavioral and social as well as biological sciences. Specialists in anthropology, sociology, and other social sciences have been added to the staff of some health organizations and their counsel sought by many. Human motivations, feelings, and attitudes are becoming subjects of study in professional health training; social organization is also receiving attention.

The ability to be both scientifically objective and expert in human relations that is required for effective practice in most of the health professions is an exceptional combination that cannot reasonably be expected in all people giving health services. To some extent, the association of persons with different skills in a team effort can provide the necessary combination, as well as allow for application of specialized knowledge. It is not uncommon, for instance, for clinic physicians to spend a minimum of time with patients, leaving detailed interpretation of their directions to nurses who have had special training in counseling. But the physician is more effective if he has some understanding of the patient as well as of the disease. The sanitarian cannot reasonably expect to take a behavioral scientist with him when he must persuade restaurant owners to change their ways.

And the health officer cannot call upon anyone else to carry out his responsibilities for influencing his staff, his board, and the many publics in his community.

MANAGEMENT SKILLS

The management and administrative skill greatly needed for efficient and effective community health services is another competence not usually considered in the basic training of professional health workers. Physicians are trained to act independently and are frequently motivated in choosing their profession by a desire to be "on their own." However, they sometimes find themselves in situations where they must be responsible for the work of others as well as for their own and for matters such as supervision, employee morale, program planning, and budget administration. These subjects are not taught in medical schools and are often treated only superficially in other professional schools.

Suchman has pointed out the following:

> The supervision of a modern public health agency, especially in a large metropolitan area, calls for an understanding of bureaucratic structure, staff organization, personnel policies, financial budgeting, and public relations, along with many other skills of executive management.[2]

Health organizations are increasingly recognizing these requirements. Hospital management is becoming the responsibility of specialists trained for the work. Administration is usually included in the graduate training required for many executive positions in health, and some health agencies place all management activities under the general direction of trained administrators.

The importance of planning in the management of health programs is receiving growing recognition, and a new professional field of health planning is in the process of development. The skills required, discussed in Chapter 18, draw heavily upon the social sciences, but familiarity with the rationale as well as the organization of health services is essential.

[2] Edward A. Suchman, SOCIOLOGY AND THE FIELD OF PUBLIC HEALTH (New York: Russell Sage Foundation, 1963), p. 101.

Table 4

Educational Requirements for Selected Health Professions

Profession	Undergraduate Education	Professional Education	License Required	Number of Specialties and Requirements	Additional Information
Administrator General........4 years		Not required, may be needed for advancement	No		
Hospital........4 years		1 year plus 1 year of administrative residency	No		
Behavioral science..4 years (anthropology, political science, social psychology, sociology)		1–3 years of graduate study	No		
Dentist...........2–4 years		4 years	Yes	8 dental specialties, requiring at least 2 years special training and examination	APHA[1]
Dental hygienist....Preferably at least 2 years		2 years	In some states		APHA[1] Dental hygienist must be supervised by a licensed dentist
Dietitian or Nutritionist......4 years, major in home economics		1-year dietetic internship. Graduate study usually required for advancement	No		Membership in Amer. Dietetic Ass'n requires academic training and either internship or 3 years experience APHA[1] for nutritionist
Health educator....4 years, major in social or biological sciences or education		Preferably at least 1 year in public health	No		APHA[1]
Laboratory scientist........4 years, major in biological sciences		Needed for advancement, Ph.D. preferred	No	10 laboratory specialties requiring major emphasis in training	APHA[1]
Medical social worker.........4 years		2 years, additional often required for advancement	No	Psychiatric social work, essentially the same requirements	Membership in Amer. Academy of Certified Social

Table 4 (cont.)

Profession	Undergraduate Education	Professional Education	License Required	Number of Specialties and Requirements	Additional Information
				as medical social work	Workers, requires 2 years' grad. study and 2 years' approved experience. APHA[1] 61% of M.S.W.'s and 78% of P.S.W's had 2 or more years of graduate study, 1960
Medical technologist............At least 3 years		1 year. Additional required for advancement	No		Certification from Registry of American Society of Clinical Pathologists based on examination
Nurse (professional)..........Either 3 years for diploma, 4 years for BS or 2 years for associate degree		Graduate training often required for advancement	Yes, mandatory in 29 states; permissive in remainder, 1964	Several, requiring experience and/or study. Public health nurses need college degree to qualify for many positions	APHA[1] for public health nurses. A few states separately license public health nurses. 89% of nurses had diploma, 9% bachelor's, 2% higher degree, 1964
Occupational therapist........4 years, with major in O.T.		18 months if undergraduate work is not in O.T.	No		Registration by Amer. Occupational Therapy Ass'n open to graduates of accredited schools of O.T. who pass national registration examination
Optometrist.......4 years		At least 1 year	Yes	Several, requiring advanced study	
Osteopathic physician........3–4 years		4 years plus 1 year internship	Yes	Several; 22% of D.O.'s specialized, 1963	Licensure is limited in several states

Table 4 (cont.)

Profession	Undergraduate Education	Professional Education	License Required	Number of Specialties and Requirements	Additional Information
Pharmacist........	4 years for B.S. in pharmacy Some colleges of pharmacy require previous 2 years of general education		Yes	Research, requiring graduate study	Licensure requires examination, sometimes apprenticeship experience
Physical therapist...	4 years, in P.T. or equivalent		In some states, either mandatory or permissive		Supervised experience after training often required for employment APHA[1]
Physician.........	4 years	4 years plus 1–2 years internship	Yes	19 recognized, plus many subspecialties. Accreditation by specialty boards requires 2–4 years' residency plus 2 or more years' practice in specialty and examination. 64% of all M.D.'s specialized, 27% were board diplomates, 1961	APHA[1] for directors of public health depts., school physicians, and medical administrators of specialized health activities Certification by National Board of Medical Examiners is accepted in lieu of examination for license in many states
Podiatrist-chiropodist......	1 or 2 years	4 years; 1-year internship required for license in some states	Yes		
Psychologist (clinical)........	4 years	At least 2, usually 4 plus 1 year of internship	In a few states		Diplomate in Psychology requires 5 years' experience after Ph.D. and examination by Amer. Board of Examiners in Professional Psychology Amer. Board for Psychological Services certifies qualified

Table 4 (cont.)

Profession	Undergraduate Education	Professional Education	License Required	Number of Specialties and Requirements	Additional Information
					professional psychologists
Sanitary engineer...	4 years in engineering, major in sanitary engineering	1 year preferred	Yes	Several, requiring special training and/or experience	APHA[1]
Sanitarian........	Preferably 4 years, with biology, chemistry, social sciences		In a few states	Several, requiring training and/or experience	APHA[1] 46% of sanitarians had bachelor's, 17% had higher degree, 1962
Food technologist............	4 years		No	Research, requiring 1–3 years' graduate study	
Industrial hygienist........	4 years, major in physical sciences	1–3 years usually required for advancement	No	Several, requiring advanced training and experience	APHA[1]
Statistician........	4 years, including mathematics, statistics, biological sciences	1–3 years usually required for advancement or research positions		Several, requiring advanced training and experience	APHA[1]
Speech and hearing therapist.....	4 years (last 2 in a college offering special courses)		No	2, requiring at least 1 year of advanced training	Certification by Amer. Speech and Hearing Ass'n on basis of supervised practice and professional experience
Veterinarian.......	At least 2, preferably 4 years	4 years	Yes	Public health work usually requires graduate training in public health	APHA[1]
Vocational rehabilitation counselor.......	4 years	1–2 years	No		

Sources: U.S. Department of Labor, HEALTH CAREERS GUIDEBOOK (Washington: Government Printing Office, 1965); U.S. Department of Health, Education, and Welfare, Public Health Service, HEALTH MANPOWER SOURCE BOOK, Section 12, Medical and Psychiatric Social Workers, Section 14, Medical Specialists, Section 16, Sanitarians, Section 18, Manpower in the 1960s (Washington: Government Printing Office); Harry L. Lurie (ed.), ENCYCLOPEDIA OF SOCIAL WORK (New York: National Association of Social Workers, 1965); American Nurses' Association, FACTS ABOUT NURSING, A STATISTICAL SUMMARY, 1966 EDITION (New York: The Association, 1966).

[1] American Public Health Association has stated qualifications for public health workers in the profession.

Other Health Workers

Dominated as it is by requirements for professional expertise, the health industry at the same time depends greatly on the efforts of nonprofessional workers, who comprise half of the health labor force. Medical and public health laboratories, for instance, employ junior technicians, glass workers, animal tenders, and other people whose work is essential to the scientist's professional operations. Medical and dental assistants save practitioners' time, and homemakers help solve problems associated with illness.

Hospitals could not operate without the practical nurses, nursing aides, orderlies, or attendants who provide personal service to patients. Practical nurses have had formal training for a year or more and are licensed by the states to use the title, Licensed Practical Nurse. (In a few states, licensing is mandatory for practical nurses.) About a third as many practical nurses as professional nurses are employed in hospitals in the United States.[3] Nursing aides, orderlies, and attendants, having less training, make up an even larger proportion of total hospital nursing personnel.

Other hospital employees also give services essential to the welfare of patients. The housekeeping staff, as well as people involved in food preparation, can make the difference between good and poor hospital service, and personnel practices that recognize their contribution are an important administrative tool. A recent personnel study in a large metropolitan hospital showed that special attention to the selection, working conditions, supervision, and morale of employees in the nutrition department reduced the expensive personnel turnover rate by more than half.[4]

All health agencies employ secretaries and clerks, many of whom have continual direct contact with the public or the agency's clients. Both their competence and their attitude toward the agency and those served by it influence public relations and therefore the effectiveness of the organization. The first encounter of a person seeking health services is usually with a clerk, who may profoundly affect the response to services received. Interested, courteous, and well-informed clerical personnel have many opportunities to encourage acceptance of agency services and to minimize the difficulties of interagency referral.

Activities of health agencies often require communication with people whose language or culture differs from that of professional health workers. In such situations, nonprofessional workers familiar with the particular language or culture can serve an exceedingly useful liaison function as assistants to nurses, sanitarians, health educators, and the like. Indian or Mexican public health nursing aides have contributed significantly to programs in the southwestern states, as have Puerto Rican assistants in New York City programs. Even when language is not a barrier, the professional workers' culture may separate them in feeling from the people they wish to serve, whereas an indigenous nonprofessional aide will not usually have that handicap.

The value of the nonprofessional is recognized increasingly in programs such as those sponsored by the Office of Economic Opportunity Their contribution, beyond relieving the professional manpower problem, is emphasized in a recent report of the National Institute of Labor Education, which states:

> The deeper problem emerges when we deliberately seek to help those who do not use presently constituted services although their need is most critical. There must be a change in the character of service, a real reaching out into the community and determination to stay involved. This change can only be effected by adding a new member to the "team"— the indigenous nonprofessional. He can complement the professional by not merely taking over lesser tasks, but by fulfilling newly created ones.[5]

Volunteers

In almost every aspect of community health service, volunteers make contributions of in-

---

[3] American Nurses' Association, FACTS ABOUT NURSING, A STATISTICAL SUMMARY, 1966 EDITION (New York: The Association, 1966), pp. 16 and 167.

[4] U.S. Dept. of Health, Education, and Welfare, Public Health Service, HOSPITAL PERSONNEL (PHS Publication No. 930-C-9, [Washington: Government Printing Office, 1964]), pp. 10–11.

[5] Robert Reiff and Frank Riessman, THE INDIGENOUS NONPROFESSIONAL (New York: National Institute of Labor Education, 1964), p. 6.

terest, time, and effort. It is often volunteers who identify health needs and at whose insistence services are established. They can provide a bridge between both official and voluntary agencies and the public and, serving on the board, help set policy in the best interests of both. In campaigns to raise funds for voluntary agencies, volunteers' services are indispensable, and they often help in obtaining support for governmental health programs.

Thousands of hours of volunteer time are given to helping in hospitals and other institutions and in community programs. Sieder points out that under present conditions, in which an increasing number of married women are employed, the greatest number of potential volunteers are to be found among young and elderly persons. She sees volunteer service as helping the following goals:

(1) resocializing youth into a way of life which puts a premium on civic responsibility; (2) preventing illness and deviant behavior by substituting the satisfying experience of being needed and useful; (3) recruiting trainees for the helping professions; (4) supplementing the understaffed work force in public and voluntary agencies; (5) contributing service which, freely given, makes a unique impact on client treatment; (6) bridging the gap between social classes through firsthand knowledge of social conditions; (7) promoting community health through self-help projects; and (8) mobilizing public interest and support for programs undertaken to remedy unhealthful social conditions.[6]

In general, social agencies look more favorably upon extensive use of volunteers in the community than do health agencies. Physicians, and perhaps especially nurses, perceive their responsibilities toward patients in a way that makes them reluctant to allow either paid or volunteer nonprofessional workers to engage in activities directly serving patients which have traditionally been theirs, even when these activities are of less than professional nature. In hospitals, however, the necessity of supplementing professional nursing has resulted in demonstrating that aides and volunteers with proper training and supervision can carry out many nursing functions, leaving professional nurses

free for professional duties. A few health departments are beginning to use volunteers in clinics and health centers for service similar to that given in hospitals. However, their full potential, especially that of the indigenous volunteer who comes from the same social group as the people he serves, remains to be explored.

Shortage of Health Personnel

Although scientific and technological growth is producing a store of knowledge offering great promise for good health, its fulfillment requires large numbers of skilled manpower. As medical research discoveries have multiplied the opportunities to improve and preserve human health, and as the population for whose benefit they should be exploited has increased, the need for a significantly larger force of professionally trained people in health and medicine has become a matter of national concern.

Consideration of growth trends in the population and in professional manpower leads to the conclusion that even present vigorous national efforts will be unable to do much more than maintain the present inadequate status. For instance, between 1930 and 1950 the ratio of doctors of medicine and osteopathy to population in the United States increased from 134 to 149 per 100,000, but 13 years later, in 1963, the rate was still 149. Public Health Service projections for 1975 assume expansion of the present 92 schools of medicine and osteopathy and construction of 12 to 15 new schools, as well as the continued immigration of foreign-trained physicians; but they project an increase to only 154 doctors per 100,000 population.[7]

The dentist-to-population ratio has continuously declined from 59 to 100,000 in 1930, to 57 in 1950, to 56 in 1963. Projections based on anticipated additions to present dental training facilities place the ratio in 1975 at 53 per 100,000.[8]

---

[6] Violet M. Sieder, "Volunteers," in Harry L. Lurie (ed.), ENCYCLOPEDIA OF SOCIAL WORK (New York: National Association of Social Work, 1965), p. 832.

[7] U.S. Department of Health, Education, and Welfare, Public Health Service, HEALTH MANPOWER SOURCE BOOK 18, MANPOWER IN THE 1960s (PHS Publication No. 263, Section 18 [Washington: Government Printing Office, 1964]), pp. 20 and 38.

[8] Ibid., pp. 42 and 51.

Because of aggressive efforts on the part of official and professional agencies, the number of nurses in practice has increased in recent years from 375,000 in 1950 to 621,000 in 1966, or from 249 to 319 per 100,000.[9] The inadequacy of the present available supply of nurses, however, is indicated by the fact that 21 per cent of budgeted full-time professional nursing positions in nonfederal general hospitals in 1962 were vacant.[10] The increase in public health nurses has been proportionate to the total, but in 1962 only 43 per cent of them had public health training approved by the National League for Nursing.[11]

Although detailed information has not been assembled on shortages of other health personnel, in 1966 a joint study by the American Hospital Association and the PHS indicated that the total number of professional, technical, and auxiliary personnel employed in hospitals is about 1.4 million. An increase of about 20 per cent over present staffing would be needed to provide optimum care, the most urgent needs being for nurses, practical nurses, and aides.

Practitioners in all health professions tend to be concentrated in urban areas. Among physicians, although general practitioners are evenly distributed, relatively few specialists practice outside of metropolitan areas. The ratio of specialists to population in metropolitan areas is more than twice that of nonmetropolitan areas. The ratio of dentists is also higher in metropolitan areas. The northeastern, north central, and Pacific coast states have relatively high ratios of health professionals to population, and the southern states have low ratios. Five of the southern states have 70 or fewer private phsycians in practice per 100,000 population, whereas California, Massachusetts, and New York have 120 or more.[12]

In efforts to increase health manpower, the health professions legislation provides grants for construction of educational facilities and grants to medical, dental, osteopathic, and pharmacy schools, as well as to schools of nursing and schools of public health to enable them to establish, expand, or improve instruction in certain specified health fields. Grants and loans for graduate training of physicians, nurses, engineers, and scientists are made to institutions and to individuals.

The recently enacted Allied Health Professions Personnel Training Act of 1966 authorizes PHS support for baccalaureate or graduate allied health curriculums such as medical technology, physical therapy, occupational therapy, and dental hygiene. The four major forms of aid provided are construction grants, basic and special improvement grants for teaching programs, advanced traineeships, and demonstration grants for curriculum development and other innovative programs. The major contribution of the Office of Education in training health workers is under the permanent, ongoing program of aid for vocational and technical education.

In spite of these and other national efforts to remedy the shortage of professional personnel, the shortage will inevitably continue, and communities will have to compete for health workers. One possible approach to the problem, used by a number of areas, is to support training of medical students and others on the condition that upon completion of training they will practice for a stipulated period in the community providing the support. Guaranteed income, and assistance in obtaining and paying for professional facilities are other possible methods of encouraging professionals to settle in a community. Opportunities for practice may also be deciding factors. A high quality of hospital, laboratory, and other supporting services, and suitable office space will carry weight with physicians, as will the presence of a medical college with its resources for consultation, professional association, and continuing education. And, of course, a community must compete for health workers in terms of economic conditions, amenities, and general desirability as a place to live.[13]

[9] American Nurses' Association, *op. cit.*, p. 7.

[10] *Ibid.*, p. 19.

[11] U.S. Department of Health, Education, and Welfare, Public Health Service, NURSES IN PUBLIC HEALTH (PHS Publication No. 785 [Washington: Government Printing Office, 1964]) , p. 14.

[12] See HEALTH MANPOWER SOURCE BOOK 18, MANPOWER IN THE 1960s, *op. cit.*

[13] Health Department policies that help to attract, develop, and retain competent staff will be discussed in Chapter 19.

Organization and administration of health services can do much to relieve the shortage of professional personnel in a community. When duplication is eliminated through coordination, better use can be made of whatever professional time is available. For example, well-administered combination nursing agencies, coordinating the work of visiting nurse associations and health departments, have been notably successful. Through interagency or community health planning, professional workers can be deployed to cover a range of community activities, and special programs requiring intensification can be timed to avoid unnecessary competition for professional time. Agency planning and policies that encourage determination of realistic service priorities discourage use of professional time on less productive activities.

Efforts of those in health professions to raise their own standards and capabilities have tended to take precedence over consideration of the possible value of nonprofessionals in the total effort. In the face of projected continuing scarcity of professional talent, the increasing opportunities to improve health demand aggressive exploration of the potential contributions to be made by persons with less technical training. To derive full benefit from nonprofessional skills, it is more productive to consider them for their own value than to think of them as inferior but necessary substitutes for the professionally skilled. By selecting from the numerous functions performed in providing health services those not requiring health professional training, and building from them discrete occupations, health agencies can attract the competent employee who respects the health professions but would not be willing to spend his career entirely in their shadow. The health organization whose staff members, professional and nonprofessional, identify with its mission profits thereby in ingenuity and creativity.

An extensive discussion of the problems of manpower development and utilization is contained in the report of the National Commission on Community Health Services, *Health Is a Community Affair*. In the context of its comprehensive analysis of community health problems and opportunities, the Commission highlights the necessity of treating manpower needs not merely as a question of training or recruitment, but as an interrelated problem of utilization of skills and development of new methods of organization and service.

Part Two

Growth of Community Responsibility for Health Services

Introduction

THE HISTORY of human action concerned with community health is at least as ancient as civilization itself. Excavations of ruins dating back as far as 3000 B.C., in Asia, Africa, the Middle East, Europe, and South America, show vestiges of public water supplies and sewerage and drainage systems. The Old Testament Book of Leviticus, written some 35 centuries ago, set forth detailed sanitary regulations, including those for the isolation of persons with contagious diseases, and the Code of Hammurabi fixed physicians' fees. The Pharaohs of Egypt and other rulers in ancient times maintained a medical staff, primarily to attend the court but also to fight epidemics, supervise sanitary conditions, and sometimes to act as military surgeons.[1]

In the earliest civilizations, health and disease were believed to be supernatural phenomena, reflecting divine pleasure and anger. Cleanliness and sanitation were practiced for religious rather than for hygienic reasons, and the treatment of illness was a function of priests. Even the Jews, who recognized that some diseases could be transmitted from one person to another, believed that epidemics were a result of the wrath of Jehovah. Only as scientific understanding grew were medicine and sanitation separated from religion.

At every period of western history, the characteristics of a dominant culture have determined both the nature of additions to scientific knowledge and the manner in which knowledge has been applied. Social behavior, indeed, has to a certain extent determined the major health problems of successive periods.

In the fifth century B.C., the rationalism of the Greeks led them to recognize that ill health was associated with particular environmental conditions—that malaria for instance occurred in people who lived near undrained swamps. From this assumption, they developed the basic premise of the Hippocratic system of medicine, that health is a state of balance between man and his environment. Although the Grecian physicians failed to interpret correctly the environmental features that endangered health, and placed greater emphasis on personal hygiene than on environmental sanitation, their work provided a basis for investigation of the causes of disease that was to influence the science of medicine for 2,000 years.

The Romans added little to the Greek medical science they adopted, but they achieved certain practical improvements. Their particular genius was in engineering and administration and some of their accomplishments, such as the aqueducts to bring water long distances to the public fountains of Rome and the Cloaca Maxima that drained the marshy land at the foot of the Capitoline Hill, are still in use. The supply and purity of water and the sewerage systems were responsibilities of government officials during both the Republic and the Empire, and public authorities also exercised certain controls over the sanitation of food and over public baths, taverns, and brothels.

---

[1] Major sources consulted for historical information are René Sand, THE ADVANCE TO SOCIAL MEDICINE (London and New York: Staples Press, 1952); George Rosen, A HISTORY OF PUBLIC HEALTH (New York: MD Publications, Inc., 1958); Fred B. Rogers, A SYLLABUS OF MEDICAL HISTORY (Boston: Little Brown and Company, 1962); and John J. Hanlon, PRINCIPLES OF PUBLIC HEALTH ADMINISTRATION, Chapter 2, "The Background and Development of Public Health in the United States" (St. Louis: The C. V. Mosby Company, 4th ed., 1964).

After the decline of the Roman Empire, Christianized western Europe returned to a supernatural explanation of ill health, believing it to be a punishment for sin. Rejecting Greek and Roman ideas as pagan, the people sought to heal their ills through prayer and penance.

Living conditions in the Middle Ages did not serve the interests of health. As people congregated in quickly overpopulated towns, which could not expand beyond their fortifications, and brought with them their animals and their rural patterns of living, the physical environment soon became appalling. There were few amenities like public water supplies, baths, or even sewers. The streets were foul with refuse and excrement, and houses were dark, cold, and crowded. Poverty was usual, famine frequent.

The devastations of medieval pestilence were further encouraged by the wanderings of many people during the period. The religious pilgrimages of Mohammedans to Mecca, beginning in the seventh century, and of Christians to Palestine in the eleventh to the thirteenth centuries served to distribute cholera from India, where it was endemic, to the faithful in other lands, and leprosy from the Middle East to Europe. Travel along the developing international trade routes is considered to have been responsible for the spread of plague, or the Black Death, which according to some estimates killed half the population of the known world in the fourteenth century.

During the early medieval period, a time of general ignorance and superstition, the Catholic Church was almost the only center of learning and custody of ancient knowledge in western Europe. It was in monasteries that Greek and Roman medical knowledge was preserved and physicians were educated. The planned monastery communities had the only buildings in many areas with piped water, latrines, and facilities for heat and ventilation.

Leprosy became epidemic in many parts of Europe in the seventh century, and the Church undertook to control it. Whether it was believed to be a purely physical disease or a physical manifestation of spiritual uncleanness is uncertain, but it was recognized as contagious. Drawing upon the Mosaic rules for dealing with contagion, the Church established patterns to isolate lepers from the community, including procedures for diagnosis, ceremonies to observe the departure of victims from society, and strictures about their costume and behavior. Many of the leper houses of the period were established by monasteries or were served by them.

A number of religious orders devoted themselves to care of the unfortunate, and their ministrations included nursing the sick in their homes and even medical treatment in the frequent absence of physicians. In hospitals, usually founded by church officials or by orders of knight-crusaders, patients were cared for by monks or nuns.

Toward the end of the Middle Ages, European cities began to develop systematic methods of dealing with sanitary problems, under the administration of city councillors or aldermen. By the end of the thirteenth century many towns had piped water supplies, paved streets, and sewers and cesspools. Sanitary codes of the time set regulations for keeping and slaughtering animals and preventing adulteration of food and pollution of water. When the Black Death raged in the fourteenth century, port cities instituted maritime quarantine, and some inland towns closed their gates to strangers.

Physicians of the later medieval period were organized, like people in other occupations, in guilds that stipulated their duties and fees. Municipal physicians were retained to care for the sick poor, investigate epidemics, and advise city councillors on public health problems.

The end of the Middle Ages in Europe was a period of economic expansion, the growth of trade and manufacturing. Wealth began to be measured by money or goods as well as by land, and a new respect for the technology that could increase such wealth came into being. The prosperity of the increasing bourgeoisie stimulated greater interest in learning no longer dominated by religion.

Physicians and scientists of the Renaissance and the seventeenth century added greatly to knowledge of health and disease. Diseases that had formerly been classed together as "fever" or "pox" began to be differentiated on the basis of their clinical symptoms, and their communicability was acknowledged. Syphilis received its name in the 1530s when a physician of Verona, Girolamo Fracastoro, described it in an allegory in Latin verse.

In the seventeenth century, with the aid of primitive microscopes, investigators in several countries observed the living organisms found in matter associated with decay and disease; they came teasingly close to developing the germ theory of disease two hundred years before Pasteur. In defiance of the Church's ban on dissection, the Italian physician Vesalius stole cadavers from the gallows and began a correction of errors in the understanding of human anatomy that had been accepted for a thousand years. Harvey, in England, discovered the circulation of the blood and initiated the modern science of physiology. Beginning with Paracelsus, scientists applied themselves to investigations of medical chemistry and later of biochemistry. In England, the "political arithmetic" of Graunt and Petty in the seventeenth century was the progenitor of modern medical statistics.

The burgeoning medical science of the sixteenth and seventeenth centuries barely touched the lives of most people. For all its glories of art and science, this was a cruel time to live, a time of poverty, famine, filth, pestilence, and brutality, no better for most than the Dark Ages.

In England, whose experience was to influence social patterns in the United States, social critics like Petty pointed out the values to a nation of a healthy population and proposed national programs encompassing sanitation, medical care, hospitals, communicable disease control, and relief for the poor. But England was then too much preoccupied with wars and empire building to address herself to the condition of the people. Responsibility for sanitation and disease control fell upon the towns whose outgrown medieval patterns of operation were largely ineffective.

In England after the Reformation, hospitals previously run by the church were turned over to municipalities, which continued to run them partly as almshouses, although the concept of a hospital as a medical center for the care of the sick was advanced in the seventeenth century. The lag between the discovery of new knowledge and its application was even greater three hundred years ago than it is today.

The social changes that occurred in Western Europe in the eighteenth century were to affect health and society's attitudes about it, as they did almost every aspect of human life. From the philosophy of enlightenment, which recognized ideas as the result of intelligence and reason, was developed the concept of the social utility of widespread education, including education about health and hygiene.

The acceptance of the worth of the individual and the rights of men contributed not only to the American and French Revolutions but also to changing social attitudes about the poor. The utilitarian ideas of men like Bentham set the stage for reforms based on government's responsibility for the welfare of the masses; and the Industrial Revolution created conditions among the laboring classes that invited the indignation and effort of reformers imbued with new concern for human welfare.

The effect of eighteenth century ferment upon social conditions reached a peak in England in the middle of the nineteenth century. This period has been called the era of sanitation, but it was also a time of hospital reform, improvements in medical education, the professionalization of nursing, the institution of district nursing, and the beginning of preventive medicine, as well as of widespread social reforms in other fields. Before the end of this period of great reforms, the discoveries of Pasteur, Lister, Villemin, Koch, and other great bacteriologists uncovered definitively the causes of many of the diseases that afflicted mankind and opened the way for specific prevention and treatment.

In the United States, as in western Europe, public concern about health began with efforts to improve sanitary conditions, and these were the main concern of the few local boards of health set up late in the eighteenth century following the pattern of local responsibility borrowed from England. The country grew in the early nineteenth century without much concern for health; however, there was little of the dire poverty that created inescapable problems in European cities. Municipal governments were engrossed with providing law and order. The unsavory conditions about which European visitors wrote with disgust appear to have been accepted by most Americans as part of life in what had only recently been a wilderness. Even the report of Lemuel Shattuck, the Massachusetts citizen who brilliantly surveyed the sanitary conditions of that state in 1850, received no immediate attention, although by this time health conditions had worsened.

But as American cities grew, especially with large-scale immigration from Europe, and as the Industrial Revolution spread, conditions forced attention to matters of health, especially when epidemics of yellow fever, cholera, smallpox, and typhoid fever struck again and again. By the beginning of the twentieth century, the United States was catching up with Europe in sanitation, and many cities as well as nearly all the states had health departments. The country was engaged in reform and was gradually recognizing that industrial advancement would not in itself cure urban social ills. During this time the welfare of children and mothers began to be the object of special programs of health promotion and maintenance. This was also the time when voluntary social and health agencies sprang up, a force reflecting the industrialization that produced both misery for the poor and leisure for the well-to-do.

The United States was slow to accept public responsibility for the health of workers. Laws to protect workers, that had been enacted in England beginning early in the nineteenth century, were not enacted by most of the states until after 1900, and until 1910 this country took little official action concerning occupational health and safety. After that time, the industrial health movement advanced rapidly under the power generated by organized labor as well as by physicians and community leaders.

During the first half of the twentieth century, health services grew rapidly in the United States in the public–voluntary–private combination described in Chapters 2 and 3. By 1940, 4 per cent of the gross national product was being spent for health and medical services, the country had 1.2 million hospital beds, two-thirds of the population lived in areas with full-time local public health services, and the American Public Health Association had issued its statement of desirable minimum functions of local health departments, the "basic six."[2]

Over the centuries, action in behalf of health has been motivated by humanitarianism and also by self-interest. In the Middle Ages, philanthropy placed higher value on spiritual than on physical well-being, and the manner of dealing with the obvious threat of leprosy was influenced by this viewpoint. The social reforms in England in the nineteenth century came about through a combination of humanitarian concern for man's total well-being, recognition that diseases by then known to be communicable were a physical threat to all, and realization that a working force weakened by ill health was an economic threat to the nation.

In the United States, the need for community action in behalf of health was delayed because of the relative lateness of our population's growth and economic development, and by the lingering frontier viewpoint that the government should do little more than provide "housekeeping" services. Early in this century, however, overcrowding and poverty, attended by ill health, were becoming common in our cities. Heightening social consciousness and realization that diseases such as tuberculosis, epidemic among the poor, were a threat to the entire population brought rapid increases in health services.

The services discussed in Chapters 5 to 9 are now considered traditional. By the time they had been established in most of the United States, the perceptions of humanitarianism and self-interest had begun to define these services as a right that, like public education, protects the interests of both individuals and the community.

---

[2] U. S. Department of Health, Education, and Welfare, HEALTH, EDUCATION, AND WELFARE TRENDS, Part I, "National Trends" (Washington: Government Printing Office, 1964 ed., 1965); and Joseph W. Mountin and Evelyn Flook, GUIDE TO HEALTH ORGANIZATION IN THE UNITED STATES (Washington: Government Printing Office, 1946).

5

Environmental Health Services

ENVIRONMENTAL HEALTH SERVICES—for the control of harmful or potentially harmful effects of the physical environment—are the first line of preventive defense against many illnesses. As more understanding of the interaction of man and environment is gained, they are increasingly recognized as necessary to the promotion of good health. Aspects of the environment significant for health are continually being discovered and rediscovered as concepts of health and illness change. That significance increases as man uses and changes the environment in innumerable ways.

In the past, environmental health programs were most concerned with the detection and correction of health hazards as manifested primarily through physical contaminants and pollutants. Although such hazards are still of concern, the more subtle influences of the environment upon various physical, mental, and social aspects of the quality of life are increasingly recognized as existing and as potential hazards and deficiencies affecting man's adaptation to his surroundings. The present aim of environmental health is to realize the maximum potential in science, medicine, and engineering in order to promote man's physical, social, and mental development and adaptation to the environment.

Environmental health services are thus much more complex today than ever before, dealing both with natural and man-made factors in the environment: the air we breathe, the water we drink, the food we eat, the houses we inhabit,

the stresses we are subjected to through transportation requirements, the design of our neighborhoods, the aesthetics of our communities, and many more aspects of our industrial and predominantly urban environment. Although in most communities major emphasis in environmental health programs continues to be given to sanitary activities that were of concern thousands of years ago—disposal of domestic waste and assurance of an adequate supply of clean water—the scope of modern programs must be far wider.

Development of Sanitation Services

Sanitary engineering had its beginning in antiquity, and sanitary measures of some sort were taken by governments in every century; but sanitation services as we now know them had their beginning in nineteenth century England. Even at this relatively late period such services were based not on knowledge of the specific dangers involved but on the inescapable observation that disease attended the frightful conditions in city slums.

Edwin Chadwick, the Englishman who is generally considered the originator of modern public health science, was a follower of Bentham's utilitarian philosophy. He had for some years been associated with Poor Law reform when he turned his attention to sanitary reform as a means of improving the health and lengthening the life of the poor. In 1842, as head of a

FIGURE 3. *Physical variables which bring health problems to urban environment include air pollution, water pollution, adulteration of food by pesticides, sewage disposal, dilapidated housing, radioactive materials, urban ugliness, noise, and odors*

commission to investigate the sanitary conditions of the poor, he reported that epidemic and endemic diseases were "caused, or aggravated, or propagated chiefly among the labouring classes by atmosphere impurities produced by decomposing animal and vegetable substance, by damp and filth, and close and overcrowded dwellings . . ."[1]

Chadwick's interpretation of the causation (or propagation or aggravation—he carefully hedged) of disease was mistaken, but his detailed and graphic report of unsanitary conditions, their implications, and their correlation with mortality was impressive. His recommendations for remedy by organized preventive services as a substitute for relief resulted in the first systematic public health legislation, passed by Parliament in 1848. Chadwick's thorough and methodical approach in making his survey,

and his principles for reform, became the basis of modern sanitation and public health activity.

In the United States, several sanitary surveys —general investigations of the circumstances of the people—were made in the 1840s, including those of the newly organized American Medical Association, but they had little effect. In 1850, Lemuel Shattuck's famous report of the health situation in Massachusetts not only revealed urgent needs for action but recommended procedures in public health organization, vital statistics, environmental sanitation, control of food and drugs, and many other areas familiar to the modern public health world. Shattuck's contemporaries were not stirred by his revelations, and it was not until 1869, 10 years after Shattuck's death, that his recommendation for a state board of health was put into effect.

In New York City, establishment of a board of health was an outgrowth of a civic reform movement under the auspices of the Citizens' Association formed in 1864. The Association in

---

[1] Chadwick's report, "The Sanitary Conditions of the Labouring Population of Great Britain, 1842," quoted in René Sand, THE ADVANCE TO SOCIAL MEDICINE (London and New York: Staples Press, 1952) , p. 167.

turn appointed a Council of Hygiene and Public Health made up of prominent physicians whose survey uncovered deplorable conditions. Under Citizens' Association leadership, a public health law was drafted and enacted by the state legislature in 1866 establishing a Metropolitan Board of Health with jurisdiction in the city and surrounding areas.

When the New York City Health Department was created in 1870 to serve only the city, then constituting the present boroughs of Manhattan and the Bronx, its bureaus were Sanitary, Sanitary Permits, Street-cleaning, and Vital Statistics.[2] The department's emphasis on cleaning up the city was in keeping with the general belief that disease was caused by contamination of the atmosphere by filth. This was the usual pattern for health departments in the following years, even after the emerging science of bacteriology challenged accepted notions of causation.

As the germ theory of disease began to be understood, however, its implications had a material effect on public health practice. Laboratories were established, and environmental sanitation began to be an exact science, directed specifically to the control of disease organisms that are carried in the environment and communicated to man. Activities like street cleaning and waste removal were no longer considered health-related functions and in many cities became responsibilities of another governmental department, usually public works or sanitation, with only surveillance responsibilities in the health department. (The change has not been completely accepted by the public, however, and even today citizens who wish to complain about filth in the streets are likely to call the health department.)

The progress of sanitary science has been steady from the early years of the century. With filtration and disinfection of water supplies and improved sewerage, cholera disappeared from this country and typhoid fever, frequently epidemic in the nineteenth century, is today a rare disease. Pasteurization and control of milk processing have all but eliminated bovine tu-

berculosis, which once hunched the spines of thousands of children, and have reduced the danger of many other milk-borne diseases. Through control of rats infested with disease-carrying fleas, plague has been conquered; because of mosquito control, yellow fever no longer occurs in the United States, and malaria cases number less than 100 a year. This success does not indicate that the work is finished, since effective, unbroken control of all these diseases requires continuing vigilance against reintroduction into our environment of the causative organisms that still exist in humans and animals in this country and elsewhere in the world.

Urbanism and Technology

The more urban the society the more subject it is to risks of disease. Further complications to environmental health are the new dangers brought on by advanced technology. A population distributed over a wide area provides fewer opportunities for the spread of disease through contamination of the environment than does a highly concentrated population. The pattern of population growth in this country in recent years has been one of increasing urbanization, and sanitary services have been hard put to keep pace. In addition, the advancing technology that has encouraged urban growth, and in fact made it possible, produces new environmental hazards.

POPULATION GROWTH

In the United States as a whole, the population has nearly doubled in the 50 years from 1910 to 1960. At the same time the proportion living in urban areas has increased from less than half to almost three-quarters. Thus, while the rural population has increased only slightly, the urban population has risen from about 42 million in 1910 to more than 135 million in 1960. Since 1950 a number of cities have increased their population by more than 100 per cent. Around the largest cities, however, suburbs have been growing much faster than the cities themselves.

When a city doubles in size, it needs twice

[2] George Rosen, A HISTORY OF PUBLIC HEALTH (New York: MD Publications, Inc., 1958), p. 246.

the number of dwellings, twice as much safe food, twice as large a water supply, and twice the capacity for sewage and waste disposal. The growth of cities depends on industrial growth, and industry also needs space, water, and waste disposal facilities; indeed, the amount of organic wastes produced by industry is now twice the amount of household and other nonindustrial municipal wastes. Growth as rapid as has occurred since 1950 in many cities soon overburdens even the most adequate sanitation systems.

The situation is actually complicated by more than simple arithmetic. A water source that is ample for a population of 50,000 and a river that can handle its sewage cannot be doubled in capacity, so that new, probably more expensive water sources must be found, and sewage treatment facilities substantially enlarged. When there are more homes to be heated, more domestic waste to be burned, more automotive vehicles to give off fumes, as well as more factories emitting smoke, gases, and chemicals, the atmosphere is likely to be burdened even if meteorological conditions are favorable, and to be severely polluted if they are not.

When growth occurs without adequate planning and control, housing becomes overcrowded, new housing is often built both in central cities and in suburbs with little thought for health or sanitation, and both present and future slums become firmly established. If the mushroom growth of suburbs precedes the provision of sewerage, septic tanks soon become a source of ground-water pollution that threatens the surrounding area. Only a carefully thought-out and consistently enforced development policy can prevent such conditions.

TECHNOLOGICAL ADVANCEMENT

Advancing technology makes the lives of most people easier and more pleasant and also makes it possible for the land to support a growing population. At the same time, it engenders environmental problems of growing magnitude. One of these problems that has had a great deal of public attention is the ubiquity of pesticides. These chemicals have helped to reduce the incidence of vector-borne disease, enormously increased the production of food, and facilitated

control of insects and other pests in homes, gardens, public buildings, and factories. Some nine hundred million pounds of pesticides are used annually and their residues, in minute quantities, are to be found everywhere. No ill effects to men have been traced directly to pesticides in the small quantities to which the general population is continually exposed, but toxicity due to amounts accumulated in the body after long-term exposure is a possibility that cannot be ignored. This problem is the subject of intensive investigation by the Public Health Service and other federal agencies.

Partly because of Rachel Carson's book, *Silent Spring*,[3] which dramatically warned of the possible danger in overuse of pesticides, these materials have been the subject of a great deal of public protest and alarm. However, this is an age of chemistry, and pesticides are only one group of the enormous number of chemical products in everyday use. Synthetic materials of a wide variety are a commonplace everywhere from the factory to the farm to the kitchen sink.

Synthetic products, and the wastes produced in their manufacture, require new approaches to water pollution control because they often do not respond to biological treatment and are not easily identified or removed. Similarly, the processing of chemicals and other manufacturing, as well as incomplete burning of automotive fuels, involve emission of chemicals into the air further complicating air pollution control. In addition, wider use of nuclear energy is compelling us to develop more widespread safeguards against radioactive contamination.

Food technology has reached a high degree of development—with multiplied opportunities for contamination or adulteration. Even food packaging, a convenience the American housewife expects, increases the amount of solid waste to be removed.

The City Environment

The benefits that cities offer—economic, social, cultural—draw a continuing stream of migration from rural areas. However, this continuing

---

[3] Boston: Houghton Mifflin Co., 1962.

growth, and the advanced technology that encourages it, can compound the environmental health problems that cities must deal with. Perceptions of health and expectations for its achievement are higher than ever before. "Health," says the World Health Organization, "is a state of complete physical, mental, and social well-being and not merely the absence of disease or infirmity." But cities are hard put to provide suitable backgrounds for health in these terms.

Writers concerned with the present plight of cities are forcing the situation to public attention. One of them has put it this way:

Perhaps when the achievements of the past century are appraised, there will be advanced as the most impressive accomplishment of this period the great extension of social justice. The majority of the population of the Western world moved from an endemic condition of threatening starvation, near desperation, and serfdom, to relative abundance, security, and growing democratic freedoms. Human values utilized the benison of science, technology, and industry, to increase wealth absolutely and distribute it more equitably. In the process, responsibility and individual freedom increased, brute hunger, bare suppression, and uncontrolled disease were diminished. It is a paradox that in this period of vastly increased wealth, the quality of the physical environment has not only failed to improve commensurately, but has actually retrogressed. If this is true, and I believe that there is more than ample evidence to support this hypothesis, then it represents an extraordinary failure on the part of Western society. The failure is more inexplicable as the product of a society distinguished by its concern for social justice; for surely the physical environment is an important component of wealth and social justice. The modern city wears the badges which distinguish it as a product of the nineteenth and twentieth centuries. Polluted rivers, polluted atmosphere, squalid industry, vulgarity of commerce, diners, hot dog stands, second-hand car lots, gas stations, sagging wire and billboards, the whole anarchy united by ugliness—at best neutral, at worst offensive and insalubrious. The product of a century's concern for social justice, a century with unequaled wealth and technology, is the least human physical environment known to history.[4]

Recognition of the urban condition and of its aspects that are inconsistent with modern as-

pirations forces new definitions of health concern and extends that concern into every aspect of community life.

The public health professions are continually reevaluating their orientation and practices in order to adapt to new opportunities for positively promoting a more satisfactory environment. This reorientation is leading to greater interdisciplinary activity and cooperative relationships with other professionals which, in turn, is stimulating public health to view the environment within a context that goes far beyond the germ theory of disease.

As great as have been the benefits to mankind of the germ theory of disease, it has tended to limit the health professions' viewpoint and the direction of their efforts to affect the physical environment for the improvement of human health. As a first and basic priority in sanitation, eliminating the dangers of disease organisms in water and food, as well as removing the insect and animal carriers of such organisms, cannot be questioned, but it stops short of eradicating all causes of disease from the environment and far short of promoting "physical, mental, and social well-being." If crowded, noisy, complex, ugly, odorous cities encourage ill health and prevent the fulfillment of positive health goals, the physical environment cannot be treated as a causative factor only so far as germs are involved. If ugliness—the "least human physical environment"—contributes to emotional breakdown and mental illness, it is an environmental health problem just like sewage-contaminated water.

In many instances, of course, the classical concept of cause and effect has not demonstrably operated. To wait for correction until all of the conditions for proof have been met is at worst to invite catastrophe and at best to lose advantage in achieving present-day health goals. In this context, it is pertinent to recall that sanitary reforms based on observation and recognition of results rather than proofs of causation were established even in the slower and less efficient nineteenth century well before the development and acceptance of the germ theory.

Today, even though we do not know the exact mechanism operating, observation of the

[4] Ian L. McHarg, "Man and Environment," in Leonard J. Duhl (ed), THE URBAN CONDITION (New York: Basic Books, Inc., 1963), pp. 50–51.

high association of cardiorespiratory disorders with air pollution, both during episodes of high exposure and over long periods of time, is sufficient basis for taking corrective action. This course is no less sensible than John Snow's insistence that the Broad Street pump be shut off during the 1854 London cholera epidemic, even though his theory was not proven valid until Koch discovered the cholera vibrio in 1883.

Modern science, furthermore, is not as confident that ill health or even particular diseases have a single cause as were scientists early in the bacteriological era. It is true that a disease known to be caused by a bacterium or virus does not occur in the absence of the specific causative organism, but it does not always occur *in* its presence.

The cause of most chronic and mental diseases is even less clear. In the continuing exploration of various possibilities, unusual stress is considered by many authorities to be a major factor. The components of stress are both physical and social and vary with individuals, but the presence of stress in the city environment is generally believed to affect all social and economic groups, the prosperous as well as the underprivileged.

If identifiable aspects of the city's physical environment contribute to stress, these would appear to call for environmental health measures as do aspects that can cause communicable disease or chemical poisoning. Thus, air pollution control should prevent the emission of unpleasant odors and grime as well as harmful gases and dust. The healthfulness of housing should be considered to include privacy, quiet, and pleasant surroundings, as well as basic sanitation. Water in sufficient quantity and quality should be available for swimming and fishing, as well as for domestic consumption, fire-fighting, and industry.

These broad concerns cannot be accepted as wholly the responsibility of the health professions. But support of and participation in efforts to ease the stress of city living is surely within their province.

Considerations of environmental health, in terms realistic for present-day needs, concern many interests in the community, both public and private. The city planning agency must bear them in mind in all the aspects of its proposals for orderly growth and wise land use. They are a major responsibility of public works departments, not only in providing water and waste disposal but in such things as constructing and maintaining public buildings, cleaning and lighting streets, and controlling traffic to make city streets pleasant and useful rather than threatening.

Industries and businesses can do much to make a community healthy as well as prosperous, and civic and service clubs should be a powerful force in that direction. Within the health department, concern with the environment cannot be limited to the work of its engineers and sanitarians, but must be shared as well by the entire staff in recognition of the effect of environment on human health.

Environmental health reaches beyond the community itself. In the United States, where health services are centered not in the federal government but in the states, and where functions and responsibilities are distributed within the states among many local jurisdictions, improving the healthfulness of the environment requires a greater degree of coordination among governments at all levels than was usual in the past. Towns once widely separated have grown toward each other, and air and water pollution do not stop at city limits. The interdependence of communities is recognized in the trend toward enactment of state and federal laws governing such matters as water and air pollution, and also in the growing number of formal and informal agreements among local governments and between states to combine their attacks on environmental problems.

Practically, environmental problems can no longer be dealt with as categorical problems of water supply and pollution, solid wastes disposal, food and milk sanitation, air pollution, radiation, and housing. The effect that each has on the other must be considered. In most cities, responsibility for the several programs is distributed among a number of different agencies with different specific competencies. However, community leadership, particularly in health, must be continually aware of the totality of the environment and of the interaction of each part with the others.

6

Environmental Health Programs

When this country was settled, towns and cities often grew up near water courses where there was convenient access to water for domestic or industrial purposes and for transportation. They were often located on lakes or rivers that seemed to offer an inexhaustible supply of water which was customarily used for every purpose, including dumping waste. Most river cities drew water upstream and dumped waste downstream, confident of the stream's ability to purify itself on its course.

Water Supply and Pollution Control

As population and industry grew, and both the demand for water and the amount of waste to be disposed of increased, cities began to find their water supplies contaminated. In recent years, there has been general awakening to the fact that the water supply is not limitless, and that it must be managed so as to continue to provide for the country's needs.

The data in Table 5 illustrate the rapid increase in national water consumption. Industry is using nearly six times as much water as it did 40 years ago, and agriculture two and a half times as much. With our rising standard of living, our daily per capita consumption for domestic and municipal purposes has also more than doubled, so that our growing population now requires nearly four times as much water for this use as in 1920. Continuation of these trends can be expected to bring the nation's

water consumption to successively higher totals.

Water for communities is drawn either from the surface of the earth—rivers, streams, lakes—or from ground water below the surface—springs or wells.[1] Usually surface water and sometimes ground water requires some type of treatment before it meets biological, chemical, and physical quality requirements. Surface water is increasingly likely to be contaminated with sewage and industrial and agricultural wastes, including residues of agricultural chemicals. Ground water often has too high a mineral content to be usable without processing, and in some areas it is also subject to biological contamination. Both surface and subsurface waters may require treatment (by aeration or chemicals) to remove unacceptable taste or odor.

One of the basic problems in protecting water for human consumption is reduction of contamination by sewage and other waste. When the volume of waste disposed in a water course is small enough to be significantly diluted, water drawn a sufficient distance from where waste is dumped may be satisfactory with limited treatment. As amounts of sewage and waste increase, however, they strain the capacity of receiving water to purify itself. Since it is not presently feasible to dispose of most liquid waste in any other way than into water, the solution must lie in more intensive treatment of

---

[1] In some still unusual instances, water is drawn from an ocean or sea and, after chemicals are removed, is used as an additional water supply.

Table 5

Trend in Water Use for Major Purposes, United States

Year	Population (millions)	Domestic and Municipal		Industry, BG/D[1]	Agricul- ture, BG/D[1]	Total	
		BG/D[1]	G/D[2] Per Capita			BG/D[1]	G/D[2] Per Capita
1920..............106		6	56	27	58	91	864
1940..............132		10	76	52	74	136	1,033
1960..............180		22	122	160	141	323	1,800

Source: U.S. Department of Health, Education, and Welfare, Public Health Service.
[1] Billion gallons per day.
[2] Gallons per day.

waste before it is discharged and of water before it is consumed.

Sewage treatment is a reasonably well-developed technology involving biological, physical, and chemical processes by which waste can be rendered innocuous. Primary treatment, consisting of screening for gross particles and settling to reduce and concentrate organic material, removes about 35 per cent of organic pollutants. Secondary treatment, in which oxidizing bacteria are used by any of a number of methods to destroy organic material, can remove up to 90 per cent of the pollutants. The effluent (used liquid returned to a water course) is usually disinfected by chlorination after both primary and secondary treatment. Industrial wastes need special treatment if they contain acids, chemicals, excessive animal or vegetable matter, or other materials not removable by conventional methods.

According to a report published by the Public Health Service, in 1962 18.7 per cent of communities with sewer systems discharged all sewage without any treatment, and nearly 30 per cent of the existing municipal sewage treatment plants were not equipped for secondary treatment.[2] Combined waste and storm sewers, not unusual in cities located on water courses, are an important source of pollution in heavily populated areas. Treatment plants cannot practically be designed to handle the large volume of waste water during storms, so that some or most of it containing raw sewage as well as street wastes including organic matter must be allowed to overflow into the stream.

In the face of increasing water requirements, the ultimate implications of continued pollution of water sources demand the attention of all communities, in addition to that of the states and the federal government. The need for clean water is so urgent for the health and well-being of a community that health officials must be concerned, regardless of where the legal responsibility is established.

LOCAL PROGRAMS[3]

Not only must the quality and safety of a city's water be ensured, but the water distribution system must provide adequate supply and pressure to meet both normal and emergency needs. Plumbing must be designed, installed, and maintained in such a way as to avoid contamination of water in the distribution system by waste or unsafe water supply. A city sewerage system must be adequate to carry off all liquid waste and therefore must be designed on the basis of neighborhood occupancy and volume of waste at peak periods during the day. In-

[2] Andrew G. Glass, STATISTICAL SUMMARY OF 1962 INVENTORY MUNICIPAL WASTE FACILITIES IN THE UNITED STATES (Washington: Government Printing Office, 1964), p. 4.

[3] For details of water and sewage program administration, see MUNICIPAL PUBLIC WORKS ADMINISTRATION, Chapter 11 and 12 (Chicago: International City Managers' Association, 1957).

BILLIONS OF GALLONS PER DAY

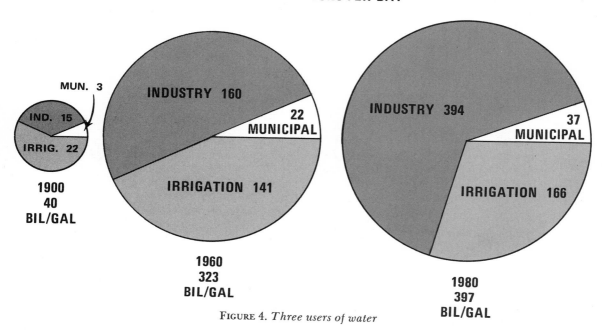

MUN. 3

IND. 15

IRRIG. 22

1900
40
BIL/GAL

INDUSTRY 160

22
MUNICIPAL

IRRIGATION 141

1960
323
BIL/GAL

INDUSTRY 394

37
MUNICIPAL

IRRIGATION 166

1980
397
BIL/GAL

FIGURE 4. *Three users of water*

dustrial waste is sometimes discharged into city sewer systems, but if the industrial waste requires more advanced processing than municipal waste, or overburdens city facilities, special arrangements must be made. In some instances the industry has its own treatment plant; in others, the city provides special treatment services and assesses an effluent charge.

Municipal water works are operated under rules and regulations issued by state health departments specifying standards of design, operation, and maintenance. Although some services are provided commercially, about three-fourths of municipal water systems, nearly all sewer systems, and half of sewage treatment plants are under local government control. They are usually the responsibility of a municipal department of public works, sometimes of a water or sanitary commission; special sanitary districts in a number of areas serve several municipalities. Communities sometimes purchase water and/or sewerage service or sewage treatment from neighboring jurisdictions or operate such facilities cooperatively. A large sewage treatment plant serving an entire drainage area is more efficient and economical than a number

of smaller plants, and a single sizable water supply system can ensure adequate supply and pressure more readily than a number of small systems.

The skills required for designing, operating, and maintaining water supply and sewerage systems include a number of specialties in engineering, laboratory science, and sanitation, as well as important contributions from inspectors, foremen, and laborers.

These essential operations of a city are expensive. Water treatment, at an average of about 5 cents per 1,000 gallons, costs some $600 a day for a city of 100,000 for its domestic and municipal supply alone—over $200,000 a year. Construction cost for an adequate sewage treatment plant for such a city ranges up to $2 million.

The return from such sizable investments is not apparent to the public. It is not easily subject to dollar measurement but lies in protection of health, improvement of recreation facilities and scenery, expansion potential for industry, and insurance of future water supply. Interpretation to the public is continually needed, and is a function that should be shared

FIGURE 5. *Major sources of water pollution include industrial processes, agricultural activity, and municipal disposal plants*

with city management and the public works department by the various other city agencies concerned: the fire department, health department, parks and recreation department, and planning agency.

The health department has a number of functions in water supply and sewage disposal. Health department engineers help plan water and sewerage systems and review operations. Health department laboratories conduct tests to measure the quality of water according to established standards.[4] Both health department and public works department personnel survey water and sewerage lines to eliminate hazards, and both departments work with the fire department on treatment requirements for auxiliary water supplies that may not be potable.

(When more than one water supply system is used in a community, the risk of contamination is increased.)

The health department also is called on to determine the quality of water from private supplies and the suitability of well locations. It has major responsibility for controlling individual sewage disposal facilities. Especially in suburbs, houses have often been constructed before sewer lines were laid, and septic tanks placed without regard to their potential for ground water pollution, nearby bodies of surface water, or drinking water systems. In most cities, health department approval is now required before building permits are issued so that the adequacy of the soil to accommodate drainage can be determined, and building specifications drawn up to prevent accidents and nuisances.[5]

[4] See PUBLIC HEALTH SERVICE DRINKING WATER STANDARDS, 1962 (PHS Publication No. 956 [Washington: Government Printing Office, 1962]) and American Public Health Association, STANDARD METHODS FOR THE EXAMINATION OF WATER AND WASTE WATER (New York: The Association, 11th ed., 1960).

[5] See U.S. Department of Health, Education, and Welfare, Public Health Service, MANUAL OF SEPTIC TANK PRACTICE (PHS Publication No. 526 [Washington: Government Printing Office, 1960]).

The problem persists, however, in some unincorporated places.

STATE PROGRAMS

The states have primary powers for control of water pollution. Traditionally, state legislation gave the health department authority to enforce water pollution control with other departments held responsible for certain aspects of the problem.

In recent years the trend has been toward a "comprehensive approach to pollution control, whose object is to preserve and improve water quality for all legitimate uses and to do this through an agency that represents all affected interests."[6] As of 1962, statutes of 35 states and Puerto Rico, reflecting this approach, generally empowered the responsible administering agency to "determine the permissive limits of waste discharges into the waters of the state, to enforce the abatement of existing pollution, and through a system of permits to regulate any new or increased discharges to prevent impairment of desired water use."[7]

With only few exceptions, however, state programs are hindered by inadequate financing. A report prepared by the Public Administration Service in 1964 indicated that state budgets for water pollution control agencies should range from $179,000 in states with fewer than 500,000 people to $2.1 million in those with more than 15 million.[8] Few states even approach such levels of expenditure. State leadership, backed by informed public interest, is necessary to accomplish water pollution control, a problem almost no community can solve independently.

FEDERAL PROGRAMS

Protection of public water supplies is the objective of several activities conducted by the Public Health Service. As part of its responsibility to prevent the interstate transmission of communicable disease, the Service enforces regulations for drinking water on interstate carriers. Carriers are required to take on water only where the municipal supply is certified as meeting PHS standards. If the water in any of some 800 watering points for trains, buses, or planes falls short of standards, the carriers cannot use it.

Another PHS function is operating a network that provides continual data on water quality. It also gives technical assistance to the states in improvement of water supplies and establishes standards for water used for drinking, shellfish and other marine food production, and bathing and other human contact with water. New municipal water systems are usually built in accordance with PHS standards, required by law in some states and also by the American Water Works Association, to which most municipalities belong. The Service develops techniques for identifying contaminants— biological, chemical, and radiological—as well as to determining their effects on human health.

Federal concern with clean water has been expressed in a series of laws passed since 1948, when the Federal Water Pollution Act (P.L. 80–845) established a permanent legislative base for action upon which subsequent amendments have been built. In 1966, an Executive Order divided the responsibility for the federal program between the Public Health Service, which had previously carried it, and the newly established Federal Water Pollution Control Administration of the Department of Interior.

Under agreement between the two departments, the Public Health Service is specifically concerned with the health significance of water pollution, and the Federal Water Pollution Control Administration has now taken over the program of grants to communities for building or improving sewage treatment facilities. (More than 6,000 communities have received grants since the program began in 1956.)

The FWPCA is also responsible for enforcement procedures, either on request of state governors or when reports indicate that pollution is occurring. The procedure stipulated by law provides for consultation with water pollution agencies allowing enough time for corrections

---

[6] A STUDY OF POLLUTION—WATER, A STAFF REPORT TO THE COMMITTEE ON PUBLIC WORKS, UNITED STATES SENATE (Washington: Government Printing Office, 1963), p. 74.

[7] Ibid.

[8] Thomas R. Jacobi, Richard A. Povia, and E. F. Ricketts, "Staffing and Budgetary Guidelines for State Water Pollution Control Agencies," JOURNAL WATER POLLUTION CONTROL FEDERATION, January, 1965, pp. 1–17.

to be made. Court action because of noncompliance with conference recommendations is only rarely necessary.

The 1966 reorganization of water pollution activities provides for a more comprehensive approach to the total water problem, as is increasingly the case in state programs. The Public Health Service, like state health departments, has major responsibility in determining the health needs in pollution control.

The federal government provides important support for water pollution activities, stimulates improvements, resolves disputes, and develops new methods, but the front line of activity is at the state and local levels.

Solid Waste Disposal[9]

Solid waste includes garbage; wastepaper, tin cans, bottles, and other rubbish; abandoned automobiles; industrial solid waste; street sweepings, leaves, and dirt; and ashes—all the miscellaneous discards of daily living. As technology has advanced and standards of living increased, the city's refuse has assumed mountainous proportions. In the United States today, the daily production of routinely collected solid waste is about 4.5 pounds per capita, equal to 225 tons each day for a city of 100,000 population. If all solid waste is included, the total is close to eight pounds per capita.[10]

The belief that decomposition of garbage produces atmospheric impurities that cause disease, which motivated Chadwick more than a hundred years ago, has long since been disproven and the health hazards involved in refuse improperly handled have been specifically identified. Garbage left standing provides a breeding place for flies and other insects that are vectors (carriers) of various communicable diseases; it also may harbor rats carrying plague. Carelessly dumped refuse can pollute both soil and ground water, and it may cause

smouldering fires that are difficult to control. Trash burned in hundreds, or even thousands, of backyards can cause significant air pollution. All refuse that is not properly handled creates a nuisance that the public no longer will tolerate.

DISPOSAL METHODS

When cities in this country were surrounded by large areas of open land, many of them disposed of refuse on a city dump located, at least at first, at a reasonable distance from where people lived. The town dump, unsanitary and unsightly as it was, became an American institution, and one that still persists in many areas. However, many cities have exhausted the readily available dump space, and as cities have drawn closer together, the daily tons of refuse would need to be hauled prohibitive distances even where dumps could still be tolerated. Cities on rivers or oceans, into which garbage and other refuse was once dumped, now face the fact that even large volumes of water cannot accommodate unlimited waste.

The major solutions now in use are the sanitary landfill and incineration. Unlike the open dump, the landfill method does not leave refuse open for vector-breeding, fires, and disagreeable odors. On land selected for the purpose, in terms of local soil and drainage conditions, the day's load is spread, packed down, and covered with a layer of earth. When the area's capacity is reached, a 2-foot earth cover is applied to seal the fill. When operations are carried out according to established standards, sanitary landfills can solve the public health and nuisance problems of solid waste disposal and in addition may result in reclamation of land that was formerly useless.

In some situations, two or more communities can join together to utilize a common sanitary landfill, sharing costs according to their refuse production, and thereby usually reducing the cost for each community.

Some cities, especially those located in areas so densely populated that space even for sanitary landfill is not available, incinerate their solid waste, except for nonburnable materials and bulky objects that must be disposed of in other ways. With modern, well-designed equip-

---

[9] For detailed description of solid waste disposal activities, see MUNICIPAL PUBLIC WORKS ADMINISTRATION, op. cit., Chapter 13.

[10] Committee on Pollution, National Academy of Sciences—National Research Council, WASTE MANAGEMENT AND CONTROL (Washington: The Academy, 1966), pp. 13–14.

ment, combustible waste can be burned at very high temperatures so that gases and odors are destroyed and air pollution is minimized, but few communities have such equipment. Incineration is more expensive than sanitary landfill, but it saves the cost of hauling waste great distances, and the residue of burning that must be carried off is only a fraction of the total load.

In areas where sewerage capacity is sufficient, garbage is now often ground, either in household grinders, at grinding stations, or at sewage treatment plants, and discharged into the sewerage system. The obvious advantages of this procedure, however, may be offset by the increased load of sewage for treatment. Refuse collection and disposal are of course still necessary.

Commercial garbage is sometimes purchased by hog farmers for use as feed. (All states have laws requiring that garbage be cooked before such use, to prevent the spread of disease.) Composting, or the conversion of organic waste to useful soil conditioner, is widely practiced in some other countries. It has not been used extensively in this country, but is receiving increased attention. If garbage is to be used for feeding or composting, or to be ground at central locations, it must be collected separately from other refuse, or separated after collection, processes that add to the difficulty and cost of disposal.

COLLECTION

Solid waste collection is involved and difficult. It is an unpleasant job little noticed when done well but subject to prompt criticism for any shortcomings. Citizen cooperation is as important to efficiency in waste collection as a smoothly operating system.

Ordinances in most cities specify in some detail such matters as where, how often, and what refuse will be collected and how it must be stored and prepared for collection, but such regulations need to be backed up by public understanding and participation. An unremitting campaign of information and education is undoubtedly a good investment; without it regulations about types of containers, separation of refuse, and other necessary household procedures will not be observed.

In many cities, waste collection and disposal are carried on by a municipal department of public works or sanitation, or a special sanitary district, but all or part of these functions may also be provided commercially under contract with the city. In areas where municipal service is not extended, or for types of refuse that are not included in the service (from some industries, for instance), private companies often contract directly with householders or businesses; this service is likely to be expensive and gives the city less control over the extent and manner of refuse disposal. Whatever system is used, an overall plan, based on professional analysis of the present and anticipated needs for collection as well as disposal of refuse, is of the utmost importance.

Although health departments are usually not directly responsible for refuse collection and disposal, both local and state health departments are active in several aspects of solid waste management to prevent not only the aesthetic offenses which are likely to arouse public protest, but also the less obvious sanitary hazards as well.

The rapidly growing problem of solid waste management was recognized as national in scope by the Solid Waste Disposal Act of 1965,[11] under which the Department of Health, Education, and Welfare is given new and specific responsibility for action. The program, administered by PHS, includes grants to states and interstate agencies for development of solid waste disposal plans; grants to public and nonprofit organizations for demonstration of new and improved disposal methods and processes; and research, by PHS itself and by others through grants and contracts, to develop new methods, evaluate health hazards, and study potential values of discarded wastes.

Insect and Rodent Control

Public health triumphs over yellow fever, plague, and malaria came from discovery that these diseases were carried by insects (in the case of plague, an insect that infests rats) and the development of techniques to destroy or re-

[11] Public Law 89–272, Title II.

duce the numbers of such insects, known as vectors. Surveillance is still needed to ensure that the species of mosquitoes that carry yellow fever and malaria do not again become common, to prevent excessive rat infestation, and to prevent uncontrolled breeding of insects.

In some parts of the country, mosquito-borne encephalitis occurs in epidemics, and while it does not affect large numbers of people, control of insects carrying the disease is urgent because of its severity and high case/fatality rates. In addition to carrying disease, insects can cause serious discomfort when they are uncontrolled, and the undesirability for any city of a large rat population is obvious.

Some vector control is part of other programs. Sanitary solid waste disposal, for instance, limits the breeding of flies and rats; proper water resource management prevents mosquito breeding in impounded waters; and both food and housing sanitation are concerned with vector control. A number of state health departments operate mosquito control programs, and the Public Health Service provides technical assistance to the states.

Most local health departments include vector control in their environmental sanitation programs. Activities may include vector surveys, direct application of insecticides, and nearly always public information to encourage practices that will prevent vector breeding.

A part of vector control that is receiving increased attention is the possible adverse effects of widespread use of pesticides. These chemicals are now present in small amounts everywhere in the environment. The possibility that they could accumulate to levels dangerous to man calls for care in using them only as they are needed, and caution is always necessary in handling them in quantity. Not only in its own operations, but also in overseeing those of private pest eradicators and in informing the public, health departments must be concerned with moderate and sensible use of pesticides.

Milk and Food Sanitation

Most civilizations have been concerned with the cleanliness of food and have had laws dealing with the sale of spoiled or contaminated food. There was little understanding of spoilage or contamination, however, until the middle of the nineteenth century when Pasteur discovered that wine spoilage during fermentation was due to the presence of foreign organisms and showed that they could be destroyed by heating at a certain temperature for a short period, the process now considered essential to safeguard milk. The discoveries made during the ensuing years of the century in the science of bacteriology provided a background for practical sanitary measures to prevent the spread of disease in milk and other food.

In 1901, W. H. Parks, who directed the first public health laboratory in this country in New York City, demonstrated that in the summer delivered milk contained millions of bacteria, and in later work showed a clear relationship between the consumption of raw milk and infant morbidity and mortality.[12] As a result, the city established a milk sanitation program, and in 1910 the Board of Health began to require milk pasteurization.

Federal action began in 1906 with passage of a law, administered by the Department of Agriculture, prohibiting the sale of adulterated and misbranded food. The interest of that Department and of the Public Health Service in food sanitation increased in following years, and even after the Food and Drug Administration was created in 1948[13] and given overall federal responsibility for protecting the purity of food, both retained certain activities in this field.

The Department of Agriculture, for instance, inspects meat and manufactured milk products (butter, powdered milk, etc.) entered in interstate commerce. The Public Health Service promotes state and local adoption of standard ordinances and codes for milk sanitation and food service sanitation and through a variety of other means, including training and standards development, encourages improvement in these areas. PHS also has special responsibilities for shellfish sanitation.

---

[12] George Rosen, A HISTORY OF PUBLIC HEALTH (New York: MD Publications, Inc., 1958), p. 359.

[13] See Chapter 3 for description of Food and Drug Adminstration functions.

State-level responsibility for milk and food sanitation usually is lodged with the agriculture or health department. State laws stipulate sanitary standards for food sold within the state in somewhat the same manner that federal laws apply to food in interstate commerce, and in about a third of the states the legislation conforms to federal legislation. The trend toward conformity is also expressed in the interstate milk shippers agreement, under which compliance with Public Health Service standards qualifies a milk supply as acceptable in all the cooperating states.

Food industry expansion has been accompanied by growing voluntary compliance with sanitary standards by producers and processers. Self-inspection of dairy farms as well as processing plants, with only occasional supervision by health authorities, is becoming common in the milk industry, especially among the larger producers. Large food manufacturers, such as chain bakeries, centralize production in new plants where sanitary control is easier. Industry organizations, such as the National Canner's Association and the American Institute of Baking, promote self-policing of sanitary conditions by their members.

At the local level where food is consumed, however, the health department must safeguard the cleanliness of the food until it gets to the consumer. In some states local authorities have responsibility for enforcing state law, and local ordinances are often more stringent than state law. The most common local programs in food sanitation cover restaurants and other places where food is served as well as milk.

Procedures for safeguarding milk from farm to table have been developed in great detail, since this food is especially suitable for the growth of bacteria.[14] Standards for production and processing of milk have been set by the Public Health Service,[15] and the American Public Health Association has published standards for bacteriologic examination of dairy products.[16] Inspection of farms and milk plants, and laboratory testing of milk before and after processing, must be performed by the health department or by industry with health department supervision. In addition, health departments should certify plans for new construction in dairy farms and milk plants.

Food service sanitation programs aim at preventing the contamination of food as it is prepared and served in restaurants, bars, lunch counters, institutions, and vending machines. Requirements are outlined in model ordinances developed by the Public Health Service,[17] which have been extensively adopted.

In most communities, sanitarians make unannounced visits to food service establishments and inspect them according to a standard schedule of factors. Time limits are set for correcting deficiencies, after which licenses or permits may be revoked.

Physical examination of food handlers, still practiced in some communities, is not recommended. It provides a false sense of security because it reflects health only at the time of examination; furthermore, most of the diseases that can be readily uncovered in the usual examination are not likely to be transmitted through food. Training food service managers and owners in the principles of sanitary food service, both in special classes and by sanitarians as they make inspections, is considered a more positive and effective approach. Plans for construction of food service establishments should be reviewed and certified by the health department.

Air Pollution Control

Although some communities had vigorous smoke abatement campaigns as early as the 1930s, the modern science of air pollution control—concerned not just with the gases and particles contained in smoke but with a variety of

---

[14] Local ordinances generally cover the sanitation of fluid milk and cream; inclusion of ice cream, cottage cheese, and sour milk and cream is recommended but is not as usual.

[15] GRADE A PASTEURIZED MILK ORDINANCE (1965) and METHODS OF MAKING SANITARY RATINGS OF MILKSHEDS (1959), (Washington: Government Printing Office).

[16] STANDARD METHODS FOR THE EXAMINATION OF DAIRY PRODUCTS (New York: The Association, 11th ed., 1960).

[17] FOOD SERVICE SANITATION MANUAL, INCLUDING A MODEL FOOD SERVICE SANITATION ORDINANCE AND CODE, 1962 and THE VENDING OF FOOD AND BEVERAGES, A SANITATION ORDINANCE AND CODE, 1965.

PHS-4006
REV. 5-65

DEPARTMENT OF ENVIRONMENTAL HEALTH
P. O. Box 1293 - Municipal Office Building - Albuquerque, New Mexico
FOOD SERVICE ESTABLISHMENTS INSPECTION REPORT

Permit No. _____

Type _____ NSD _____

NAME OF ESTABLISHMENT	ADDRESS	OWNER OR OPERATOR

Sir: Based on an inspection this day, the items marked below identify the violation in operation or facilities which must be corrected by the next routine inspection or such shorter period at time as may be specified in writing by the health authority. Failure to comply with this notice may result in immediate suspension of your permit (or downgrading of the establishment).* An opportunity for an appeal will be provided if a written request for a hearing is filed with the health authority within the period of time established in this notice for the correction of violations.

SECTION B. Food

1. FOOD SUPPLIES

Item		Specify:	Bakery products	Poultry and poultry products	Meat and meat products	Frozen desserts	Shellfish	Milk and milk products	Demerit points
1	Approved source								6
2	Wholesome—not adulterated								6
3	Not misbranded								2
4	Original container, properly identified								
5	Approved dispenser								2
6	Fluid milk and fluid milk products pasteurized								6

2. FOOD PROTECTION

Item		Preparation	Storage	Display	Service	Transportation	Demerit points
8	Protected from contamination						4
9	Adequate facilities for maintaining food at hot or cold temperatures						2
10	Suitable thermometers properly located						2
11	Perishable food at proper temperature						2
12	Potentially hazardous food at 45° F. or below, or 140° F. or above as required						6
13	Frozen food kept frozen; properly thawed						2
14	Handling of food minimized by use of suitable utensils						4
15	Hollandaise sauce of fresh ingredients, discarded after three hours						6
16	Food cooked to proper temperature						6
17	Fruits and vegetables washed thoroughly						2
18	Containers of food stored off floor on clean surfaces						2
19	No wet storage of packaged food						2
20	Display cases, counter protector devices or cabinets of approved type						2
21	Frozen dessert dippers properly stored						2
22	Sugar in closed dispensers or individual packages						2
23	Unwrapped and potentially hazardous food not re-served						4
24	Poisonous and toxic materials properly identified, colored, stored and used; poisonous polishes not present						6
25	Bactericides, cleaning and other compounds properly stored and non-toxic in use dilutions						

SECTION C. Personnel
1. HEALTH AND DISEASE CONTROL

26	Persons with boils, infected wounds, respiratory infections or other communicable disease properly restricted	6
27	Known or suspected communicable disease cases reported to health authority	6

2. CLEANLINESS

28	Hands washed and clean	6
29	Clean outer garments; proper hair restraints used	2
30	Good hygienic practices	4

SECTION D. Food Equipment and Utensils
1. SANITARY DESIGN, CONSTRUCTION AND INSTALLATION OF EQUIPMENT AND UTENSILS

Item		Good repair, no cracks	No chips, pits or open seams	Cleanable, smooth	Approved material	No corrosion	Proper construction	Accessible for cleaning and inspection	Demerit points
31	Food-contact surfaces of equipment								2
32	Utensils								2
33	Non-food-contact surfaces of equipment								2
34	Single-service articles of non-toxic materials								2
35	Equipment properly installed								2
36	Existing equipment capable of being cleaned, non-toxic, properly installed, and in good repair								2

SECTION D. Food Equipment and Utensils (Continued)
2. CLEANLINESS OF EQUIPMENT AND UTENSILS

Item		Demerit points
37	Tableware clean to sight and touch	
38	Kitchenware and food-contact surfaces of equipment clean to sight and touch	4
39	Grills and similar cooking devices cleaned daily	
40	Non-food-contact surfaces of equipment kept clean	2
41	Detergents and abrasives rinsed off food-contact surfaces	2
42	Clean wiping cloths used; use properly restricted	2
43	Utensils and equipment pre-flushed, scraped or soaked	2
44	Tableware sanitized	4
45	Kitchenware and food-contact surfaces of equipment used for potentially hazardous food sanitized	4
46	Facilities for washing and sanitizing equipment and utensils approved, adequate, properly constructed, maintained and operated	4
47	Wash and sanitizing water clean and at correct concentration	2
48	Wash water at proper temperature	
49	Dish tables and drain boards provided, properly located and constructed	2
50	Adequate and suitable detergents used	2
51	Approved thermometers provided and used	
52	Suitable dish baskets provided	
53	Proper gauge cocks provided	
54	Cleaned and cleaned and sanitized utensils and equipment properly stored and handled; utensils air-dried	2
55	Suitable facilities and areas provided for storing utensils and equipment	2
56	Single-service articles properly stored, dispensed and handled	2
57	Single-service articles used only once	
58	Single-service articles used when approved washing and sanitizing facilities are not provided	6

SECTION E. Sanitary Facilities and Controls
1. WATER SUPPLY

59	From approved source; adequate, safe quality	6
60	Hot and cold running water provided	4
62	Ice from approved source; made from potable water	6
63	Ice machines and facilities properly located, installed and maintained	2
64	Ice and ice handling utensils properly handled and stored	
65	Ice-contact surfaces approved; proper material and construction	2

2. SEWAGE DISPOSAL

66	Into public sewer, or approved private facilities	6

3. PLUMBING

67	Properly sized, installed and maintained	2
68	Non-potable water piping identified	1
69	No cross connections	
70	No back siphonage possible	6
71	Equipment properly drained	

4. TOILET FACILITIES

72	Adequate, conveniently located, and accessible; properly designed and installed	6
73	Toilet rooms completely enclosed, and equipped with self-closing, tight-fitting doors; doors kept closed	
74	Toilet rooms, fixtures and vestibules kept clean, in good repair, and free from odors	
75	Toilet tissue and proper waste receptacles provided; waste receptacles emptied as necessary	

5. HAND-WASHING FACILITIES

76	Lavatories provided, adequate, properly located and installed	6
77	Provided with hot and cold or tempered running water through proper fixtures	4
78	Suitable hand cleanser and sanitary towels or approved hand drying devices provided	

SECTION E. Sanitary Facilities and Controls (Continued)
5. HAND-WASHING FACILITIES

79	Waste receptacles provided for disposable towels	2
80	Lavatory facilities clean and in good repair	2

6. GARBAGE AND RUBBISH DISPOSAL

81	Stored in approved containers; adequate in number	2
82	Containers cleaned when empty; brushes provided	2
83	When not in continuous use, covered with tight-fitting lids, or in protective storage inaccessible to vermin	2
84	Storage areas adequate; clean; no nuisances; proper facilities provided	2
85	Disposed of in an approved manner, at an approved frequency	2
86	Garbage rooms or enclosures properly constructed; outside storage at proper height above ground or on concrete slab	2
87	Food waste grinders and incinerators properly installed, constructed and operated; incinerators areas clean	2

7. VERMIN CONTROL

88	Presence of rodents, flies, roaches and vermin minimized	4
89	Outer openings protected against flying insects as required; rodent-proofed	2
90	Harborage and feeding of vermin prevented	2

SECTION F. Other Facilities
1. FLOORS, WALLS AND CEILINGS

91	Floors kept clean, no sawdust used	2
92	Floors easily cleanable construction, in good repair, smooth, non-absorbent, carpeting in good repair	1
93	Floor graded and floor drains, as required	2
94	Exterior walking and driving surfaces clean; drained	2
95	Exterior walking and driving surfaces properly surfaced	1
96	Mats and duck boards cleanable, removable and clean	2
97	Floors and wall junctures properly constructed	2
98	Walls, ceilings and attached equipment clean	2
99	Walls and ceilings properly constructed and in good repair; coverings properly attached	1
100	Walls of light color; washable to level of splash	2

2. LIGHTING

101	20 foot-candles of light on working surfaces	
102	10 foot-candles of light on food equipment, utensil-washing, hand-washing areas and toilet rooms	2
103	5 foot-candles of light 30" from floor in all other areas	
104	Artificial light sources as required	2

3. VENTILATION

105	Rooms reasonably free from steam, condensation, smoke, etc.	2
106	Rooms and equipment vented to outside as required	2
107	Hoods properly designed; filters removable	2
108	Intake air ducts properly designed and maintained	1
109	Systems comply with fire prevention requirements; no nuisance created	2

4. DRESSING ROOMS AND LOCKERS

110	Dressing rooms or areas as required; properly located	1
111	Adequate lockers or other suitable facilities	1
112	Dressing rooms, areas and lockers kept clean	2

5. HOUSEKEEPING

113	Establishment and property clean, and free of litter	2
114	No operations in living or sleeping quarters or direct openings	2
115	Floors and walls cleaned after closing or between meals by dustless methods	2
116	Laundered clothes and napkins stored in clean place	2
117	Soiled linen and clothing stored in proper containers	1
118	No live birds or animals other than guide dogs	2

*Applicable only where grading form of ordinance is in effect.

DEMERIT SCORE OF THE ESTABLISHMENT _____ Date _____ Public Health Sanitarian _____

REMARKS: (Use Reverse Side) _____ Operator's Signature _____

P161100

FIGURE 6. *Food service establishments inspection report, Albuquerque (N.M.) Health Department*

harmful and irritating ingredients from other sources—had its beginning in the 1940s, chiefly in Los Angeles.[18]

Los Angeles had almost no heavy, smoke-producing industries; it was using little of the fuel known to cause smoke problems in other cities when it began to experience frequent episodes of what came to be called smog—a hazy, sun-dimming atmospheric condition that caused distressing symptoms such as eye irritation. Los Angeles pioneered in developing and adopting air pollution control measures, and their findings stimulated national attention. Air pollution catastrophes in Donora, Pennsylvania; London, England; and New York City, all attended by significant illness and mortality attributed to concentration of air pollutants, dramatically illustrated the hazards.

In 1953, the New York State Health Department began to develop an air pollution control program. The first federal program was established in PHS in 1955, and the Clean Air Act of 1963 and amendments of 1965 extended and strengthened its activities, providing support for state and local efforts. Most of the states and many local governments now have laws of some kind regarding air pollution, and programs directed toward its control.

Air pollution has definite effects on health. It irritates the membranes of the eyes, nose, throat, and respiratory passages, thus causing a range of symptoms from tears in the eyes to severe bronchial distress that may be fatal in persons with chronic respiratory disease or other conditions of lowered vital capacity. Heavy air pollution is associated with higher-than-usual incidence of acute respiratory illness.[19] The effects on health of long-term exposure to polluted air are not fully understood, but it is recognized as an important factor in urban stress.

The estimates of economic loss due to air pollution place it at $11 billion annually in "wasted fuel, agricultural damage, deterioration, corrosion, and soiling of physical structures of all kinds, reduction in visibility, and others. None of the estimates that have been made include the costs in human health and irritation."[20]

SOURCES AND COMPONENTS OF AIR POLLUTION

Air pollution is a by-product of population growth, advancing technology, and concentration of both in a relatively small proportion of our total land area.

Industry is an important source of air pollution. Nearly all industrial operations involve burning fuels, producing emissions of gas and particles. Combustion of coal and oil means emission of sulfur dioxide, a major factor in the pollution of cities like New York and London. A large proportion of the sulfur dioxide discharged to the atmosphere is produced by burning coal and oil, both containing sulfur as a naturally occurring impurity. Other manufacturing processes may produce additional pollutants such as dust, odor, and a vast array of chemicals. The toxicity of some is known, but others have not even been biologically tested.

The automobile is a national source of air pollution and a major contributor to the smog that plagues many areas such as Los Angeles. Burning automotive fuel produces carbon monoxide, nitrogen oxides, and hydrocarbons, all highly toxic gases. The effect of sunlight upon the latter two gases produces the atmospheric condition known as photochemical smog.

In addition to manufacturing and automotive vehicles, the domestic, commercial, and municipal activities of heating buildings and water, disposing of refuse, and in some areas consumption of fuel to produce electric power add to the air's load of pollutants. All communities have an air pollution potential; local severity depends on topography and climatic conditions as well as industry, automobiles, and local practices.

THE AIR SUPPLY

Most of the earth's vast surrounding atmosphere, which makes possible life as we know it,

---

[18] Thomas F. Williams, "Polluted Air—A Social Challenge," NATIONAL TUBERCULOSIS ASSOCIATION BULLETIN, January, 1965, pp. 3–5.

[19] F. Curtis Dohan, "The Complexity of the Relationship Between Air Pollution and Respiratory Health," NATIONAL CONFERENCE ON AIR POLLUTION PROCEEDINGS (PHS Publication No. 1022 [Washington: Government Printing Office, 1963]) , pp. 137–39.

[20] Williams, op. cit., p. 5.

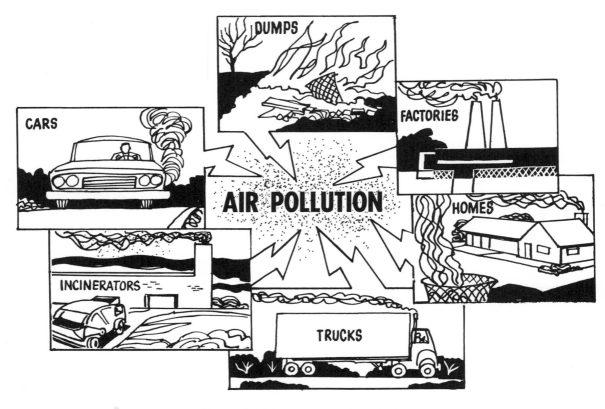

FIGURE 7. *Major sources of air pollution*

is massed in a layer above the earth's crust large enough to provide an ample total resource. In any given location at a given time, however, the amount of air available for dispersing and diluting pollutants may be limited because of meteorological or topographical conditions—for example, by light winds or calm, by temperature inversion that prevents the normal flow of air upward, or by hills or buildings that restrict ventilation. These conditions aid in the formation of smog and generally polluted air in many urban areas. They were associated with the catastrophes that occurred in Donora and in London.

In recent times meteorology has developed a great deal of knowledge about local climate in relation to air pollution potential. It is now able to "offer sound engineering advice to assist in site selection, site planning, facilities design, the establishment of operational procedures, and the evaluation of existing problems."[21]

LOCAL PROGRAMS

Although federal and state governments have important regulatory and financial functions in air pollution control, the preventive work must be done where pollution occurs. Air cannot be purified after it is polluted, and it is therefore necessary to control pollutants at their source.[22]

The legal power to regulate air pollution is part of the state's police power[23] and is possessed by local governments according to the extent and nature of the state's delegation. Legislation that provides adequate authority to con-

---

[21] Maynard E. Smith, "The Status of Meteorological Knowledge as a Factor in Air Pollution Control,"

NATIONAL CONFERENCE ON AIR POLLUTION PROCEEDINGS, *op. cit.*, p. 264.

[22] Vernon G. MacKenzie, "Air Pollution—A General Discussion," presented at Seminar on Urban Planning for Environmental Health, Mayaguez, Puerto Rico, January 29, 1965.

[23] See Chapter 3. For legal factors in air pollution control, see Harold N. Kennedy, "The Mechanics of Legislative and Regulatory Action," NATIONAL CONFERENCE ON AIR POLLUTION PROCEEDINGS, *op. cit.*, pp. 306–14; and Melvin I. Weisburd (ed.), AIR POLLUTION CONTROL FIELD OPERATIONS MANUAL (PHS Publication No. 937 [Washington: Government Printing Office, 1962]), pp. 57–70.

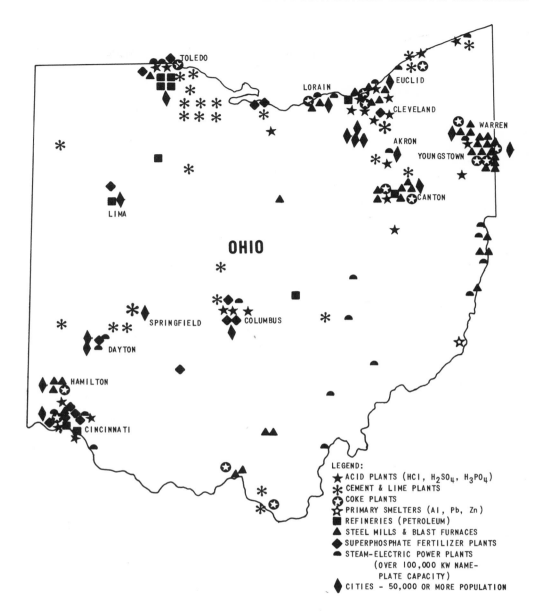

FIGURE 8. *Map shows location of major industrial processes causing air pollution. Similar mapping can be helpful in a metropolitan area, county, or large city as a guide to more effective enforcement*

trol air pollution usually requires intensive public education efforts, since the need for legislation may not be obvious.

For local air pollution programs, a commission or board is usually the rule-making body; control and enforcement operations may be carried out by an independent agency or by a bureau of the health, public works, or sanitation department. Since air pollution does not respect local boundaries, control programs at the local level are most effective when based on a region with a common problem, usually including more than one governmental jurisdiction.

In the acceleration of air pollution control activity in recent years, the elements of a local program suitable for any community have been stated by a number of authorities who are in general agreement. The *Air Pollution Control Field Operations Manual,* prepared by staff of the Los Angeles Air Pollution Control District and published by the Public Health Service, lists these elements:

1. Research and Investigation. Identification and evaluation of causes and effects of, and solutions to, both the community-wide air pollution or smog problem, and specific or localized air pollution problems.

2. Control Standards. Promulgation of control standards based on confirmed research findings and air quality standards.

3. Source Registration. Registration of the sources of air pollution in order to determine pollution potentials for (1) locating the need for remedial or preventive measures, (2) estimating trends in pollution potentials and atmospheric concentrations, (4) [sic] establishing evidence for anti-pollution legislation, and (5) planning field control operations.

4. Field Control Operations. Inspection of the sources of air pollution and enforcement of the air pollution law to obtain minimum pollution potentials and solutions to specific air pollution problems.[24]

Requisite professional skills include engineering, laboratory science, and meteorology. Inasmuch as a successful program requires public understanding and cooperation, the field staff should have skill in human relations, and professional help in public relations or health education is very useful.

While a large number of communities carry on some type of air pollution control activities, they frequently fall short of the type of program described above. A statement by a Public Health Service official indicated that fewer than one quarter of the 596 counties with populations of 50,000 or more have adequate programs.[25]

Reluctance in some communities is based on fear that enforcement of air pollution controls will cause industry to move elsewhere. The experience of Los Angeles, which has the strictest control program in the country, does not support this fear. The possibility that a city with clean air would attract more industry than one without pollution control seems worth considering. Industry has contributed significantly to techniques of control, and amicable working relationships of control staff and industry have been established in many areas.

STATE PROGRAMS

State legislation may provide for prevention and abatement in all areas; it may allow for establishment of air pollution control districts by local option or provide for a research and technical assistance program. Some state laws have all three provisions, and several have two.[26]

While there is considerable expert opinion that air pollution control should be a local government function, the state has an important responsibility to enable local governments not only to establish their own programs, but also to join in united, regional efforts to deal with pollution. States with effective control programs are active in defining such zones and in stimulating and assisting local programs. Some state programs also provide funds, service, and advice to local areas for research, investigation, and enforcement. Negotiation or action on interstate air pollution problems is also the function of state governments.

Air pollution control activities at the state level are usually carried on by health departments, sometimes under the guidance of an air pollution committee or board representing interests other than health.

FEDERAL PROGRAMS

The Clean Air Act of 1963, although recognizing that air pollution control is a responsibility of state and local government, acknowledged that federal action is also necessary and provided for federal grants by PHS to state and local air pollution control agencies for initiating, developing, or improving their programs. Grants are made to match local funds that must be in addition to amounts previously spent, so that the aid will stimulate rather than substitute for local effort. Because of the regional na-

---

[24] *Ibid.,* p. 71.

[25] Charles D. Yafee, "Air Pollution Control Program Grants—The First Year of Experience," presented at the Meeting of the Air Pollution Control Association, Toronto, Canada, June 20–24, 1965.

[26] Samuel M. Rogers, *et al.,* A DIGEST OF STATE AIR POLLUTION LAWS (Washington: Government Printing Office, 1963 ed., 1963), and (Washington: U.S. Department of Health, Education, and Welfare, 1964 Supplement, 1964).

ture of the problem, matching requirements for intermunicipal or interstate programs are more liberal than those for local programs.

The Secretary of Health, Education, and Welfare may institute abatement proceedings on his own initiative or on official request for interstate problems, and on request of state officials when the situation is within a single state. The procedures authorized are similar to those of the Water Pollution Control Act described earlier in this chapter.

The 1963 Act greatly expanded research, technical assistance, and training programs by the Public Health Service and directed attention to such special pollution problems as sulfur oxides and automobile exhaust fumes, criteria for guidance of states and local areas in establishing standards, and development of new control methods.

In 1965, important amendments to the Clean Air Act[27] gave the U.S. Department of Health, Education, and Welfare responsibility for promulgating and enforcing national standards for pollutant emissions from motor vehicles. These standards will apply to all new cars and light trucks fueled by gasoline, beginning with 1968 models, whether manufactured in or imported into the United States. They require significant reduction in emissions of hydrocarbons and carbon monoxide through exhaust tailpipes, as well as 100 per cent control of hydrocarbon emissions from the engine crankcase.

The 1965 amendments also authorize the Department to investigate potential new sources of pollution and to hold public conferences on such situations. Findings and recommendations of the conferences will be advisory, but will be admissable into the record of any abatement proceedings should these become necessary.

Control of Radiological Hazards

In the years between the discovery of the X ray and radium and the beginning of the atomic era, the use of radiation in medical and dental practice was well established. Application in both diagnosis and therapy was developed, along with increasingly effective machinery and

skill, and radiology became a recognized specialty of medical practice. At the same time, the harm that excess radiation can cause, which was known within a short time after the X ray was discovered, came to be somewhat more fully understood. By 1945, standards for use of both X-ray equipment and radium had been set at levels now considered far too lenient, but at least concern was shown for limiting exposure of both patients and professional people.

In the years since the atomic bomb first demonstrated the destructive potential of ionizing radiation, concern for the adverse effect of man-made nuclear energy has brought about national and international efforts to control population exposure. In the United States, as atomic energy was developed for peaceful uses, including extensive use in medical diagnosis and therapy, strict standards were set by the Atomic Energy Commission, which retains control over the distribution and uses of by-product materials, source materials, and special nuclear materials.

The Public Health Service, through a surveillance system in all the states, monitors levels of radioactivity in air, water, milk, and food. With financial support from PHS, all of the state health departments carry on some activities in radiological health; some of them, such as California and New York, have bureaus of radiological health staffed with a variety of experts— physicists, engineers, radiochemists, for instance —and engage in a full range of activities, including surveillance of the environment, control of X-ray installations and radium sources, and public information programs.

Some of the states have assumed the regulatory control of certain nuclear materials by agreement with the Atomic Energy Commission. In the majority of states, medical X-ray equipment is inspected in programs that vary from occasional inspection on request to a comprehensive effort including registration, inspection of all X-ray installations, follow-up for compliance, and education of operators and owners.[28] About half the states have programs to control use of radium.

---

[27] Public Law 89–272, Title I.

[28] U.S. Department of Health, Education, and Welfare, Public Health Service, REPORT OF STATE AND LOCAL RADIOLOGICAL HEALTH PROGRAMS, FISCAL YEAR 1964

Emergencies, such as local accidents that may result in environmental contamination, are covered by meticulously detailed plans of assistance by federal and state agencies, geared to take immediate action.

Only a few local governments engage in radiological health programs. Public anxiety about excess radiation has been centered in fear of fallout from weapons testing and leakage from nuclear plants; both are matters of federal and state concern. However, in 1966, aside from natural background radiation, the sources causing the greatest degree of population exposure are medical X ray and radium, both used in local communities where local action is most suitable. The use of these important medical tools when they are needed should not be discouraged, but needless exposure from such use should be prevented.

State programs to inspect medical X-ray installations, having reached about 45,000 of the 123,000 units at least once, have uncovered a large percentage that did not meet all state standards.[29] For example, the data show that 40 to 90 per cent of the equipment components considered most significant in contributing to unnecessary exposure did not meet the standards. It is therefore highly desirable for local health departments to participate in this effort. The numbers of highly trained specialists to do such inspections may be insufficient for all inspections needed in a given area. However, where professional supervision or consultation is available, inspections can be made by less highly qualified persons especially trained to check the parts of equipment most likely to be faulty. Because substandard equipment exposes operators as well as patients, inspection is a service to the whole community.

The use of radium and accelerator-produced isotopes has been made subject to licensure in some states, but it is not under Atomic Energy Commission control. Many physicians obtained supplies of radium before considerable knowledge of radiobiology was available and before modern technology had developed monitoring

tools. Because it was once very expensive, those who have a supply of radium are unlikely to dispose of it, even though they no longer use it and despite the sharp drop in the price. Under such circumstances, radium has been found in many instances to be either an actual or a potential source of radioactive exposure and contamination.[30] A local health department working with the medical profession to ensure the proper storage and use of all radium supplies makes a significant contribution to protection of the public health.

Housing and Land Use

In the early years of the public health movement both in England and in the United States, the miserable housing conditions of the poor were among the evils that sanitary reformers sought to remedy. Indeed, Shattuck's 1850 report went beyond housing for the poor to recommend planning of new communities in order to provide for an ample supply "in purity and abundance, of light, air, and water; for drainage sewerage, for paving, and for cleanliness." He also included recommendations on health provisions for public buildings and on reservation of open space.

In the present century, the American Public Health Association's Committee on the Hygiene of Housing, carrying on the tradition inherited from Shattuck, established the principle that improvement of housing conditions must extend beyond the confines of the structure itself to the total community environment. Early experience in public housing augmented this concept by showing that slum clearance sometimes simply moved slums to new locations and did little to halt the deterioration of cities. Housing, it was found, cannot be wisely planned except in relation to the social, economic, and physical life of the community. The requirement for community land-use plans and controls that was included in federal urban re-

(Washington: PHS Division of Radiological Health, 1965), p. 20.

[29] Ibid.

[30] See U.S. Department of Health, Education, and Welfare, Public Health Service, MEDICAL USES OF RADIUM AND RADIUM SUBSTITUTES (Washington: PHS Division of Radiological Health, 1965).

newal legislation in the 1950s was a recognition of the failure of partial approaches.[31]

Community leaders undertaking such planning must face a variety of undesirable conditions, in addition to dilapidated housing, that result from total lack of planning or uncoordinated planning in the past. Some of these such as inadequate public water systems, sewerage, and sewage treatment plants as well as uncontrolled air pollution are obvious threats to human health.

From the beginning of the housing and urban renewal movements in this country, the importance of health considerations has been acknowledged and participation of health agencies invited. Public health experts assisted, for instance, in setting standards for plumbing, septic tanks, ratproofing, and other health protection factors in public housing.

In recent years, public health engineers have gone beyond the specific techniques of sanitary engineering to introduce into city planning expert decisions about land and its use that will help develop and preserve a truly healthful physical environment. The two-week course on urban planning for environmental health, sponsored by the Public Health Service with participation of federal, state, and local health, housing, and planning agencies and professions, is an example of efforts to encourage comprehensive evaluation of environmental health conditions to serve as a basis for rational community development programs.[32]

In addition to its usefulness in evaluating housing, the approach used in public health to determine the nature and extent of disease problems also has application in determining need for health services and facilities. Health departments and other health agencies have responsibilities to help in shaping the distribution of these services within the context of city planning.[33]

Improvement of existing housing depends to a great extent on community housing codes or ordinances. Until relatively recently, codes in many communities were limited to building codes whose coverage extended only to construction of new buildings or substantial alteration of existing buildings, and even these codes were often out-dated in terms of growing technology. Modern, adequate codes, though they will not in themselves eliminate urban blight, are effective tools in preventing deterioration. Such codes provide not only for structural safety and fire protection, but also for health protection through appropriate facilities for cleanliness and waste disposal, light, heat, and freedom from vermin. A number of model codes[34] have been developed by national organizations and some states. Local codes must of course be developed within the framework of state-delegated powers.

Administration of codes involves periodic inspection and efforts to bring about compliance. In most instances, explanation and persuasion are sufficient, but if these techniques are not successful, administrative hearings may be necessary or even court action.[35] Enlistment of support through public information programs, as well as consistently reasonable and impartial administration of codes, encourages voluntary compliance.

In the usual community pattern, administration of building codes concerned with new construction and housing codes concerned with existing residential buildings is the responsibility of several agencies,[36] among them the health department that must inspect for environmental sanitation. Careful planning and coordination

[31] Charles R. Adrian, GOVERNING URBAN AMERICA (New York: McGraw-Hill Book Company, 1961), p. 454.

[32] Charles L. Senn, "Planning of Housing Programmes," in World Health Organization, HOUSING PROGRAMMES: THE ROLE OF PUBLIC HEALTH AGENCIES ("Public Health Papers," No. 25 [Geneva: WHO, 1964]), p. 56.

[33] A more detailed discussion of community planning for health will be presented in Chapter 16. See also

International City Managers' Association, PRINCIPLES AND PRACTICE OF URBAN PLANNING (Washington: The Association, 1968).

[34] For model codes and ordinances, see American Public Health Association, A PROPOSED HOUSING ORDINANCE (New York: The Association, 1952), and Housing and Home Finance Agency, CODE ADMINISTRATION FOR SMALL COMMUNITIES, (Urban Renewal Service Technical Guide 19 [Washington: Government Printing Office, 1965]), pp. 23–24.

[35] For legal bases of inspection, condemnation, administrative hearings, and other procedures, see Frank P. Grad, PUBLIC HEALTH LAW MANUAL (New York: American Public Health Association, 1965).

[36] MUNICIPAL PUBLIC WORKS ADMINISTRATION, op. cit., Chapter 15, "Inspectional Services."

Assignment

No._____

Serial No. S ____ ____

STRUCTURE SCHEDULE

Address _____ District No. _____ Block No. _____ Structure No. _____

Owner or Agent _____ Not Available for Occupancy ☐

S1 NUMBER OF UNITS

	Total	Vacant
Dwelling units	—	—
Rooming units	—	—
Business units	—	—

S2 NUMBER OF STORIES

Total	Nonres.
—	—

S3 EXTERIOR WALLS

Wood	Other
☐	☐

S4 STRUCTURE TYPE

Attached	Detached
☐	☐

S5 NUMBER OF TOILETS AND BATHS

Toilets	Baths
—	—

S6 LIVING UNIT IN BASEMENT

Yes	No
☐	☐

S7 MAIN ACCESS

Street	Rear Yard	Alley
☐	☐	☐

S8 WATER SUPPLY

Public	Private	None
☐	☐	☐

S9 SEWER CONNECTION

Public	Private	None
☐	☐	☐

SUPPLEMENTARY APPRAISAL

S8a WATER SUPPLY
Nonpublic water supply acceptable to Health Dept.

Yes	No
☐	☐

S9a SEWER CONNECTION
Nonpublic sewage disposal acceptable to Health Dept.

Yes	No
☐	☐

S16a DAYLIGHT OBSTRUCTION

Side	This Str.	Adjacent Structure		
	No. of Windows	Height in Stories	Distance in Feet	Horiz. Obstr.
	a	b	c	d
Front				
Left				
Right				
Rear				

(office entries)

Obstruction Factor: Total h/Total e _____

Side	Adj. a	Table	f x d	e x g
	e	f	g	h
Front				
Left				
Right				
Rear				

Total e _____   Total h _____

DHEW-ATLANTA,GA.

S10 STAIRS AND FIRE ESCAPES (for two-story tenements and all structures of three or more stories)

☐ Item Not Applicable

	Front Stairway		Rear Stairway		Outside Fire Escapes	
	None ☐		None ☐		None ☐	
	Yes	No	Yes	No	Yes	No
Free from obstruction	☐	☐	☐	☐	☐	☐
Clear egress at ground level	☐	☐	☐	☐	☐	☐
Fireproof construction throughout					☐	☐
Free from vertical ladders above first story					☐	☐

S11 PUBLIC HALL LIGHTING

☐ No Public Hall

	No	Yes	Ext.
Daytime lighting deficient	☐	☐	☐

	None	Part	All
Halls lacking light fixtures	☐	☐	☐

S12 DETERIORATION INDEX

Inside Stairs	Deg. 0	Deg. 1	Deg. 2
Steps deteriorated	☐	☐	☐
Rails deteriorated	☐	☐	☐
Public Hall Walls, Ceilings			
Hole or surface worn	☐	☐	☐
Surface broken or loose	☐	☐	☐
Public Hall or Porch Floors			
Hole or surface worn	☐	☐	☐
Surface broken or loose	☐	☐	☐

S13 INFESTATION INDEX

	Not Evd.	Re-ptd.	Ob-svd.
Rats in structure or yard	☐	☐	☐
Other vermin	☐	☐	☐

S14 SANITARY INDEX

	No	Yes	Ext.
Refuse containers defective	☐	☐	☐
Garbage accumulated	☐	☐	☐
Other refuse accumulated	☐	☐	☐

S12 DETERIORATION INDEX

Outside Stairs	Deg. 0	Deg. 1	Deg. 2
Steps deteriorated	☐	☐	☐
Rails deteriorated	☐	☐	☐
Outside Walls			
Hole or surface worn	☐	☐	☐
Surface broken or loose	☐	☐	☐

S15 BASEMENT CONDITION INDEX

☐ No Basement

	Not Evd.	Re-ptd.	Ob-svd.
Leakage or backflooding	☐	☐	☐
Stairs hazardous	☐	☐	☐
Combustibles accumulated	☐	☐	☐

S16 DAYLIGHT OBSTRUCTION

Condition warranting supplementary appraisal	No	Yes	Ext.
	☐	☐	☐

REMARKS (refer to items by number)

_____

_____

_____

_____

_____

Inspected by_____ Date_____

Time begun_____ Time finished_____ Total time_____

Office check_____ Field check_____

Form DS-1: Copyright 1944, Committee on the Hygiene of Housing, American Public Health Association

FIGURE 9. *Structure schedule*

are necessary both to avoid duplication and to develop consistent policies in housing activities of the various agencies. In a few communities, responsibility for several licensing functions is delegated to a combined licensing agency.

Public health participation in housing and urban renewal should be guided by the principle that prevention of future health problems is as important as meeting present needs. Thus the interest of health cannot be served by simply dealing with the diseases that are encouraged by crowded, unsanitary housing but also requires support of the community in preventing the development of such conditions. When slum areas are redeveloped, for instance, health agencies should lead in making sure of the healthfulness not only of new housing but also of the housing into which relocated families will be moved. They must be concerned both with the adequacy and enforcement of housing codes to prevent deterioration of housing, and with zoning to promote healthful residential environments.[37] When new areas are subdivided, they must make sure the opportunity is not missed to anticipate and provide for the new community's needs for water, waste disposal, and other health services, as well as an orderly pattern of land use.

The various agencies of local government concerned specifically with housing and land use—housing authority, planning commission, parks and recreation departments, and public works—are all set up in the public interest. Health is so important a factor in the public interest that it must be represented, and health department participation in the decision-making councils of these agencies is indispensable.

---

[37] World Health Organization Technical Report Series No. 297, ENVIRONMENTAL HEALTH ASPECTS OF METROPOLITAN PLANNING AND DEVELOPMENT (Geneva: WHO, 1965), pp. 46–48.

7

Communicable Disease Control

THE DEVELOPMENT of the germ theory of disease at the end of the nineteenth century provided the basis for a dramatic increase in the ability of communities to act effectively against many of the infectious diseases that have repeatedly harassed mankind. In the years since, detailed knowledge has been accumulated about the characteristics of hundreds of organisms that cause human disease. The specific causative organism can now be identified for most cases of infectious disease. The body's reaction to the invasion of such organisms has been clarified, and the mechanisms of immunity explored. The life history of many microbes, the circumstances of their introduction into the human body, and to some extent the way in which they cause disease have been revealed.

In the two decades since a technique of culturing viruses was developed, knowledge of these minute disease agents has been enormously extended. Since about 1950, the number of identified viruses that cause human disease has increased from 35 to over 200. The diseases in which they have been implicated comprise not only poliomyelitis, measles, and smallpox but also a large number of acute respiratory diseases (including influenza and the common cold), and gastrointestinal and neurological conditions. We know now that viruses are involved in the development of some forms of cancer.

Continually expanding knowledge of infectious agents has made it possible to study in detail the extent to which they cause human infection and disease, as well as their cycle of propagation in the environment, in animals, or in man. Such knowledge has also made possible the development of immunization materials for preventing a number of communicable diseases, and drugs or biological products for use in treating them.

Techniques of Control

Communicable disease control is based on accumulated knowledge in various scientific areas. Although the procedures emphasized are different for different diseases, the overall program consists of a combination of the broad knowledge of (1) the behavior of disease agents or epidemiology, (2) laboratory work, (3) immunization, and (4) treatment.

EPIDEMIOLOGY

The Hippocratic works of the fifth century B.C. represented the first systematic efforts to determine the causes of disease. Physicians of that time, for instance, noted that some diseases were always present in the population to a certain extent and that some occurred in outbreaks. The first were named endemic and the second epidemic, terms still used in the same sense. These ancient writings formed the basis of the modern science of epidemiology, which is "the study of the distribution of a disease or pathological condition in the population, and of those host, agent, and environmental factors that influence this distribution."[1] Although the techniques of epidemiology were first developed for control of communicable diseases, it also has application for other diseases and conditions, so that today the application of epidemiology to chronic diseases, mental illness, or accidents is accepted as important to their control.

The epidemiology of a communicable disease deals principally with:

—the source of the causative organism—the *reservoir;*

—the means by which the disease is transmitted to man;

—the groups in the population that are susceptible and those resistant to it, and the circumstances associated with susceptibility and resistance;

—the frequency of occurrence—*incidence* or *morbidity;*

—the frequency of deaths caused by the disease—*mortality,* or in relation to numbers of cases, *case-fatality;*

—the period during which a person or animal with the disease (host) excretes causative organisms—*period of communicability;*

—manifestations of the disease.

Together, these factors provide the basis for action to control and prevent the disease.

Epidemiology has discovered numerous patterns of disease. Some, especially those communicated directly from man to man, occur in any geographical area. Other diseases occur only in certain areas, usually either because of the presence of an animal species that serves as reservoir or of a particular species of insect that transmits the causative organism. The epidemic diseases may occur in a short, sharp outbreak, or in a long-term gradual rise and recession.

Typhoid fever provides an example of how knowledge of the epidemiology of a disease is applied. Typhoid fever is caused by a bacillus whose reservoir is man. It is transmitted both by direct contact with a patient or his excretions and by contaminated water or food. The entire population is susceptible except for those who have had the disease or have been vaccinated. Although typhoid fever is common in many areas of the world, fewer than 600 cases have occurred in the United States in each recent year, chiefly in single cases or small epidemics; it has caused fewer than 20 deaths annually in this country since effective antibiotic treatment became available. The period of communicability varies, usually ending with convalescence but sometimes lasting for three months. In a few cases patients continue to excrete organisms permanently—that is, they are chronic carriers.

On the basis of this type of information, the notably successful typhoid fever control measures include protection of water supplies, sanitary sewage disposal, protection of milk and other food, treatment and isolation of patients, precautions to prevent their spreading disease, investigation of the source of their disease, and identification and supervision of carriers. Vaccination is recommended for contacts, persons associated with patients or with carriers, and some international travelers, but not as a routine community measure.

LABORATORY IDENTIFICATION

Table 6 shows in brief summary the major groups of infectious organisms[2] and some diseases associated with them. The ability of an organism to cause disease, called its pathogenicity, varies with different organisms and may even vary with different strains of the same organism. Some organisms multiply and cause disease in only certain kinds of body tissue, and are assumed to be innocuous in others. Organisms also vary widely in the ease with which they are able to enter the body, and therefore in the number of people they are likely to affect.

The relative danger of a communicable disease to public health depends upon the pathogenicity of the causative organism, the likeliness that the disease will become widespread, its severity, and the immune status of the population. Rabies, for instance, is caused by a highly pathogenic virus. It is always fatal to man, and

[1] Abraham M. Lilienfeld, "The Epidemiological Approach to Chronic Disease," in CHRONIC DISEASE CONTROL (Continuing Education Series, No. 88 [Ann Arbor, Michigan: University of Michigan School of Public Health, 1960]) , p. 15.

[2] The word "organisms" as used here refers to all biological agents of disease, although technically viruses are not organisms.

Table 6

Organisms That Cause Human Disease

Organisms	Diseases
Plantlike organisms	
Funguses	Ringworm, *et al.*, Histoplasmosis, Coccidioidomycosis, *et al.*
Bacteria	
Cocci (round)	"Strep throat" and scarlet fever, boils and "staph" infections, gonorrhea, *et al.*
Bacilli (rod-shaped)	Tuberculosis, typhoid, whooping cough, diphtheria, leprosy, plague, *et al.*
Spirilli (spiral-shaped)	Syphilis, leptospirosis, *et al.*
Animal organisms (parasites)	Amebic dysentary, malaria, *et al.*
Rickettsiae	Typhus, Rocky Mountain spotted fever, *et al.*
Viruses	Smallpox, rabies, poliomyelitis, viral encephalitis, measles, mumps, chickenpox, influenza, common cold, *et al.*

Source: Franklin H. Top, COMMUNICABLE AND INFECTIOUS DISEASES (St. Louis: The C. V. Mosby Company, 1964).

humans have no natural immunity to it. Thus continued efforts to control rabies are necessary, even though it occurs only rarely in man. Some of the childhood diseases, such as measles, that affect a great many children are usually rather mild; but most infectious diseases, even those usually less severe, can cause death or lasting disability in a small proportion of cases.

The technical laboratory work of identifying disease organisms precisely is important both to the health department and to clinicians treating patients. Knowledge of the specific organism that is causing an unusual amount of illness permits the health officer to judge accurately the necessary control measures in epidemiologic terms. Laboratory information may help the physician differentiate the disease his patient has from others that cause similar signs and symptoms, or tell him whether the disease he has diagnosed by clinical observation is caused by a virulent type or strain of organism.

In some instances when drugs or antibiotics have been used over a period of time to treat a disease, strains of the causative organism resistant to that therapy develop through natural selection. Determination of such resistance not only points to a need for different treatment, but may also indicate the need for special procedures to prevent the spread of resistant organisms.

IMMUNIZATION

Long before formulation of the germ theory of disease, it was observed that people who had recovered from smallpox would not have it again. Inoculation of well persons with material from a person with a mild case of smallpox was practiced quite extensively in many areas of the world, including the American colonies, by the eighteenth century. This risky procedure was replaced by vaccination after 1798 when Jenner, an English country doctor, reported that inoculation with cowpox material conferred immunity against smallpox without causing disease or the danger of spreading it.

Nearly a hundred years elapsed before the biological processes that account for the success of vaccination began to be understood. In the past 75 years, however, the science of microbiology has opened the way for immunization against many diseases, as well as the related techniques of skin and blood testing to determine existing infection or immune status for many diseases.

Immunization is a major tool of communicable disease control. It has dramatically reduced the incidence not only of smallpox but diphtheria, whooping cough, tetanus, and poliomyelitis as well. Now it offers the opportunity for dramatic reduction of measles.

The success of immunization programs depends not only on the efficacy of the immunizing material, but upon people's behavior with regard to it. Measles vaccine was available several years ago, but did not have an immediate effect on the incidence of the disease because it was not generally used. Parents had become accustomed to this widespread childhood ailment. If they did not know or were apathetic about

COMMUNICABLE DISEASE CONTROL 83

the fact that it can result in mental retardation, middle ear infection, pneumonia, or other serious conditions, they were not motivated to seek measles vaccination for their children. (A sharp reduction in reported cases in 1965 indicates a change in this situation.)

On the other hand, smallpox is generally known to be a serious disease, but because it is now rare in this country people tend to think smallpox vaccination is not necessary—a notion that disregards the role of immunization in achieving and maintaining low levels of incidence. An indispensable part of an immunization program is a campaign to inform the public and bring about their participation.

TREATMENT

Since 1940 drugs and antibiotics have been discovered that act specifically on the bacteria and rickettsiae[3] causing many infectious diseases for which previous therapy consisted only of general measures. When such drug treatment (chemotherapy) shortens the duration of a disease, it also usually shortens its period of communicability and thus helps reduce the number of cases. In addition to reducing death rates, chemotherapy reduces the likelihood of lasting damage (sequelae) that may follow many infectious diseases in a certain number of cases. (Similar treatment used to prevent overt disease in those who have been infected or to prevent infection itself is called chemoprophylaxis.)

Levels of Communicable Disease

In the United States, disease and death due to most infections are at relatively low levels in comparison with those in many other countries. Yet the data in Table 7, showing recent morbidity and mortality in the United States due to 21 communicable diseases,[4] indicate that such diseases are still a significant cause of both illness and death. In addition to those listed,

some cases and a number of deaths are reported each year due to such serious diseases as botulism, leprosy, and malaria. Moreover, the list does not include major diseases such as influenza, rubella (German measles), and staphylococcal infection, which are not reported nationally except in major epidemics, nor pneumonia.

All the infections listed are endemic in at least some areas of the United States, and most also occur in epidemics. Several diseases do not ordinarily occur in cities because their reservoirs or means of transmission are rare in the urban environment. Others, notably tuberculosis and the venereal diseases, tend to be concentrated in cities.

Several of the diseases listed attack children more often than adults, and others occur more commonly in young adults than in the elderly; but no age group is totally resistant to any. They affect both males and females, but incidence is generally greater among males. Both white and nonwhite races are susceptible to all of the diseases; more frequent occurrence of a number of them among nonwhites in the United States is at least partially due to socioeconomic factors. For some obvious reasons and for others not fully known, high incidence of communicable disease is associated with poverty and deprivation.

Elements of Control

Long before science provided specific measures, steps were taken to prevent some communicable diseases on the basis of their observed communicability. The isolation of lepers and quarantine against plague are examples. The practice of protecting the community from infection through regulations restricting the freedom of those who may spread disease was established long before the beginning of the modern public health movement. In the United States, early state public health laws, some of which have not been changed, authorize such regulatory actions as compulsory immunization, isolation and quarantine, and compulsory hospitalization.[5]

---

[3] Drugs are used, somewhat less successfully, in treating fungus and animal parasite diseases. Neither drugs nor antibiotics useful against viruses are available yet.

[4] Notifiable diseases that are reported by all the states, of which more than 150 cases were reported in 1965.

[5] See Frank P. Grad, PUBLIC HEALTH LAW MANUAL, A HANDBOOK ON THE LEGAL ASPECT OF PUBLIC HEALTH

PHS 4.2428 (CDC)
3-62

DISEASE CASE REPORT

FORM APPROVED
BUDGET BUREAU NO. 68-R579

DISEASE | DATE OF REPORT | DATE OF ONSET

PATIENT'S NAME | AGE | SEX | RACE

ADDRESS
STREET NO. (R. F. D. if rural) | APT. NO.
CITY OR COUNTY

NAME OF HEAD OF HOUSEHOLD

REMARKS

NAME OF REPORTING PHYSICIAN, HOSPITAL, OR OTHER AUTHORIZED PERSON

OFFICE ADDRESS

DEPARTMENT OF
HEALTH, EDUCATION, AND WELFARE
PUBLIC HEALTH SERVICE
COMMUNICABLE DISEASE CENTER

☐ CHECK HERE IF ADDITIONAL CARDS ARE NEEDED

NOTIFIABLE DISEASE CASE REPORT FOR WEEK ENDING _____

DISEASE	PATIENT		COUNTY OR CITY	AGE	SEX	RACE
	NAME					
	ADDRESS					
	NAME					
	ADDRESS					
	NAME					
	ADDRESS					
	NAME					
	ADDRESS					

NAME OF PHYSICIAN, HOSPITAL, OR OTHER AUTHORIZED PERSON

OFFICE ADDRESS

Please sign and mail this card promptly even if you have no cases to report.

PHS 4.2429 (CDC)   3-62

FORM APPROVED
BUDGET BUREAU NO. 68-R579

FIGURE 10. *Disease case report and weekly report forms*

Knowledge about the communicable diseases developed in the past 75 years has provided means to control most of them without rigorous restriction of personal freedom. Moreover, research into personal attitudes and behavior regarding health has shown people to be more readily influenced by means other than official regulation. The public is likely to regard compulsory personal health regulations as an unjustified invasion of individual rights and privacy, an attitude that is often shared by private practitioners of medicine. Experience indicates that measures to prevent and control infectious diseases, such as examination, immunization, isolation, and even treatment, are best presented as services to individuals and explained as such. When this is done the need for legal enforcement is minimized.

Thus, in controlling communicable disease, the present-day health department acts more often through education, persuasion, and service than through regulation and enforcement. Patient and persistent communication with people who may not be receptive is often necessary. Communicable diseases flourish among the economically disadvantaged, whose level of education and cultural perceptions about disease and about governmental authority often make them indifferent or even resistant to health department efforts. However, if they can be led to see that a *service* is proposed, and if their personal feelings are given reasonable consideration, indifference and resistance can be overcome.

The astute health department communicates that it wants to control disease rather than people. Its employees make special efforts to be helpful in the exceedingly trying circumstances that sometimes surround communicable disease, and they avoid being aligned against the community, a position that can seriously interfere with control efforts.

Basic to control of all communicable diseases is a knowledge of cases that occur. Because private physicians are often the first to identify cases, all states by law require physicians to report cases of certain diseases that come to their attention.

Provisions vary among states and localities, but in general action is recommended in three types of situations: (1) When cases of any of the six diseases subject to international sanitary regulation (cholera, plague, louse-borne relapsing fever, smallpox, louse-borne typhus fever, yellow fever) are diagnosed or suspected, local health authorities must be notified immediately by telephone or telegraph. (2) When other diseases reportable by state or local regulations are diagnosed, local health authorities must be notified at once if the disease is one that requires their immediate action, such as a first case of typhoid fever, and otherwise weekly by mail. (3) Outbreaks or unusual incidence of diseases not otherwise reportable, such as food poisoning or influenza, should be made known to health authorities by telephone or telegraph.[6] In areas

---

ADMINISTRATION AND ENFORCEMENT (New York: American Public Health Association, 1965), Chapter 6.

[6] See American Public Health Association, CONTROL OF COMMUNICABLE DISEASES IN MAN (New York: The Association, 10th ed. 1965), pp. 6-7.

without a local health department, cases are reported to the state health department.

Notifications of communicable disease cases are forwarded by local health departments to state health departments and in turn weekly to the federal Communicable Disease Center of the Public Health Service in Atlanta, Georgia. (When international quarantinable diseases occur, or epidemics of other diseases, the CDC is notified at once, and prompt action is taken.) This channeling of information allows for continual observation of disease incidence and suitable action in case of epidemics.

The procedures followed by a local health department upon receipt of a communicable disease report depend upon the disease. In some cases, the health department may provide public health nursing service to instruct families on caring for the patient and protecting other members. A prompt epidemiologic investigation may be indicated, including determining the source and means of transmission, identification of others exposed, and action to prevent spread of the disease and further exposure.

This kind of follow-up involves health department physicians, sanitarians, public health nurses, and laboratory staff. In some instances it may require specially trained personnel from the state or federal government. Not only technical skill is required, but also consideration for patients and their families and ability to carry out the work without antagonizing or unduly alarming the public or interfering unnecessarily with the physician's care of his patient. Notifications that warn of a possible growing problem in the community call for other action —efforts to more adequately immunize the susceptible and to increase public information activities, for instance.

In addition to responding to infectious disease, communities provide continuing preventive programs. Table 7 shows diseases carried in contaminated water supplies (amebiasis, shigellosis, typhoid fever), in contaminated milk and food (salmonellosis, typhoid fever), by insects (acute infectious encephalitis,[7] typhus fever),

---

[7] This disease is sometimes caused by mosquito-borne viruses but may have other modes of transmission or other causative agents.

Table 7

Cases (1965) and Deaths (1964) for 21 Communicable Diseases in the U.S.

Disease	Reported Cases 1965	Deaths 1964
Amebiasis	2,768	65
Aseptic meningitis	2,329	2,464[1]
Brucellosis (undulant fever)	262	4
Diphtheria	164	42
Encephalitis, acute infectious	1,722	534
Hepatitis	33,856	745
Measles	261,904	421
Meningococcal infections	3,040	750
Pertussis (whooping cough)	6,799	93
Salmonellosis, excluding typhoid fever	17,161	67
Shigellosis (bacillary dysentary)	11,027	125
Streptococcal sorethroat and scarlet fever	395,168	95
Tetanus	300	179
Trichinosis	199	1
Tuberculosis	49,000	8,303
Tularemia	264	6
Typhoid fever	454	14
Typhus fever, tick-borne (Rocky Mountain spotted)	281	17
Venereal diseases		
Syphilis	112,842	2,619
Gonorrhea	324,925	13
Other	2,015	10

Source: U.S. Department of Health, Education, and Welfare, Public Health Service, MORBIDITY AND MORTALITY WEEKLY REPORT, ANNUAL SUPPLEMENT SUMMARY, 1965, October 14, 1966.

[1] Meningitis except meningococcal as listed in VITAL STATISTICS OF THE UNITED STATES, 1964, VOLUME II—MORTALITY, PART B (Washington: Government Printing Office, 1966), p. 7–385, Table 7–7.

and by animals (brucellosis, trichinosis, tularemia). For control of these, the basic sanitation measures described in preceding chapters are of the utmost importance.

For several diseases, most of which are communicated more directly from man to man either through the air or by contact, control can be accomplished by widespread immunization (diphtheria, measles, pertussis, poliomyelitis, smallpox, tetanus). Most local health departments provide immunization programs as part of their activities to improve child health.[8] As

---

[8] See Chapter 9.

part of their continuing activities, health departments sponsor immunization programs either regularly, during special campaigns, or in attempts to head off threatened epidemics. In addition, many health departments supply immunization materials for use by private physicians, and medical societies sometimes conduct or participate in immunization projects. In a special national effort, Congress appropriated funds in several years for grants administered by the Communicable Disease Center to communities attempting to accomplish complete immunization of all children under five years old against diphtheria, whooping cough, tetanus, polio, and measles.

Communicable disease control is an important part of the work of public health nurses. In addition to servicing known cases, they teach prevention of communicable diseases as part of counseling the families under their care for other reasons. In observing families during home visits, they often recognize the first signs of infection and refer patients for diagnosis and care; thus they are an important source of intelligence for the health officer about the occurrence of communicable disease. Public health nurses also participate in programs directed at special population groups, such as mothers and children and industrial employees, in which infectious disease control is a major concern.[9]

Health education has also always been an important component of communicable disease control. While much of it is done by physicians, nurses, sanitarians, and others in person-to-person encounters, most health departments both engage in special campaigns, to promote immunization for instance, and provide continuing public information service. Clear and consistent information about epidemics is particularly important in controlling them.

Although most cases of the more common and less severe communicable diseases can be treated at home, hospitalization is necessary for others. At one time, many cities had infectious disease hospitals, but because of expense and the relatively low incidence of highly communicable diseases, the present trend is toward the use of special wards or single isolation rooms in general hospitals.

The role of laboratory science in communicable disease control was recognized early in the United States, and the major function of public health laboratories has always been identification of disease-causing organisms. Modern treatment and control of infections demands more highly technical procedures than were formerly required. As a result, the volume of communicable disease laboratory work has not decreased in proportion to the reduction in incidence of these diseases. In order to make best use of the skills that present-day laboratory work calls for, centralization of laboratory functions has become a usual pattern. All state health departments operate laboratories, and many of them have regional branches that carry out certain procedures. Local health departments may refer all specimens, or all but those requiring only simple procedures, to a state laboratory. However, a number of large local health departments operate their own laboratories, some of which are designated as state branches.

The continual collection and use of information about the incidence and prevalence[10] of communicable disease in the community is basic to measurement of community health status. This subject will be discussed in Chapter 16.

Tuberculosis and venereal disease control are often the subject of special programs in health agencies. Both are endemic in the United States and occur in large numbers of cases. The nature of tuberculous infection and disease and the mode of transmission of the venereal diseases increase the need for consideration of social factors in their control. Accordingly, they are separately treated in the following pages.

Tuberculosis Control

The tubercle bacillus is a slow-growing organism that does not produce immediate symptoms when it begins to multiply in the human body. After infection is established it may progress to disease, slowly and often without identifiable

---

[9] See Chapter 9.

[10] "Incidence" measures the new cases of disease that occur during a stipulated period. "Prevalence" measures the cases that exist at a stipulated time.

symptoms, causing primary tuberculosis, which is ordinarily mild but may lead to serious complications, especially in children. Usually primary tuberculosis heals, but a focus of inactive infection remains from which active pulmonary tuberculosis may develop at a later time. Persons once infected may carry such foci throughout life. One who has had active disease is more likely to have it again than a person who has never had it.

DEVELOPMENT OF TUBERCULOSIS CONTROL

At the end of the nineteenth century, tuberculosis was so prevalent in the United States that few families were unaffected by it. One person in every 500 died of it each year in the country as a whole, and rates were even higher in the crowded slums of cities.

Tuberculosis was so common that physicians of that time spent much of their effort in treating it, frequently without success. The recommended treatment was fresh air, a hearty diet, and rest and the best place for it was away from the city, both for the benefits of country air and for isolation to protect others. Recovery, when it occurred, came only after many months or years of this treatment, so that most people, even the more prosperous, could not afford the "cure."

Leaders in the medical profession saw the chief hope of controlling tuberculosis in preventing its spread. Recognizing the need for widespread public understanding and support, a group of physicians founded the National Tuberculosis Association in 1904.[11] The Association was conceived as a partnership of physicians and laymen, and broad community representation was sought in the organization of its local affiliates. The chief objectives were to educate the public about the disease, especially about its communicability, and to promote public action.

What the early educational activities launched by the tuberculosis associations lacked in polish and professionalism was compensated for by enthusiasm and persistence. An exhibit that presented in somewhat gruesome

[11] It was called the National Association for the Study and Prevention of Tuberculosis at first. Several state or local tuberculosis associations had already been founded.

detail the miseries caused by tuberculosis drew crowds all over the country. Tracts about the disease were pressed on all who would take them—and they were eagerly accepted even by some who could not read. In addition, tuberculosis associations directed all the support and influence they could muster toward the establishment of tuberculosis sanitoria and tuberculosis services in health departments—or even establishment of health departments themselves where they did not exist. A pattern was set for voluntary community action that was to become typical in American communities.

Public health nursing as a health department service also developed as part of tuberculosis control. "District nursing" or "instructive nursing" services were provided to the sick poor in a number of American communities under voluntary auspices which were to continue as Visiting Nurses' Associations. Following their pattern, health department public health nurses taught protective procedures to patients and their families and gave nursing care to the ill. Through all the phases of tuberculosis control, public health nurses have carried a large share of responsibility and continue to do so.

During the first half of this century, the tools of tuberculosis control were much improved. By 1950, the X ray had long been an important diagnostic aid, and the photofluorograph, which had come into use in the 1940s, allowed large-scale screening of the presumably well population for signs of this insidious disease. Fresh air and special diets were by that time known to be less important than rest. Prolonged sanatorium treatment was still the major therapy, and in this country there were more than 100,000 beds in hospitals and sanatoria for tuberculosis. In view of the urgency of diagnosing tuberculosis early in its active course, both to prevent its spread and to enable successful treatment, control efforts were concentrated on case finding, and chest X-ray surveys were undertaken in attempts to screen entire communities.

The amount of tuberculosis had decreased significantly, but tuberculosis was still among the 10 leading causes of death, and caused so much illness that many diagnosed cases had to wait months for admission to a hospital. Moreover, chest X-ray surveys showed that there was much unrecognized active disease.

In the early 1950s, effective drug treatment for tuberculosis was generally introduced. It had an almost immediate effect on the number of deaths from tuberculosis and a somewhat slower but significant effect upon the number of new active cases reported in the next 10 years. In more recent years, however, numbers of newly reported cases have declined more slowly, totaling nearly 50,000 each year in the United States.

EPIDEMIOLOGY OF TUBERCULOSIS

The major reservoir of tuberculosis is man.[12] The disease is communicated from person to person through the air.

All groups of the population are considered to be susceptible to tuberculous infection. Once infected, risk of active disease is greatest for children less than four years old, adolescents, and young adults. However, probably because the older people now living were more often infected in youth than today's younger people are, more than half of all new active cases occur in those over 45 years old. In general, more males than females have tuberculosis, and case rates are higher in the nonwhite races.

Geographically, tuberculosis tends to be concentrated in urban areas, especially the slums of very large cities. The disease is associated with poverty, both in city slums and among the very poor in rural areas. Persons who have at some time been infected are at greater than usual risk of disease when they have other health problems or illnesses.

Recent research indicates that tuberculosis is not as highly communicable as it was once thought to be. The disease can be communicated when it is active in the infected person and when tubercle bacilli are being discharged from the body. Some persons with active tuberculosis are found, treated, and their disease rendered inactive without their ever excreting bacilli. Others have communicable tuberculosis when diagnosed and can be presumed to have been spreading infection. Confirmatory diagnosis of tuberculosis requires laboratory tests. Adequate treatment with drugs in most cases eliminates communicability within a few weeks, although this situation may be reversed if drugs are discontinued prematurely.

Inasmuch as infection usually results only from association over a period of time with a person excreting tubercle bacilli,[13] the group most likely to have tuberculosis in most of this country are the contacts of newly diagnosed cases. Studies have shown that about 2 per cent of them have active disease when they are first examined, and nearly another 1 per cent will develop disease in the following year if they are not treated. In some overcrowded slums of the largest cities where levels of tuberculosis are very high, most of the people live under conditions of similar risk.

MODERN DIAGNOSIS AND TREATMENT

The diagnosis of tuberculosis is a slow process except in far-advanced cases. The tuberculin skin test tells only whether a person has been infected, not whether he has active disease. Inasmuch as infection indicates a degree of risk of disease, the test is an important screening tool. X-ray diagnosis is difficult except in the hands of experts and even then may have to be repeated periodically to determine activity of disease. Laboratory diagnosis, using modern methods, requires a minimum of three weeks; it is essential in determining the susceptibility of bacilli to the major drugs, and also in ensuring that the bacilli recovered are true tubercle bacilli rather than related, atypical organisms, a number of which are common in this country.

Adequate treatment of newly diagnosed cases usually requires from two to six months of hospital care, followed by 18 months or more of continued drug treatment. After disease becomes inactive, patients should be examined at least every six months for five years, because relapse is most likely to occur in this period. Re-

---

[12] Several species of animals are susceptible to tuberculosis, and at one time milk from infected cows caused a considerable amount of tuberculous disease, especially scrofula, which is glandular tuberculosis, or tuberculosis of the spine and other bony structure. An aggressive campaign to eliminate tuberculosis in cattle, plus the practice of pasteurizing milk, have made bovine tuberculosis very rare in this country.

[13] A very few persons with active tuberculosis have an unusually communicable form of the disease and may infect persons around them on less prolonged exposure.

treatment of relapsed or inadequately treated cases takes much longer and is more difficult because bacilli have often become resistant to the usual drugs.

Prognosis is very good for the newly diagnosed case under adequate treatment, especially when disease is diagnosed before extensive lung damage has occurred. It is less good in cases where retreatment becomes necessary for any reason. A certain proportion of patients in tuberculosis hospitals who fall in the second group will not recover sufficiently to be able to leave the hospital. Because of the risk and seriousness of relapse, persons who have had active tuberculosis should be given detailed advice about health checkups.

A very effective tool for control is isoniazid, the most common tuberculosis drug, to prevent active tuberculosis in persons who have been infected. Daily doses of this cheap and not unpleasant drug taken for a year are recommended for contacts of new cases, children under four years old who react to tuberculin, and other groups whose disease risk is high.

SOCIAL FACTORS IN TUBERCULOSIS CONTROL

The prevalence of many communicable diseases is greatest among economically and socially disadvantaged groups, and tuberculosis has a particularly obstinate hold in such populations. Overcrowded living promotes the spread of infection, and the stresses of poverty encourage progression of infection into disease. Controlling this disease among people preoccupied with the immediate pressures of their daily lives is complicated by the time needed for every step— screening, diagnosis, and treatment. The cultural gulf and frequently a language barrier between professional workers and patients are obstacles at every point.

Many of these people fear tuberculosis, some even consider it a disgrace, and it is a serious economic threat to people whose existence is already marginal. When people are very poor, they are too much engrossed with the present to be much concerned about the future, and inasmuch as tuberculosis often does not cause acute symptoms until it is very far advanced, they may handle their emotions about it by ignoring it—to the exasperation of professional workers.

People who live even in dire poverty are as strongly attached to their families as those who live comfortably, and the separation involved when they are hospitalized for tuberculosis for the months that may be thought necessary is as great a hardship to them. A physician seeing their homes and living situations as utterly undesirable may fail to recognize their urge to return and even extend the length of hospitalization recommended, not on medical grounds but because he truly cannot believe a patient could prefer to go back to such a home environment.

When patients leave the hospital, they may be lost to public health supervision not necessarily because they are recalcitrant, but because their pattern of living in the immediate present does not provide for keeping appointments made months ahead. The possibility of relapse which they learned about in the hospital becomes part of that vague future they do not think about. Because many people with tuberculosis are in the highly mobile populations of both cities and rural areas, when they are "lost," they are hard to find.

In the control of tuberculosis, as in other fields of public health and medical care, professional expertise must include ability to recognize the personal and cultural factors that influence patients' behavior, to realize that patients do not necessarily share professional attitudes and aspirations, and to modify professional behavior accordingly.

The potential for significant further reduction in the level of tuberculosis in the United States depends to a great extent on providing the kind of service that will encourage response from people in the lower socioeconomic groups.

In a number of areas, such service is provided and patients are treated and contacts are examined and kept under prophylactic treatment— with success that even the sponsors did not anticipate. The extra ingredients in such programs are not highly technical. They are such things as convenient hours and location of clinics, sufficient staff to spend time with patients, definite clinic appointments at short enough intervals to emphasize their importance, and manifest interest in the people who are served. If this kind of service appears to be too expensive, the community should consider the fact that a year of hospitalization for one tuberculosis patient costs about as much as a year of intensive outpatient treatment for 33 patients, or prophylactic treatment and medical supervision of about 230 contacts or infected children. Inasmuch as well over $300 million a year is being spent in this country for tuberculosis hospitalization, investment in prevention is money well spent.

PRESENT-DAY TUBERCULOSIS CONTROL

The prospect of a continuing problem of tuberculosis at its present level has called for a reassessment of tuberculosis control programs. Many communities that had begun to reduce their control efforts have had to face the fact that the time for relaxation has not yet come. The trio of casefinding, isolation and treatment, and rehabilitation, long the basis of tuberculosis control, has had to be redesigned.

Mass X-ray surveys in the general community often no longer find cases, and the need to eliminate unnecessary exposure to X rays has made low-yield surveys unsuitable. Cases now occur more usually in groups that are not responsive to community campaigns; different techniques are needed to uncover these cases. Contacts of new cases, always considered candidates for examination, now assume new importance as a source of potential cases that can be prevented. The spread of infection can now be controlled more readily by chemotherapy, but treatment must be provided chiefly in the community rather than in a possibly distant hospital.

Rehabilitation in the old sense of retraining for sedentary occupations is no longer needed, since now most recovered patients are physically able to return to former occupations. However, new effort to keep them under treatment for long periods of time is needed to prevent relapse, as well as training for those whose ability to make a living was inadequate before they became ill.

In 1963, a rational task force considered the status of tuberculosis and issued a report outlining the components of tuberculosis control programs appropriate for the United States today. The task force recognized that the precise pattern would vary with communities, but considered the framework of the plan adaptable to local situations, and it has been widely accepted.

Services for Patients. The community should provide services in and out of hospitals for patients with tuberculosis from the time of their diagnosis until five years after disease becomes inactive. (Hospital care for tuberculosis patients is provided under state or local government auspices in all the states. In some states it is free for any patient needing it; others have means tests or residence requirements or both. A limited period of tuberculosis hospitalization under some circumstances is covered under the new Medicare legislation.)

Service for Contacts of New Cases. Contacts should be tuberculin tested, and X-rayed if they react. Cases found among them should be referred for treatment. All the remaining contacts should receive prophylactic treatment under clinic supervision for a year. (While drug treatment may not be necessary for contacts who are not infected, all contacts should be under clinic supervision, and giving antituberculosis drugs to all family members has been found to be more successful administratively than prescribing for only the infected.)

In highly mobile population groups, a year of prophylactic treatment under continued supervision may be impossible. In such situations, those contacts who do not react to tuberculin may be given BCG vaccination. BCG is a vaccine used widely in areas of the world where tuberculosis rates are high and other control measures inadequate. It offers some protection to the uninfected but makes them react to tuberculin, therefore making it more difficult to determine their status in the future. It does not protect those already infected, who are at greater risk than the uninfected in our country.

Services for Others at Risk. Because children once infected may continue to be at some risk of developing active tuberculosis throughout their lives, special efforts should be directed toward preventing infection among them. The task force proposed a child-centered program to find the sources of infection in children who react to tuberculin on entrance to school, as a means of preventing infection of other children. A youngster five or six years old has had a sufficiently limited number of close associates in his lifetime that if he is infected, the source of his infection should be identifiable with some effort. Family members and other close associates of children who react should have examinations and all appropriate preventive procedures, as should teachers and other school employees; the active cases among them should be treated to prevent further spread of infection. When youngsters reach the age of 14, and are entering a period of high risk if they are infected, they should be tested and reactors X-rayed, and the opportunity used to motivate them to protect themselves and the children they may have in the future.

Every community should have a facility in a clinic, hospital, or doctor's office, that provides prompt and complete diagnostic services for "suspects" found in the child-centered program or any other casefinding activity. Such a facility will also serve persons referred by their own physicians or who present themselves because of symptoms or previous history of tuberculosis.

In communities where the level of tuberculosis is not high and the services described above are adequate, other casefinding activity is usually unnecessary. In other areas, especially in the larger cities, routine chest X-ray examinations of people admitted to general hospitals and clinics, who are also a special-risk group, are recommended. In very large cities, there are often some neighborhoods in which the incidence of tuberculosis is exceedingly high and the circumstances such that a child-centered program is not feasible. When this is the case, neighborhood chest X-ray surveys may be indicated.

In making its recommendations, the task force expressed this belief:

. . . it is in the interest of the Nation's health that services necessary for tuberculosis control be available to all persons who need them without regard to their ability to pay or legal residence, and that they should not be withheld as a means of punishment.[14]

---

[14] U.S. Department of Health, Education, and Welfare, THE FUTURE OF TUBERCULOSIS CONTROL, A REPORT TO THE SURGEON GENERAL OF THE PUBLIC HEALTH SERVICE BY A TASK FORCE ON TUBERCULOSIS CONTROL (PHS Publication No. 1119 [Washington: Government Printing Office, 1963]) , p. 19.

Tuberculosis control services are chiefly carried on at the local level, with varying degrees of participation by or support from state health departments. Until recently, the federal government's financial contribution has been a rather small proportion of the total. On the basis of the recommendations of the task force, annual appropriations have been increased to provide for more and larger grants to state and local health departments.

Venereal Disease Control

The two venereal diseases that are major problems in cities in this country are syphilis, caused by a spirochete, and gonorrhea, caused by the gonococcus. Both diseases are highly communicable by sexual contact. Syphilis can be communicated to children by mothers who have the disease when they are pregnant, and gonorrhea can cause blindness in a child exposed to it in the birth canal. Both diseases when untreated can result in serious sequelae. Without treatment, syphilis may result in heart disease, insanity, blindness, or even death, and congenital syphilis in various severe deformities. Gonorrhea is the less serious of the two diseases in terms of late manifestations, but there are many more cases of gonorrhea than of syphilis, and some of them result in complications such as sterility, infection in the urinary tract, or arthritis.

A blood test for the detection of syphilis was first developed by Wasserman in 1906, and in the ensuing years this type of test has been greatly refined so that serological screening can be done quickly. Diagnosis, however, requires examination by a physician as well as laboratory procedures, since some persons may have false positive blood tests.

No satisfactory blood test for gonorrhea has yet been developed, so that screening is not practical. Diagnosis of gonorrhea also requires a laboratory test.

Although various treatments have been used over the centuries for both venereal diseases, not until penicillin was discovered was it possible to clear up either effectively and promptly. Today, a single massive injection of long-acting penicillin is usually effective in treating early (primary, secondary or early latent) syphilis, when it is communicable. Penicillin remains the drug of choice for gonorrhea although in recent years there has been an increase in penicillin-resistant gonococci.

DEVELOPMENT OF VENEREAL DISEASE CONTROL

Although gonorrhea appears to have been known at least from Biblical times, and to be the subject of some of the Mosaic sanitary regulations, syphilis was not recorded in the western world until the fifteenth century, when it swept over Europe in a severe epidemic. The means of its transmission were known very early, but no stigma was attached to the disease, and knowledge about it was widely disseminated. Control efforts of that time resembled those for other communicable diseases, such as leprosy and plague, except that they were more stringently directed against prostitutes. The epidemic of syphilis subsided in the seventeenth century, and the disease became endemic, as it is now. At the same time, cultural changes gradually resulted in the growth of social stigma associated with the disease.

In this country, venereal disease was a problem from early colonial times and apparently a serious one by the middle of the nineteenth century. For instance, medical records of the Civil War indicate that there were 77,382 cases of syphilis diagnosed in the Union Army.[15] In the 1870s, several prominent physicians urged public health control of syphilis, but no action was taken, probably because the mores of the time made public discussion of venereal disease impossible. As late as 1908, a carefully worded bulletin prepared by the Public Health Service to inform merchant seamen about these diseases was disapproved by the Secretary of the Treasury on the basis that it contained matter "not in keeping with the dignity of the fiscal department of the Government."[16]

After the United States entered the first World War, a federal control program, under which clinics were operated in most of the states, was established and grants for venereal disease control were made available. The program was closely related to the war effort, however, and was discontinued shortly after the war ended. Venereal disease again became one not to be mentioned publicly; few people were informed and many had erroneous information. Relatively few communities took official action against the disease. For more than 10 years, aside from a program maintained at a reduced level by the Public Health Service, much of the effort toward venereal disease control was made by a voluntary agency, the American Social Health Association.

When funds became available after the passage of the Social Security Act in 1935, the Public Health Service launched an aggressive campaign against syphilis with the energetic leadership of Surgeon General Thomas Parran who was determined to bring the subject to general attention. By 1943 a national system of Rapid Treatment Centers had been established "to curb the spread of syphilis in military camps and to prevent undue absenteeism from war jobs."[17]

"Rapid" treatment in those days meant anything less than the recommended 72-week schedule. It was commonly either eight days of hospital treatment or eight to 12 weeks of injections given in camp facilities. When penicillin was first introduced, it had to be administered in repeated injections several times a day, so that hospital treatment was necessary. Long-acting penicillin preparations became available in 1948 and made outpatient treatment practical. Today most cases of early syphilis need not be hospitalized.

In the early years of the VD campaign, many cases were found through large-scale blood-testing programs of service personnel and in areas where incidence was believed to be high. The number of cases found reached a peak in 1947 when 372,963 were reported, of which 106,539 were in the communicable stage. From then until 1957, new cases of infectious syphilis

---

[15] Thomas Parran, SHADOW ON THE LAND (New York: Reynal and Hitchcock, Inc., 1937) , p. 74.

[16] Ibid., p. 80. The Public Health Service was under the Treasury Department from its founding until 1939.

[17] U.S. Department of Health, Education, and Welfare, THE ERADICATION OF SYPHILIS, A TASK FORCE REPORT TO THE SURGEON GENERAL, PUBLIC HEALTH SERVICE, ON SYPHILIS CONTROL IN THE UNITED STATES (PHS Publication No. 918 [Washington: Government Printing Office, 1962]) , p. 9.

steadily declined. During this time, more emphasis in case-finding was directed toward interviewing newly diagnosed cases in an effort to identify their sex contacts. Interviewing techniques were studied and developed in efforts to increase the yield of these procedures. (In the technical language of venereal disease control, interview-investigation procedures to find sex contacts of cases are called epidemiology.)

By 1955, the declining syphilis rates had resulted in the reduction of federal financial support for VD control. State and local expenditures remained at about the same level, but federal funds, which had made up about half of the total and were the chief support of casefinding activities, were cut by two-thirds between 1955 and 1957.

Reported cases of infectious syphilis increased in every year from 1957 until 1964; there was a slight decrease in 1965. Both federal and state and local expenditures have been increased since 1963. The aim of the present federal program is to reduce the problem by 1976 to the point where new cases of syphilis do not occur in this country.

Control of gonorrhea has made very little progress over the years mainly because of the lack of a simple method of identifying gonorrhea in females, where it is usually asymptomatic.

EPIDEMIOLOGY OF VENEREAL DISEASE

The only reservoir of either syphilis or gonorrhea is man; both diseases are transmitted almost entirely by sexual contact; and all human beings are presumably susceptible.

In the United States today, numbers and rates of reported cases of both infectious syphilis and gonorrhea are highest in the age groups between 15 and 39. In the 15-to-19 group the syphilis rate is slightly higher for females than for males, but in all other age groups it is much higher for males. Gonorrhea is reported in males more often than in females at every age. Reported case rates for both diseases are higher in nonwhites than in whites.[18]

and venereal disease rates are higher in cities than in rural areas.

Syphilis is communicable only in its earlier stages. After four or five years, however, when it is in the later stages, the disease may cause severe damage. Gonorrhea is communicable during all of its course. Communicability of both diseases is ended promptly by adequate treatment.

SOCIAL FACTORS IN VD CONTROL

As recently as the midthirties when Dr. Parran launched his campaign against syphilis, venereal disease was considered to be chiefly related to prostitution. However, this pattern began to change early in World War II, and prostitution is no longer the most important social factor in the spread of venereal disease. The alarming increase in cases occurring among teenagers undoubtedly reflects changes in sexual mores as well as many other social attitudes and conditions. Many of these young people live in slums under conditions of deprivation hardly conducive to mental and emotional wholesomeness.

However, a significant number of venereal disease cases occur in both teenagers and young adults who have social and economic advantages. The complexity of the problem of teenage venereal disease is brought out in such studies as that directed by Deschin, in which it was found that 600 teenagers attending VD clinics could not be categorized "inasmuch as there were both favorable and unfavorable aspects in their social environment as well as in their behavior."[19]

PRESENT-DAY VENEREAL DISEASE CONTROL

The major elements of venereal disease control programs are casefinding, treatment, and education.

Casefinding. Large-scale screening for syphilis has become an established procedure in the United States. In order to prevent congenital syphilis many states require premarital serologic tests as well as the testing of pregnant women so that mothers who have syphilis can

---

[18] U.S. Department of Health, Education, and Welfare, Public Health Service, VD FACT SHEET—1965 (PHS Publication No. 341 [Washington: Government Printing Office, 1965]), pp. 12–13. Data are for calendar 1964.

[19] Celia S. Deschin, TEEN-AGERS AND VENEREAL DISEASE, A SOCIOLOGICAL STUDY (Atlanta, Georgia: U.S. Department of Health, Education, and Welfare, Public Health Service, Communicable Disease Center, 1961), p. 111.

SIX-WEEK EPIDEMIC OF SYPHILIS IN A SMALL MANUFACTURING TOWN

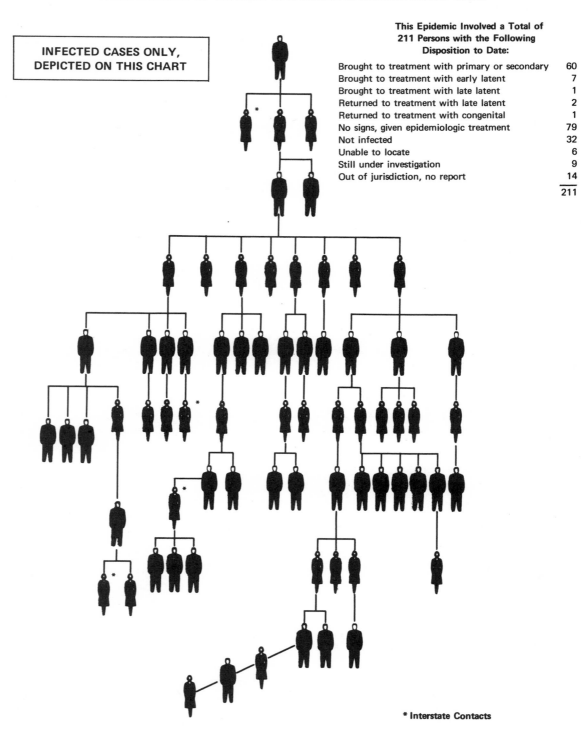

INFECTED CASES ONLY, DEPICTED ON THIS CHART

This Epidemic Involved a Total of 211 Persons with the Following Disposition to Date:

Brought to treatment with primary or secondary	60
Brought to treatment with early latent	7
Brought to treatment with late latent	1
Returned to treatment with late latent	2
Returned to treatment with congenital	1
No signs, given epidemiologic treatment	79
Not infected	32
Unable to locate	6
Still under investigation	9
Out of jurisdiction, no report	14
	211

* Interstate Contacts

FIGURE 11. *Diagram illustrates six-week epidemic of syphilis in a small manufacturing town*

be treated and congenital syphilis can thus be prevented in their unborn children. Serologic tests are included as part of routine physical examinations under a number of circumstances. Such routine testing uncovers several thousand cases of syphilis each year, but casefinding is somewhat hampered by the position taken by some private laboratories that unless the local health code specifically requires it, reporting positive tests to health authorities is unethical.

At present, a large proportion of new syphilis cases is found through "epidemiology." Contact follow-up succeeds when patient interviews yield the names of sex contacts, who are in turn interviewed and examined. Experience with these procedures has shown that many patients with syphilis have friends who are not among their sex contacts but through whom other cases of syphilis are likely to be found. Interviewing groups of nonsex contacts is called cluster testing; it has been notably successful in increasing the yield of syphilis case-finding and is recommended for all health departments. In larger urban areas with a substantial homosexual population, casefinding and cluster testing take on an added and often more difficult dimension since this population provides a significant reservoir for venereal disease.

Interviewing patients with syphilis in an effort to identify their contacts, locating contacts, and persuading them to be tested require special skills. In most urban communities, this work is done by special personnel called variously VD investigators or epidemiologists. They are usually young men with college training who have been given intensive orientation in the venereal disease problem and in interviewing techniques. Many are assigned to state and local health departments by the Public Health Service.

Treatment. Prompt and adequate treatment of all diagnosed cases is essential to control. Many communities have public venereal disease clinics. When these clinics are free and are located and administered so as to encourage their use, they are an effective aid to control. However, whether or not public clinics are available, and whatever their quality, a considerable proportion of VD cases is diagnosed and treated by private physicians. Although

syphilis and gonorrhea are reportable diseases in all the states, physicians often fail to report cases, and health departments therefore cannot investigate sources of infection to prevent further transmission of disease.

A concerted effort has been made by a number of groups in recent years to improve private physicians' understanding about venereal disease and to encourage the reporting of cases. In one PHS-sponsored program visits are made to physicians individually to put the problem before them, provide them with information, and assure them of the discretion of health department procedures. Health departments and medical societies also provide information and conduct educational activities to modernize professional knowledge of venereal disease and to enlist physician support.

Public Education. The need for public education about venereal disease has been accepted by health officials for decades, but until relatively recently the demand was limited. Because of widespread feelings and attitudes, the idea that VD was not a fit subject for public discussion persisted. As a result the information that many people had about VD was meager, if not totally lacking or inaccurate. In her 1960 study of 600 teenagers attending VD clinics, Deschin found that only 10 per cent had a good knowledge of the diseases, although most had gone to school at least for some time beyond the elementary grades.[20]

The situation that stultified VD educational efforts appears to be changing. A 1964 Joint Statement by the Association of State and Territorial Health Officers, the American Venereal Disease Association, and the American Social Health Association indicated:

During the past year, national magazines, newspapers, radio and TV devoted more space and time to venereal disease than at any other time in the past. Every aspect of the venereal disease problem was covered—statistics showing the rising rate of infection; the rate of infection among teenagers and its link to sexual promiscuity; the under-reporting of cases treated by private physicians; and even detailed and dramatic presentations of the procedures by which infections are traced from one person to another and persons exposed to infection brought to

---

[20] *Ibid.,* pp. 83 and 114.

diagnosis and treatment. [State and city health departments reported that] the increased public awareness caused by the mass media exposure of the VD problem had created greatly increased demands for information and education about the venereal diseases from schools, PTA's, youth-serving agencies, civic organizations, doctors, nurses, social workers and the public in general.[21]

Authorities on VD control generally agree that education on the subject should be provided in the schools. One group concerned with the subject recommended that "VD education should be systematically integrated within the school curriculum whenever it relates reasonably," and also that it "properly includes biological, pathological, historical, epidemiological, and sociological aspects of VD, broadly embracing causes, effects, prevention, transmission, recognition, treatment, and community responsibility for control."[22]

These recommendations presuppose that instruction in health is an established and vital part of the school curriculum. That is not always the case. A study of school health education in the United States, conducted in 1961–63, found that "there certainly are a majority of situations where health instruction is virtually nonexistent, or where prevailing practices can be legitimately challenged."[23] In such circumstances, the interests of VD control can be served only through efforts to initiate or improve general health education in the schools by cooperation of all appropriate community forces. The framework into which instruction about the venereal diseases can be fitted "where it relates reasonably" is essential.

[21] TODAY'S VD CONTROL PROBLEM (New York: American Social Health Association, 1964), p. 26.

[22] U.S. Department of Health, Education, and Welfare, Public Health Service, VENEREAL DISEASE EDUCATION, A

REPORT OF THE SPECIAL SUBCOMMITTEE OF THE PUBLIC ADVISORY COMMITTEE ON VENEREAL DISEASE CONTROL (PHS Publication No. 1190 [Washington: Government Printing Office, 1964]), p. 3.

[23] Elena M. Sliepcevich, SUMMARY REPORT OF A NATIONWIDE STUDY OF HEALTH INSTRUCTION IN THE PUBLIC SCHOOLS (Washington: School Health Education Study, 1964), p. 12.

8

Hospital and Hospital-related Services

THE WORD "HOSPITAL," derived from the Latin *hospes* meaning guest, was used in the early medieval period to describe monastery shelters for strangers. Later in the Middle Ages, monastery hospitals became refuges for the unfortunate—not only the sick but the orphaned, the old, and the infirm—who had no other place to go. This pattern persisted for centuries, even when hospitals began to be operated by governments or philanthropic groups not related to the church.

Until the nineteenth century, the hospital was primarily a charitable institution—so much so that the conceptions of hospital, poorhouse and orphanage were more or less linked in people's minds. Victims of a cruel fate sought shelter there and were succoured with compassion which was all there was to hope for or to offer.[1]

As the science of medicine advanced in the nineteenth century, hospitals were separated from other charitable institutions and were devoted exclusively to the care of the sick. Most hospitals in the United States, founded later, of course, than European hospitals, were established solely to provide health care for those who could pay as well as the poor. Until well into the present century, however, illness was usually treated at home, most babies were born at home, and the hospital was a last resort, only for surgery and extreme illness. Understandably, mortality in hospitals was relatively high, and most people feared hospitalization,

equating it with fatal illness. (Some elderly people still feel this way about hospitals.)

In the past half century, increasingly effective medical practice has come to depend more and more on diagnostic and therapeutic techniques that cannot practically be used in the home or the doctor's office. The character of the hospital has changed to accommodate the needs of medical practice, and today hospitals offer a variety of supporting services, skills, and equipment that allow the physician to practice modern medicine. The list of services provided in general hospitals shown in Table 8 suggests the complexity of present-day hospital service.

Functions of Hospitals

The major reason now for the existence of hospitals is care of the ill. In addition, many provide educational activities for physicians, nurses, or other health professionals, and an increasing number of hospitals participate in research.

PATIENT CARE

In the usual pattern of voluntary hospitals in the United States, a personal physician decides whether a private patient should have hospital care, arranges for his admission, and prescribes his treatment and care while he is in the hospital. If the patient's illness requires treatment in a specialty in which the physician is not qualified, referral to a specialist is made either be-

---

[1] René Sand, THE ADVANCE TO SOCIAL MEDICINE (London and New York: Staples Press, 1952) , p. 98.

Table 8

Per Cent of Nonfederal Short-Term General and Other Special Hospitals[1] with Specified Services 1965, by Size of Hospital

Facility or Service	Under 25 (407)	25–49 (1,216)	50–99 (1,327)	100–199 (1,081)	200–299 (531)	300–399 (304)	400–499 (129)	500 and over (163)	Total (5,158)
Blood bank	13.51	37.25	61.34	77.89	85.69	90.46	92.25	95.09	61.42
Clinical lab	87.22	96.71	98.57	99.35	99.81	99.34	99.22	100.00	97.63
Pathology lab	5.90	17.11	47.78	86.40	98.49	100.00	100.00	100.00	56.59
Electroencepha-lography	9.83	12.91	12.89	26.64	51.60	76.97	81.40	96.93	27.67
Dental facility	8.35	14.56	24.79	39.59	54.05	66.45	68.22	85.28	32.65
Pharmacy	11.79	21.30	48.91	87.23	98.87	99.67	100.00	100.00	58.53
Occupational therapy	3.44	1.89	3.47	8.14	19.96	35.53	50.39	79.75	11.24
Physical therapy	14.99	21.55	40.69	69.66	90.21	95.72	96.12	97.55	51.74
Premature nursery	28.26	40.05	56.29	70.40	82.49	88.82	93.02	93.87	59.93
Intensive care unit	3.44	5.92	12.89	29.14	61.39	72.70	86.05	89.57	26.68
Outpatient dept	41.77	32.32	25.09	31.91	56.31	74.34	85.27	95.71	39.40
Emergency dept	78.62	91.20	91.94	95.47	97.36	98.36	96.90	99.39	92.75
Home care program	1.97	2.38	1.36	3.89	8.10	14.80	17.05	32.52	5.04
Operating room	89.19	96.71	97.51	99.07	99.44	100.00	100.00	100.00	97.48
Obstretrical del. room	86.00	89.64	86.96	89.08	93.03	95.07	96.90	96.32	89.61
Post-op. recovery room	15.97	35.44	70.76	93.52	98.12	99.34	99.22	100.00	69.02
Social work dept	5.90	2.63	4.07	13.51	42.94	59.87	68.22	85.89	17.33
X-ray diagnosis	89.43	98.03	99.17	99.63	99.81	100.00	100.00	100.00	98.39
X-ray therapy	1.97	5.18	16.80	55.97	82.67	94.74	95.35	100.00	37.07
Radioactive isotope facility	.74	2.63	9.04	39.87	75.33	92.11	96.12	99.39	30.09
Psychiatric inpatient care unit	.98	2.14	4.45	10.45	25.99	42.11	63.57	82.82	13.28
Rehabilitation unit	.74	1.23	2.34	5.83	13.75	20.07	25.58	52.15	7.06
Cobalt therapy	.49	.49	2.41	8.88	21.47	37.50	51.94	68.10	10.51
Radium therapy	1.72	2.88	13.56	45.33	74.95	87.83	89.15	97.55	32.01
Family Planning Service	1.47	.74	.98	3.05	8.29	13.49	22.48	44.79	4.81
Chest X-ray on adm	32.68	35.44	30.60	33.58	35.78	41.12	45.74	57.67	34.92

Source: HOSPITALS, JOURNAL OF THE AMERICAN HOSPITAL ASSOCIATION, August, 1966 (Guide Issue), Table 4, pp. 466–71.
[1] Hospitals treating a variety of conditions or a special condition other than mental illness or tuberculosis, on a short-term basis (less than one month). Data are for the reporting hospitals, 5,158 of 5,736.

fore or upon admission. Under these circumstances the specialist is the patient's physician during his hospital stay, although his personal physician may participate in his care.

In European countries, most physicians who practice in hospitals are highly trained specialists on salary who do not practice in the community. The personal physician does not himself care for patients in the hospital but refers those who need it to a hospital where their medical care is provided by a team of specialists. In voluntary hospitals in this country, treatment of patients who cannot pay for medical care[2] is supervised by members of the medical staff, who spend a certain amount of time in such work without remuneration as an obligation of their staff membership. Public hospitals, both general and special, often have the same system, although some of them pay fees for physicians' services or have salaried physicians.

A hospital that is part of or has a primary teaching affiliation with a medical school may have some full-time salaried medical staff, similar to that of European hospitals, although physicians in private practice frequently are part-time faculty members, with or without remuneration. In many hospitals, either voluntary or public, a radiologist or pathologist, or both, may be employed by the hospital on salary or commission; or they may rent space and equipment from the hospital.

The specific nature of a patient's treatment —diagnostic tests, medication, therapeutic or rehabilitative procedures, special diet—is prescribed by his own physician. Such services are administered by the hospital but only on medical direction. (Certain routine procedures applied for all patients, or for those with certain diagnoses, are agreed upon by the medical staff.)

The hospital itself provides the setting and facilities for the patient's medical care, as well as nursing service and other personal care. The skills of various professional and nonprofessional workers, described below, are required, and blending their efforts for a therapeutic environment is the hospital's mission. As one writer has said:

> Care of high quality involves both the appropriate application of relevant scientific knowledge for the benefit of every patient and the compassionate understanding of each patient as a human being living in society in particular circumstances that are, in every case, unique.[3]

Outpatient Services. Many voluntary and public hospitals, especially the larger ones, conduct clinics under the auspices of their various medical departments called collectively the outpatient department but not usually operated as a single, unified service. Traditionally the clinics serve indigent patients, although some outpatient departments accept paying patients as well.

Especially in large city hospitals, the outpatient department has often been in low favor with the medical staff, and service in its clinics carries little prestige. Many of the people who come to outpatient departments suffer from long-term conditions such as chronic diseases and mental illness, complicated by their unfavorable social situation. The treatment they receive is frequently disease centered and fragmented in clinics concerned with various diseases or conditions. Often it fails entirely in dealing with the patient as a total person and is thus both unsatisfactory to the patients and wasteful of professional time.

Although he notes exceptions, Dr. J. H. Knowles, General Director of the Massachusetts General Hospital, has called the outpatient department "the stepchild of the urban hospital," and has said:

> The long, hard bench with the 4-hour wait, multiple referrals, incredible discontinuity of care, and various other indignities suffered in an antisocial and decadent environment remains the order of the day in most ambulatory clinics in this country. A two-class system of care has prevailed whether it be the contrast between inpatient and outpatient or private versus clinic patient.[4]

---

[2] Often called "ward patients," although modern American hospitals no longer have the large open wards from which the term was derived.

[3] Cecil G. Sheps *et al.*, MEDICAL SCHOOLS AND HOSPITALS, INTERDEPENDENCE FOR EDUCATION AND SERVICE (Evanston, Illinois: Association of American Medical Colleges, 1964), p. 66.

[4] "The Role of the Hospital," BULLETIN OF THE NEW YORK ACADEMY OF MEDICINE, January, 1965, p. 71.

The hospital's potential to provide comprehensive medical care by the effective use of both its outpatient and inpatient services, as well as the teaching potential of the outpatient service, is receiving growing consideration by authorities on medical care. In addition to providing physicians in training an opportunity to see patients who are not hospitalized, strengthened outpatient services offer the obvious practical benefit of preventing the need for some hospitalization. Federal legislation providing hospital insurance for the elderly will no doubt increase the demand for hospital beds; at the same time, because the insurance also covers payment for diagnostic service in outpatient departments, it may very well help to improve these facilities and make them a more productive element in total medical care.

Emergency Services. More than 90 per cent of all short-term general hospitals provide emergency medical and surgical service, as do many long-term hospitals. In the past 20 years, the use of hospital emergency services has increased sharply throughout the country. Weinerman and Edwards attribute this trend to medical and sociological factors:

As medical practice has become more specialized, more highly structured and less personal, physicians are not as readily available for sudden call and not as willing to handle a wide variety of acute problems. An increasingly mechanized, synthetic, and high-speed environment engenders steadily rising rates of accidental injury, toxic reaction, and hypersensitivity. Higher costs of medical care and health insurance coverage for care in, but not out of, the hospital contribute to the popularity of the emergency service. Also, alert patients soon learn the advantages of the quick care offered in the emergency department over the long waits for a clinic or private office appointment.[5]

Working people who are not paid for sick leave may go to an emergency service in the evening or on a weekend rather than lose pay to meet either clinic or private physicians' office hours. Other factors influence the situation, including the rapid growth of population in some areas without a similar growth in the number of physicians, especially family physicians, and facilities and supporting services available in the hospital that encourage physicians to refer patients to the emergency service.

Emergency services do not generally suffer from the low status of outpatient departments, and the condition for which treatment is sought usually receives adequate attention. However, even for the large number of people who use it in lieu of a family doctor, the service as a rule contributes little to comprehensive medical care, since the patient's visit is seldom used as an opportunity to prevent or interrupt the progression of either the condition which causes the "emergency" or of other health problems.

Dr. George James tells a "parable" about a 60-year-old woman who comes to an emergency service with a cut finger for which she receives excellent treatment—but no one discovers that her eyeglasses no longer correct her vision, a situation that could easily contribute to other accidents; nor is she given any screening tests that could uncover possible chronic disease to which her age group is especially subject.[6] (Similar parables might well be told of such medical service provided elsewhere than in emergency services.)

In a hospital with a well-organized outpatient department, the emergency service is appropriately a division of that department, and its functions are coordinated with those of the other divisions.

EDUCATION

The clinical portion of medical education is received in hospitals. While still in medical school, students serve in teaching hospitals in a capacity called clerkship in which, as members of a medical team under the leadership of a physician faculty member, they begin to observe and participate in patient care. After medical school graduation, they serve an internship combining service and learning. Some continue in a hospital after internship as resi-

[5] E. Richard Weinerman and Herbert R. Edwards, "Changing Patterns in Hospital Emergency Service," HOSPITALS, JOURNAL OF THE AMERICAN HOSPITAL ASSOCIATION, November 16, 1964.

[6] "Medical Advances in the Next Ten Years: The Implications for the Organization and Economics of Medicine," in THE EXPANDING ROLE OF AMBULATORY SERVICE IN HOSPITALS AND HEALTH DEPARTMENTS, *op. cit.*, p. 22.

dent physicians in a speciality and take increasing responsibility in patient care. Both interns and residents work under direction of the hospital medical staff, even though they are full-time hospital employees.

Interns and residents (called house staff) are in the hospital primarily to be trained, but they also provide important patient care services. To ensure that hospitals furnish an appropriate environment for learning, the Council on Medical Education of the American Medical Association has a system of approving hospitals for internships and for residencies in 29 specialty fields (including general practice).[7] Lists are published each year and distributed to third- and fourth-year medical students. This publication serves as the directory of the National Intern Matching Program. The Program, sponsored by the Council jointly with several hospital associations and other organizations, helps in placing interns to their own and the hospitals' satisfaction.

For the 1964–65 year, 757 hospitals in the United States were approved for 12,728 internships; they were able to fill 10,097 (79 per cent) of them with graduates from United States (7,276) and foreign (2,821) medical schools.[8] Approval was given to 1,317 hospitals for 5,440 programs under which 38,373 residencies were offered and 30,797 (80 per cent) were filled.[9] Obviously the demand for interns and residents is greater than the supply. Their presence in hospitals is valued not only because they contribute to patient care but also because the education program required in order for a hospital to be approved for internship and residency generally enhances the quality of the hospital's service.

Continuing education for hospital medical staff is necessary in all hospitals. In those with internship and residency programs, the fact that staff members act as the faculty stimulates them to further their own excellence. In all hospitals formal staff meetings, informal professional conferences, and devices to ensure the quality of medical care should provide continuing education for physicians. For instance, if a hospital's medical staff has effective utilization and medical audit teams to evaluate hospital records in terms of the appropriateness and adequacy of care, the evaluation reports can serve an educational purpose with respect to the quality and economic validity of patient care.

More than 800 hospitals in this country operate schools of nursing offering diploma programs.[10] In addition to course work, student nurses care for patients, taking increasing degrees of responsibility during their three-year course. Although most training programs for practical nurses are under vocational education auspices, over 150 hospitals conduct state-approved practical nurse training.[11]

Hospital training or supervised experience is also necessary for a number of other professions, such as hospital administration or dietetics, and of course most hospitals need continuous on-the-job training for aides, food service employees, and other nonprofessional workers.

RESEARCH

A significant part of the research in the medical sciences is clinical in nature and takes place in hospitals. A great deal is sponsored by medical schools, either in their own or in affiliated teaching hospitals. Increasingly, however, research projects are conducted in hospitals not affiliated with medical schools. Such research is usually supported by grants from outside sources, such as the National Institutes of Health of the Public Health Service, rather than by the hospital itself.

The direct advantages to the hospital of a medical research program are perhaps greatest in its effect on the medical staff. As one author says:

Anything that promotes an atmosphere of active and purposeful inquiry into the diagnostic and treatment problems of the sick is apt to have a constructive effect on the type of medicine practiced in an institution. The carrying-on of research (or, at least, the existence of the research point of view) creates such a stimulus. . . . It is doubtful, however, whether a sustained research effort can be main-

---

[7] See American Medical Association, DIRECTORY OF APPROVED INTERNSHIPS AND RESIDENCIES, 1965 (Chicago: The Association, 1965).

[8] *Ibid.*, p. 5.

[9] *Ibid.*, p. 10.

[10] American Nurses' Association, FACTS ABOUT NURSING (New York: The Association, 1965), p. 99.

[11] *Ibid.*, p. 185.

tained in institutions dependent exclusively upon the part-time contributed services of clinicians.[12]

In addition to medical research, hospitals may engage in studies and demonstrations in various aspects of administration, such as design and use of space, coordination of community medical facilities, costs of institutional care, nursing care, medical records, and many others. Grants for studies in these and related areas are available from the Public Health Service as well as from other sources.

Administrative Structure

In voluntary hospitals, described briefly in Chapter 2, authority is usually vested in a self-perpetuating board of trustees that has legal responsibility for the care rendered. An administrator is responsible to the board for general operation of the hospital. The medical staff consists almost entirely of physicians in private practice who are not hospital employees. Public hospitals differ somewhat in that their board members are usually appointed by government officials, and at least some members of the medical staff are paid employees of the hospital.

A division of responsibility between medical staff and administration exists in most hospitals, whether under voluntary or public auspices. However, the activities of the medical and administrative staffs are interdependent and cannot be conducted separately. One of the most difficult and sensitive areas of hospital administration and hospital board activity is promotion of harmony between the two complementary lines of authority.

MEDICAL ADMINISTRATION

The medical staff, whose members are appointed by the board on recommendation of the active staff, is ordinarily governed under by-laws that specify the way the staff will be organized, as well as the qualifications for membership and procedures for appointment and dismissal; that establish provisions for maintaining standards of medical care; and enumer-

ate staff responsibilities for medical training.

The number of officers and committees of the staff depends on the size of the hospital. The Joint Commission on Accreditation of Hospitals requires that certain functions be conducted by staff committees although it does not stipulate that a separate committee must exist for each function. Executive committee duties, in addition to coordinating and acting for the staff, include action on reports of other committees, such as medical records and tissue committees. The credentials committee reviews applications for appointment to the staff and makes recommendations. The joint conference committee is the official liaison among the medical staff, the board of trustees, and the administrator, although it has no operating authority. The medical records committee not only supervises the maintenance of records but evaluates from them the quality of patient care and reports findings to the executive committee. The tissue committee reviews and evaluates surgery performed in the hospital and also reports its findings to the executive committee.[13]

Certification of hospitals as providers of care under hospital insurance for the elderly (Medicare) requires that they have formal plans for utilization review. Beginning in 1966, the Joint Commission has also required staff committees on utilization to review admissions and discharges and evaluate the use or misuse of scarce hospital beds.

Hospital infections, which can be a serious threat if special effort is not made to control them, are sometimes a committee responsibility, as is the use of drugs.

Medical staffs in all but very small hospitals are divided into departments, usually called services, according to areas of medical practice. The major services in general hospitals are internal medicine, surgery, pediatrics, and obstetrics-gynecology. To be approved for internship, a hospital must have at least three of these services.[14] In large hospitals, departments are often

---

[12] Herbert E. Klarman, HOSPITAL CARE IN NEW YORK CITY (New York and London: Columbia University Press, 1963), p. 311.

[13] Joint Commission on Accreditation of Hospitals, STANDARDS FOR HOSPITAL ACCREDITATION (Chicago: The Commission, 1964), pp. 7–8. The Commission is sponsored by the American College of Physicians, The American College of Surgeons, the American Hospital Association, and the American Medical Association.

[14] American Medical Association, op. cit., p. 119.

further specialized within the four areas, and in addition there may be departments of anesthesia, general practice, and dental service. Smaller hospitals may have only medical and surgical departments.

The chief of each service is generally responsible for the medical administration and character of professional care of patients on the service and makes recommendations about the qualifications of staff as well as about administrative matters concerning patient care.

Regular meetings of medical staff are essential, and the Joint Commission on Accreditation requires that monthly meetings be held by either the active staff or departmental staffs, or at least by the medical records and tissue committees.[15] The medical staff by-laws determine the frequency of staff meetings as well as attendance requirements.

Because physicians are professionally independent of the hospital administration, the quality of medical care provided in the hospital depends largely on their own efforts. Staff organization should promote the members' efforts to strengthen and discipline each other, and medical leadership must be responsible for conscientious and effective functioning of the organization. The hospital board must answer for hospital care and assure itself that medical organization and leadership promote a high quality of care.

INSTITUTIONAL ADMINISTRATION

A hospital is not an ordinary business; it has objectives that are more social and humanitarian than economic. Yet communities expect their hospitals to be run economically. The essential work of hospitals is done by physicians who are free from nonmedical supervision, and by persons in a number of other professions who are under hospital supervision but must adhere to their own professional standards and defer to the physicians' leadership. Procedures in patient care increasingly call for highly technical and expensive equipment, but they still must include considerate personal service. The hospital's "customers" are sick human beings whose needs and expectations are highly indi-

vidual, but the hospital is supported by and answerable to the community as a whole.

Administration of such an institution requires talents not easily borrowed from other fields. It is increasingly recognized as requiring special professional training that includes background in management and executive leadership as well as orientation to the hospital environment, the medical and other professions, and the hospital's relationship with the community.

As the hospital assumes an expanded role as a center for community health services, the administrator's concern with community relationships must also grow. The administrator's training should enable him to make the decisions his position demands, objectively and tactfully, with due consideration for all the interests involved. Professional training in hospital administration is now available in 16 universities in the United States.

The specific functions within the hospital for which the administrator must be responsible include nursing service, other professional or technical services, food service, housekeeping and plant maintenance, and business and financial management.

Nursing Service. By far the largest proportion of hospital employees is in the nursing service, and in the average hospital nursing employees outnumber all others.[16] Fewer than half of them are graduate nurses; the remainder are practical nurses, nurses' aides, orderlies, and other assistants. Although the use of nonprofessional personnel in hospitals is sometimes considered a stopgap, when duties are appropriately assigned under thoughtful administration, this can be an indispensable means of extending scarce professional skills.

The number of employees involved, the importance of nursing service to patient care, and the delicacy of professional relationships mean that the director of nursing is a key figure in hospital administration. She ordinarily has full charge of all aspects of nursing service, for which she is responsible to the administrator. In a hospital that trains student nurses, she may also be director of nursing education, although

[15] Joint Commission on Accreditation of Hospitals, *op. cit.,* p. 8.

[16] Laura G. Jackson, HOSPITAL AND COMMUNITY (New York: The Macmillan Company, 1964), p. 98.

preferably this is the responsibility of a specially trained nurse educator. When ever possible, the director's qualifications should include advanced training in nursing administration.

Nursing service in the hospital is organized by areas with professional and nonprofessional staff assigned according to the needs of patients in various areas. Intensive-care units or premature nurseries, for instance, should be staffed at all times by professional nurses caring for relatively few patients, whereas a floor occupied by patients needing less attention may have only one professional nurse, assisted by several nonprofessionals. In addition to round-the-clock service in nursing units, nurses are assigned to special services, such as the operating room and the emergency service and outpatient department. Some state and local licensure laws set forth required nursing staff, or at least minimum staffing patterns.

Other Professional Services. Although patient records detailing diagnosis and treatment procedures and progress are made or approved by the physician in charge of each case, the medical record librarian is responsible for filing and indexing the records, preparing statistics, and sometimes summarizing records for medical audit. Medical records provide one of the chief means of measuring the quality of care given in a hospital, and to qualify for either accreditation or approval for internship hospitals must have trained record librarians.

A number of schools associated with hospitals provide training for record librarians approved by the American Medical Association. After such training, success in examinations administered by the American Association of Medical Record Librarians qualifies the candidate as a Registered Record Librarian (R.R.L.).[17]

The hospital medical library, also required for accreditation and internship approval, must be staffed by persons competent to provide the services needed by the medical staff and house officers. The Medical Library Association has established standards of training for medical librarians.

The Joint Commission's standards for accreditation also require that the hospital have a

pharmacy or drug room under the direction (either full- or part-time) of a registered pharmacist; a laboratory with staff capable of carrying out clinical examinations in chemistry, bacteriology, hematology, serology, and microscopy; the services of a pathologist to examine tissues removed at operations; and radiological services, including interpretation of X rays by a qualified physician.

Medical social workers, acting as part of the patient care team, contribute professional insights about the strengths and weaknesses of the patient's social and emotional condition that may affect his recovery. Especially for patients with long-term illness, the social worker plays an important role in helping patients accept their situation, keeping them in touch with families and friends, helping them with financial and family problems, and arranging for further service in the community after hospitalization.

Qualified medical social workers are in short supply; in many hospitals some of their duties are carried out by persons with less training. (The social service department in some hospitals is concerned only with determining the patient's eligibility for free care and is staffed by workers with a minimum of professional training. Their functions should not be confused with the practice of professional medical social work.)

Occupational therapy, conducted by trained professionals under medical supervision, provides special means for patients to spend their time in the hospital in a manner that will promote their recovery. The purpose is more than to relieve boredom, and projects are chosen in terms of the patient's physical and mental needs. Long-term patients are sometimes helped to develop vocational skills, although occupational therapy is not oriented to vocational rehabilitation.

The physical therapy department, in some hospitals under the direction of a specialist in physical medicine, provides treatment through the agents of heat and cold, electricity, water, massage, and therapeutic exercise, on the physician's prescription. Its aims are "to combat the cumulative effects of prolonged physical and mental illness; to shorten the hospital stay; to

---

[17] The initials M.R.L., sometimes used by persons working on medical records, have no official status.

reduce physical disability; to hasten convalescence; and to contribute to the return of patients to normal living economically and socially."[18] Physical therapy plays a major part in the prevention of disability, and most hospitals, including short-term general, use it in treating many conditions.

Food Service. The food served to patients may strongly influence their opinion of the hospital care they receive. A food service that provides well-cooked, appetizing meals and serves them at proper temperatures contributes importantly to the patients' well-being.

Hospital food service requires a variety of skills and experience, in management as well as nutrition and menu planning for both special and normal diets. In some hospitals, it is under the direction of a professional dietition, but because of the shortage of qualified dietitians, food service managers are employed in many hospitals. When this is the case, dietetic guidance may be obtained through consultation or sharing with other hospitals. In many areas, complete hospital food service, including therapeutic dietetics, can be supplied by commercial food service management concerns.

Housekeeping and Plant Maintenance. Hospital housekeeping is somewhat similar to that in a hotel except that standards of cleanliness must be more exacting and much of the housekeeping must be done in the patient's presence without unduly disturbing him. Some units and services—operating rooms and nurseries, for instance—require housekeeping by specially trained personnel to avoid the possible spread of infection. Laundry and linen service, of great importance in patient care, requires skillful management; it is sometimes purchased from commercial vendors or shared among several hospitals.

The physical plant of a hospital must be maintained with consideration for both the comfort of patients and their safety from fire and other hazards. Emergencies, such as failure of light and power, can be catastrophic in a hospital; the Joint Commission specifies the key areas in which emergency lighting must be available.

Business and Financial Management. Although a voluntary hospital does not operate for profit, fulfillment of its purposes demands the use of sound business and financial management principles. Systems to control receipts and disbursements, the use of materials and supplies, and the effective use of personnel are as necessary to a hospital as to a business enterprise. As Dr. John R. McGibony has said:

Principles of good hospital administration include all of the facets and factors usually found or implied in administration or management technics, procedures or services. In addition, a difference exists between the ordinary concept of administration and hospital administration. This difference lies in the realm of humanitarianism. The successful hospital is not necessarily the most efficient, machine-like business management, a fact too often over looked.

On the other hand, while administrative efficiency often must be subordinated to clinical requirements, there is a limit to the economic position of the institution and the community. A sustained, equitable balance is a part of good hospital administration.[19]

Although the basic principles of accounting, budgeting, purchasing, and personnel management are the same for hospitals as for other enterprises, there is an extensive literature on their applications to hospitals. The American Hospital Association publishes manuals and other materials on these and a variety of other pertinent subjects.[20]

In 1964, the Association's House of Delegates approved a statement of *Principles of Organization, Management and Community Relations for Hospitals.*[21] To help hospitals evaluate themselves in comparison with these principles, the Association has set up a Hospital Management Review Program for all member hospitals. The need for these efforts is stated in the published principles:

In recent years there has been an insistent and increasing demand for the development and adoption by hospitals of standards of performance extending beyond safety and quality of professional care to include community responsibility, effective organization, and sound management.

---

[18] Laura G. Jackson, *op. cit.,* p. 121.

[19] PRINCIPLES OF HOSPITAL ADMINISTRATION (New York: G. P. Putnam's Sons, 1952) .

[20] See American Hospital Association, PUBLICATIONS CATALOGUE EFFECTIVE JANUARY 15, 1965 (Chicago: The Association, 1965) .

[21] Chicago: The Association, 1964.

Rising costs, resulting from the expanding role of hospitals in health care, education, and research, and the heavy and persistent demands for capital funds for expansion, have resulted in the receipt by hospitals of increasing amounts of public money. This fact, and the great resources held and operated in trust for the community, and the unsought for but unavoidably monopolistic position of many hospitals, all affect our hospitals with the public interest and subject their operations to critical scrutiny by governments, third-party payers, and the general public. Hospitals must establish and maintain standards of performance that will satisfy this scrutiny.[22]

Hospitals in the United States

Hospitals are a widely used community health resource in this country. Although the nearly 29 million annual admissions to all hospitals (Table 9) include a number of multiple admis-

[22] *Ibid.*, pp. 1–2.

sions, they do indicate that hospitals serve a very large proportion of the population. Most of the admissions are to short-term hospitals, but other facilities for extended care are increasingly important in meeting present-day needs.

SHORT-TERM HOSPITALS

In 1965, the 5,736 nonfederal, short-term general and special hospitals in this country had over 26 million inpatient admissions, about 140 for every 1,000 persons in the population, and an average daily census of more than half a million.[23] Over 92 million outpatient or emergency visits were made in the 4,693 hospitals reporting about these services. More than 3.4 million children were born in short-term hospitals, 90

[23] HOSPITALS, JOURNAL OF THE AMERICAN HOSPITAL ASSOCIATION, August, 1966 (Guide Issue), Table 1, p. 439, and Text Table 6, p. 432.

Table 9

Hospitals in the United States, 1965

Type of Hospital	Number of Hospitals Total	Number of Hospitals % Accredited	Number of Beds Total	Number of Beds % Accredited	Number of Admissions	Average Daily Census	Occupancy Rate (%)	Average Lgth. of Stay	Full-time personnel per 100 Patients	Expense per Patient Day
Total	7,123	60.5	1,703,522	66.3	28,811,925	1,402,625	82.3		139	$25.29
Federal	443	79.7	173,962	94.6	1,640,087	149,783	86.1		133	28.67
Nonfederal	6,680	59.2	1,529,560	63.1	27,171,838	1,252,842	81.9		140	24.89
Psychiatric	483	37.7	685,175	38.3	490,670	607,148	88.6		45	7.50
Tuberculosis	178	57.3	37,196	71.7	52,073	26,040	70.0		111	17.39
Long-term general and other special	283	47.3	65,897	51.6	166,217	56,230	85.3		115	19.79
Short-term general and other special	5,736	61.7	741,292	86.6	26,462,878	563,424	76.0	7.8	246	44.48
Under 25 beds	562	0.9	10,024	0.9	332,776	5,310	53.0	5.8	243	37.56
25–49	1,445	27.9	51,451	29.8	1,935,707	32,037	62.3	6.0	222	36.76
50–99	1,482	67.5	103,120	69.7	3,915,776	69,982	67.9	6.5	230	39.30
100–199	1,108	91.6	154,336	92.1	5,952,872	115,086	74.6	7.1	242	41.78
200–299	541	97.6	131,388	97.7	4,998,442	104,626	79.6	7.6	250	45.62
300–399	306	98.7	104,180	98.7	3,786,395	84,630	81.2	8.2	258	47.62
400–499	129	97.7	57,240	97.8	2,030,075	47,065	82.2	8.5	253	46.76
500 and over	163	96.3	129,553	96.6	3,510,835	104,688	80.8	10.9	253	48.93

Source: HOSPITALS, JOURNAL OF THE AMERICAN HOSPITAL ASSOCIATION, August, 1966 (Guide Issue), Table 2, p. 442, and Table 5, p. 472.

per cent of all those born in 1965. Modern medical care has shortened the time needed for hospital treatment of many diseases and conditions, and the average stay in these hospitals is now less than eight days, even though some, particularly the large public hospitals, accept patients who require care over extended periods of time. The average length of hospital stay varies among localities and even among regions of the country; the east and north central parts of the country tend to have longer average lengths of hospital stay than the southern and western regions. In most regions, the average stay in state and local government hospitals is longer than in voluntary or proprietary hospitals.

In the past two decades, under the Hill-Burton program of federal assistance to the states for construction of hospitals, the once acute shortage of beds for short-term care has been considerably eased. In 1948, according to the first Hill-Burton state inventories of facilities, the nation had only 59 per cent of the general hospital beds estimated as needed. In 1965, state agencies reported that there were 83 per cent of needed short-term beds, estimated in terms of a considerably larger population and increased per capita use of hospitals.

However, as the data in Table 9 show, 14 per cent of short-term beds are in hospitals not accredited by the Joint Commission on Accreditation of Hospitals. Seventy per cent of the beds in the 1,445 hospitals with between 25 and 49 beds are not accredited. Furthermore, the data in Table 8 on some specific services of hospitals also point up the relative incompleteness of the small hospital. If a small hospital is part of a planned, cooperative system, it may very well be able to provide good care without an entire range of services on its own premises. Indeed, effective planning should prevent unnecessary duplication of some services in several hospitals in a community.

The data do suggest, however, that although the number of short-term hospital facilities has been much improved since 1948, the increase has not always been accompanied by establishment of services to allow modern medical practice. Further, many older hospitals that do provide complete care, and are accredited, are housed in physical plants that are in urgent need of modernization, a matter to which the Hill-Burton program is applying special emphasis.

LONG-TERM HOSPITALS AND RELATED SERVICES

Although 85 per cent of all nonfederal hospitals are primarily for short-term care, more than half of the beds in nonfederal hospitals are long-term hospitals. Forty-five per cent are in psychiatric hospitals (see Table 9). Because of the extended duration of hospitalization in long-term hospitals, these facilities provide more than half of the patient days of care in nonfederal hospitals, but they have only about 3 per cent of the admissions.

Hospitals for Mental Illness and Tuberculosis. Nearly 87 per cent of the long-term beds in nonfederal hospitals are used for mental illness, another 5 per cent for patients with tuberculosis. In both of these conditions, modern treatment can significantly shorten the period of hospital care for most newly diagnosed cases. In both psychiatric and tuberculosis hospitals, however, there are many patients who became ill before improved treatment was available or who for some other reason did not have the benefit of it, so that their condition may require lifelong institutional care.

Hospitals for tuberculosis and mental illness have long been considered a public responsibility, and most of them are operated by state governments. They were often established in locations geographically remote from population centers, and this distance now makes it much harder to coordinate their services with other components of modern community programs for mental illness or tuberculosis—clinics, posthospital care, and other services for patients and their families. As the usual periods of hospitalization for both conditions become shorter, the trend toward including facilities for psychiatric and tuberculosis treatment in general rather than special hospitals will undoubtedly accelerate. (Community needs and facilities for treatment of tuberculosis and mental illness are discussed in Chapter 7 and 11.)

Chronic Disease Hospitals. The hospitals listed in Table 9 as "Long-Term General" and "Other Special" are chiefly hospitals for treatment of chronic diseases. Because a large proportion of the population is now in the older age groups especially subject to chronic diseases, these institutions have growing importance. The services they provide are similar to those of a general hospital, with more emphasis on physical and occupational therapy, medical social service, and recreational activities—all especially important for long-term patients. Some chronic disease hospitals are closely related to, or part of, general hospitals; others are independent. Some accept patients with any long-term condition; others are specialized.[24]

Nursing Homes. An important resource for the care of the chronically ill is the nursing home that provides skilled nursing care under medical supervision. In response to growing needs and the demand of new programs of care for the chronically ill and elderly, considerable progress has been made in recent years in upgrading the quality of care in nursing homes and increasing the number of available beds. Since the publication in 1961 of the Public Health Service *Nursing Home Standards Guide,*[25] a number of states have revised their nursing home licensure requirements to make them consistent with the *Guide's* recommendations, and the requirements of the Medicare program are serving to raise the quality of nursing home services to an even higher level.

In 1966, the Joint Commission on Accreditation of Hospitals, together with the American Association of Homes for the Aging and the American Nursing Home Association, initiated a program of accreditation for extended care facilities.[26] The standards for accreditation approximate those of Medicare.

To qualify as an extended care facility under Medicare, a nursing home must have a written agreement with at least one participating hospital providing for transfer of patients between the two facilities when this is considered necessary by the attending physician. Health care of each patient in the nursing home must be under a physician's supervision, and there are other requirements to ensure that the service given is a health care service and not simply custodial.

In 1966 about three-quarters of nursing home beds were in proprietary homes. Some of those under voluntary or government auspices are units of general hospitals; more than 450 hospitals over the country have such units.

In the past, nursing homes were often operated in converted buildings inappropriate for the purpose, and they provided only custodial care. The eligibility standards for providing service under the 1965 Amendments to the Social Security Act—both Medicare and new provisions for care of the indigent and medically indigent[27]—are changing this pattern.

Rehabilitation Centers. Modern medical care for disabling illness or injury includes, from the beginning, procedures aimed at rehabilitation—restoration of patients to their fullest potential of physical function and mental and social competence. Rehabilitation should therefore be a part of the service of short-term general and chronic disease hospitals, and of nursing homes and home care programs as well. In addition, there are over 200 centers, some of them services of general hospitals, that offer comprehensive rehabilitation of the disabled through coordinated medical, psychological, social, and vocational services. Most of these centers accept patients with any of a number of types of disability, but some provide treatment for only one type. They are located chiefly in or near large cities, but usually serve larger geographic areas.

Home Care Programs. The first of the modern home care programs was organized to compensate for the shortage of hospital beds caused by the rising prevalence of chronic disease. Experience and investigation have shown, however, that an organized home care program, coordinated with hospital and other institutional facilities, has its own place in the total complex of care facilities.

The type of care in the home in support of

---

[24] For additional discussion of chronic disease hospital and nursing home services, see Chapter 10.

[25] U.S. Department of Health, Education, and Welfare, Public Health Service (Washington: Government Printing Office, 1961, reprinted 1963).

[26] STANDARDS FOR ACCREDITATION OF EXTENDED CARE FACILITIES AND SUPPLEMENT TO THE STANDARDS FOR ACCREDITATION OF EXTENDED CARE FACILITIES (Chicago: The Commission, 1966).

[27] See Chapter 14.

the physician's care that is most commonly available is home nursing service. Such service is provided in the majority of cities with a population of more than 25,000. It is usually under the auspices of a visiting nurse association, but is sometimes offered by the health department or a combination (official and voluntary) service. Although nursing alone fills an important need, many patients at home require other help or professional service—medical social services, physical therapy, occupational therapy, nutrition counseling, dental care, or loan of equipment, for instance. Some nursing agencies have facilities and staff trained to offer some of these, or they may be available from other community agencies, either for all patients or for those with certain diseases or conditions.

Often the kind of help a homemaker–home health aide provides is greatly needed. Originally, most homemaker services were developed to help families with children when they were threatened with disruption, but by 1963 more than two-thirds of the homemaker agencies offered service to families with ill or disabled adults as well.[28] Homemakers trained to give personal care to the ill under supervision of professional health staff are called homemaker–home health aides. To be reimbursable under Medicare, such service must be prescribed by the physician and supervised by a registered professional nurse.

A growing number of communities have organized coordinated home care programs, which have been defined[29] as follows:

A coordinated home care program is one that is *centrally* administered, and that through *coordinated planning, evaluation, and followup procedures* provides for *physician-directed* medical, nursing, social, and related services to *selected patients* at home.

The terms used in the definition above were further interpreted as:

Centrally administered—responsibility for the administration of the program is delegated to a single organization.

Coordinated planning, evaluation, and followup procedures—the organization maintains an operational unit to:

Plan and arrange for the participation of resources organized to provide patient services including at least: physician care, nursing care, social service, and ready access to inpatient facilities.

Hold periodic joint conferences with physicians and other professional or allied personnel to determine the medical, nursing, and social needs of all patients on the program. These needs are to be determined on an individual basis at the time of admission and discharge and during the course of care.

Coordinate the individual service schedules of patients consistent with their needs and with efficient distribution and utilization of services within the total caseload.

Physician directed—direction and supervision of all direct patient services (medical, nursing, social and related) are the responsibility of the attending physician.

Selected patients—the program is primarily reserved for patients whose health needs: do not require hospitalization and cannot be met on an ambulatory or outpatient basis; require a complex of medical, nursing, social, and related services over an extended period of time; and can feasibly be met by the program in a suitable physical and psychological home environment.[30]

Coordinated home care programs vary in their clientele; some provide service only to patients with chronic illness or even certain categories of chronic illness. However, the trend is toward "broader acceptance of both the acute and the long-term patient, of the convalescent as well as the terminal patient, of the patient who needs minimum service as well as the severely handicapped and complex patient."[31]

In addition to the medical, nursing, and social services required by the definition, a coordinated home care program may provide any or all of a long list of other services: dental,

[28] U.S. Department of Health, Education, and Welfare, Public Health Service, DIRECTORY OF HOMEMAKER SERVICES (PHS Publication No. 928 [Washington: Government Printing Office, 1964]), Table 6.

[29] Jointly by the American Hospital Association, American Medical Association, American Public Health Association, American Public Welfare Association, National League for Nursing, Blue Cross Commission, Blue Shield Medical Care Plan, and the Public Health Service.

[30] U.S. Department of Health, Education, and Welfare, Public Health Service, SURVEY OF COORDINATED HOME CARE PROGRAMS (PHS Publication No. 1062 [Washington: Government Printing Office, 1964]), pp. 3–4.

[31] Claire F. Ryder and Bernard Frank, "Coordinated Home Care Programs in Community Health Agencies, A Decade of Progress," presented at Annual Meeting of American Public Health Association, Chicago, Illinois, October, 1965.

physical therapy, occupational therapy, speech therapy, nutrition, homemaker, laboratory, X ray, medications, equipment, prosthetic appliances—even transportation.

The advantages of a coordinated home care program to the patient are readily apparent. It also can save the physician time while assuring him of the continuity of his patient's care. And it has the virtue of helping the community make the best and most productive use of its health care resources.

Local Hospital Needs

Experience in planning hospital facilities has shown that plans should be based on areas broader than those contained in most local governmental jurisdictions. An urban region for hospital planning purposes, for instance, should encompass the central city, its suburbs, and the part of the surrounding territory that depends upon the primary area for services.

For a designated area, gross health care needs can be defined on the basis of population projections, hospital utilization experience, and a factor representing desirable occupancy rates. For short-term hospitals, the occupancy rate for medical and surgical services should usually be 80 to 85 per cent, although it will be lower for obstetrical and pediatric services. For long-term facilities it should be 90 per cent or higher. In some isolated areas with low population density, lower occupancy rates must be accepted.

No type of hospital facility can be wisely planned without regard to an area's total resources for both hospitalization and such other services as diagnostic centers and home care programs. Hospital planning authorities are developing competence in application of more sophisticated methods of determining hospital bed needs based upon consideration and utilization of alternative methods and sources of care. A community that has a large short-term general hospital with a low occupancy rate may find adapting part of it for long-term care more sensible than building a new facility for the purpose. Or to relieve overcrowding in a short-term hospital that accepts long-term patients, a nursing home or home care program may be a better approach than another general hospital.

Hill-Burton statewide planning provides general guidance for areas within the state and specifically influences the construction of new health facilities with federal assistance. In some states, further positive steps have been taken. The California legislature has established a Hospitals and Related Health Facilities and Services Planning Committee to coordinate regional planning and to provide impartial review of decisions of voluntary planning groups. New York legislation has gone even further by placing the responsibility for approving all new construction of hospital and nursing home beds with the state health department, and specifically directing consideration of availability of home care and other out-of-hospital services as alternative ways of meeting needs.

The Hospital in Comprehensive Medical Care

The general hospital has emerged in many areas as the community's central resource for the application of modern medical science. In doing so, it has tended to concentrate its functions on one aspect of personal health services —inpatient care of acutely ill people. Its outpatient functions have rarely been more than peripheral, and hospital concern with home care programs or even nursing homes has only recently begun to appear.

A society in which the chronic diseases are the health problems affecting the largest proportion of the population cannot limit application of the kind of expertise and equipment found in the best of the general hospitals to treatment of acute illness in that hospital. And as the demand grows for health services of high quality for all the population, communities will have to make fullest use of their health service resources. The trend is undoubtedly toward a broader role for general hospitals in total community services for comprehensive medical care, not only in extending direct services to include prevention, diagnosis, and perhaps home care, but also in closer coordination and cooperation with other institutions and services.

9

Programs for Special Groups

THE SITUATION OF CHILDREN in this country at the beginning of the twentieth century was probably no worse than it had been in pioneer days or in the beginning of industrialization. But unlike earlier times, this period experienced a rise of social consciousness and growing unwillingness to tolerate evils that could be remedied. Early child health services were an expression on the part of philanthropists and charitable organizations of their humanitarian desire to turn pale, hungry, ailing children into robust, happy youngsters who would reflect the American ideal.

Children and Mothers

A few local health departments began child health programs early in the century. Extensive state and local government activities in this area, however, came after establishment of the federal Children's Bureau in 1912 as the end result of the vigorous efforts of such social reformers as Lillian Wald, founder of the Henry Street Settlement in New York City, and Florence Kelley of the National Consumers League. They had begun to push for federal action in behalf of the welfare of children in 1903.[1] Authority under the "general welfare" clause of the Constitution had not previously been used so broadly, and when the bill was finally enacted nine years later, it was an innovation in federal legislation. While this federal action was new in applying to a welfare problem of the whole nation, the state and local action for

child health that followed was innovative in applying to one group of the population rather than to the community as a whole.

The early Children's Bureau studies and publications, and the energetic efforts of its chief and her staff, aroused new awareness of children's needs which moved states and communities to launch new service programs. In 1921, on the basis of the Bureau's presentations, the Maternity and Infancy Act (Sheppard-Towner Act) was passed, providing formula grants to the states and requiring that state agencies be designated for the Children's Bureau to work with. By the time the Act expired in 1929, maternal and child health services were accepted as essential activities of all state and local health departments.

The Social Security Act of 1935 reestablished grants to the states from the Children's Bureau for maternal and child health and also instituted grants for crippled children and for child welfare services. Appropriations in these three categories have grown steadily over the years; for fiscal 1966, $45 million was appropriated for each.

More recently, Congress has also provided funds to the Children's Bureau for special project grants. The 1963 Maternal and Child Health and Mental Retardation Planning Amendments authorized a five-year program of grants to state or local health departments to pay up to 75 per cent of the cost of projects providing maternity care for women at high risk and their infants. The 1965 Social Security Amendments authorized special project grants to pay up to 75 per cent of the cost of programs of comprehensive health care for children of school and preschool age. These latter grants go

---

[1] See Dorothy E. Bradbury, FIVE DECADES OF ACTION FOR CHILDREN, A HISTORY OF THE CHILDREN'S BUREAU (Washington: Government Printing Office, 1962).

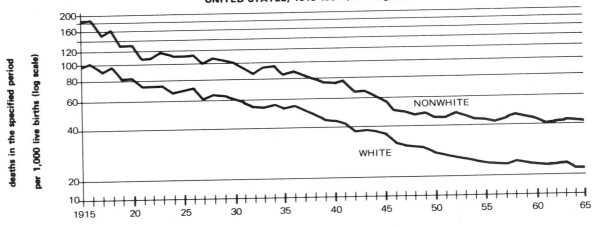

MORTALITY RATE OF WHITE AND NONWHITE INFANTS (under 1 year)
UNITED STATES, 1915-1961 (birth registration area)

FIGURE 12. *Mortality rates of white and nonwhite infants*

to state and local health departments, crippled children's agencies, medical schools, or teaching hospitals for programs of screening, diagnostic, and preventive services for all children and, in addition, treatment, correction of defects, and aftercare for children who would not otherwise receive them.

The national interest in maternal and child health is clearly expressed, but the programs in its behalf are state and local programs. Maternal and child health is one of the "basic six" programs considered the minimum for local health departments a quarter of a century ago. In recent years, state and local governments have been spending about three times as much as the federal government for MCH programs.

HEALTH STATUS OF MOTHERS AND CHILDREN

The 1965 infant mortality rate (deaths of children under a year old per 1,000 live births) in the United States was 24.7, only one-quarter of the 1915 rate of 99.9. The rate declined by between 20 and 30 per cent in each of the four decades after 1915. From 1955 to 1964, however, it declined only 6 per cent.

The possibility that the country is so close to an irreducible minimum that significant further progress against infant mortality cannot be expected is unacceptable when comparisons are made with other countries. The 1959–61 average infant mortality rate for the United States was higher than the rates of nine other coun-

tries—Netherlands, Sweden, Norway, Australia, Switzerland, Finland, Denmark, United Kingdom, and New Zealand. Five of these countries had lower average rates than the United States in the 1949–51 period; all nine of them had a higher per cent decrease between 1949–51 and 1959–61 than did the United States.[2]

High infant mortality rates are associated with low socioeconomic status. Rates are generally higher in states or counties with lower-than-average per capita income and levels of education, and in other areas among population groups with these characteristics. For instance, nonwhites, who as a group have lower incomes and fewer years of schooling than whites, had an infant mortality rate in 1965 of 40.3 per 1,000 live births, compared to 21.5 for whites (see Table 10).

Improvement in prenatal and obstetrical care and enormously greater frequency of hospitalization for childbirth helped to bring the maternal mortality rate from 60.8 per 10,000 live births in 1915 down to 3.2 in 1965. However, in 1965 the rate for nonwhites was four times that for whites.

Mortality is only one measure of the adequacy of maternal and infant care. Another is the incidence of low birth weight.[3] Low birth

[2] Eleanor P. Hunt, "Lags in Reducing Infant Mortality," WELFARE IN REVIEW, April, 1964, p. 1.

[3] A newborn weighing 2,500 grams (5.5 pounds) or less is considered to be in the low-birth-weight group.

Table 10

Births, Infant and Maternal Mortality, United States, 1965

	Total	White	Nonwhite
Registered live births	3,760,358	3,123,860	636,498
Per Cent in hospital.............	97.4	98.9	89.8
Per Cent not attended by physicians..........	1.8	0.5	8.2
Infant mortality (deaths at age under 1 year per 1,000 live births)............	24.7	21.5	40.3
Per Cent of births with low birth weight...	8.3	7.2	13.8
Maternal mortality (deaths per 100,000 live births)........	31.6	21.0	83.7

Source: U.S. Department of Health, Education, and Welfare, PHS, National Center for Health Statistics, VITAL STATISTICS OF THE U.S., 1965, Vols. I and II.

weight and premature termination of pregnancy increase the risk not only of death but also of mental and physical defects in infants who survive. Low birth weight has been increasing in recent years, from 7.7 per cent of live births in 1960 to 8.2 per cent in 1963 and 1964 and 8.3 per cent in 1965.

This condition is also associated with low socioeconomic status, and the rate of low birth weight among nonwhites is nearly twice that among whites. Studies cited by Lesser indicate the coincidence of inadequate prenatal care with premature delivery and low birth weight.[4] In New York City in 1957, for instance, the rate of premature delivery among 70,952 women who had adequate prenatal care was 7.8 per cent; among 8,683 women who had no prenatal care, it was 20.3 per cent.

Infant mortality, maternal mortality, and low birth weight occur more frequently when babies are born to mothers who are not married, probably because these mothers are least

likely to have adequate prenatal care. A study by the New York City Health Department[5] revealed that rates of infant mortality and premature delivery were about twice as high, and maternal mortality more than four times as high when mothers were unmarried. The study also showed that about half of unwed mothers received only late prenatal care or none.

Among children from 1 to 14 years old, mortality rates have been dramatically reduced. At the same time, the major causes of severe illness in children have changed.

The kinds of diseases that used to fill pediatric services in hospitals, such as rheumatic fever and rheumatic heart disease, osteomyelitis, mastoiditis, pneumonia, streptococcal infections, meningitis, polio, and others, have sharply declined. The major group of illnesses to be found in the average large children's in-patient service today are conditions that are prenatal in origin, a considerable contrast to a generation ago when infectious diseases of various kinds prevailed.[6]

Accidents continue to be a major cause of injury and death in children. Most children have many episodes of mild acute illness while they are growing up, and a considerable number have a chronic condition. In 1959–61, the National Health Survey found that 18 per cent of children under 17 years old had some chronic affliction. Over-all rates of chronic conditions reported were higher in the higher income groups. However, since this information was obtained through household interviews, it probably reflects the facts that children in families with higher incomes receive more adequate medical care and their parents pay more attention to illness, rather than an actual difference in chronic disease rates. Low-income families had higher rates of the obvious chronic conditions—paralysis and orthopedic impairments, blindness and visual impairments, hearing loss, and speech defects.[7]

[4] Arthur J. Lesser, CURRENT PROBLEMS OF MATERNITY CARE, THE FIRST JESSIE M. BIERMAN ANNUAL LECTURE IN MATERNAL AND CHILD HEALTH (Washington: U.S. Department of Health, Education, and Welfare, Children's Bureau, 1963), p. 10.

[5] Jean Pakter, Henry J. Rosner, Harold Jacobziner, and Frieda Greenstein, "Out-of-Wedlock Births in New York City, Part I, Sociological Aspects," AMERICAN JOURNAL OF PUBLIC HEALTH, May, 1961, pp. 683–96, and "Part II, Medical Aspects," June, 1961, pp. 846–65.

[6] U.S. Department of Health, Education, and Welfare, Children's Bureau, HEALTH OF CHILDREN OF SCHOOL AGE (Washington: Government Printing Office, 1964), p. 3.

[7] *Ibid.*, p. 4.

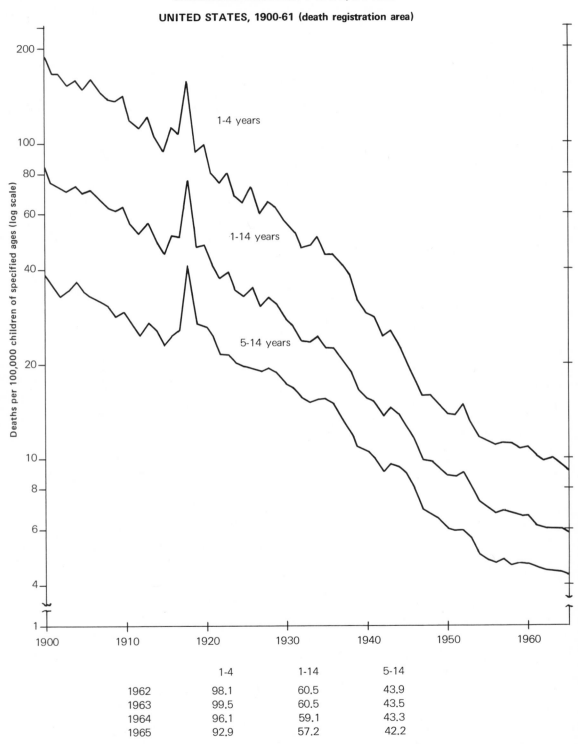

CHILDHOOD MORTALITY RATE, BY AGE:

UNITED STATES, 1900-61 (death registration area)

	1-4	1-14	5-14
1962	98.1	60.5	43.9
1963	99.5	60.5	43.5
1964	96.1	59.1	43.3
1965	92.9	57.2	42.2

FIGURE 13. *Childhood mortality rate by age*

Dental caries is another chronic condition that often does not receive attention in low-income families; it affects many children by the time they are five years old, and most by the time they are 10. Imperfect alignment of teeth (malocclusion) is also a common defect; in many children it is sufficiently serious to require orthodontia and in a few it may be so severe as to be crippling if not corrected.

Emotional disturbance in children of school age, sometimes existing when they enter school, has assumed major proportions. Studies have shown from 10 to 20 per cent of school populations to be sufficiently maladjusted to need child guidance service.

Illness, disability, and death among children are important problems in themselves, but failure to correct childhood health deficiencies also can result in adult health problems. Among the more than 20 per cent of draftees rejected for military service for medical reasons in the years 1961 to 1964 are many with conditions that could have been prevented or corrected.[8] Military service may require different standards of physical and mental health than civilian life, but it is likely that the major causes of these draft rejections—orthopedic defects, emotional disorders, circulatory system diseases, and sight defects—would also often interfere with normal civilian life.

In the majority of instances, the abnormal conditions had existed for a number of years, and the early period of the defects, when many are most readily amenable to correction, had been allowed to pass either because the condition was not recognized or because medical care had not been sought or was not available.

The concept that services to promote the health of children are an investment in the future, pervading the early child health movement, is as sound today as it was a half century ago. The concern is not limited to ensuring that a child born today has a future, but includes effort to make his future healthy and productive.

SERVICES FOR MOTHERS, INFANTS, AND PRESCHOOL CHILDREN

Basic to the ultimate physical and emotional health of a child is his being wanted and planned for before his birth. Ideally, family planning services should be available to all parents before they have their first child. With only few exceptions, family planning services in the United States until recently have been limited to those provided by private physicians or by affiliates of the Planned Parenthood Federation of America. Dr. Mary S. Calderone (formerly Medical Director of the Planned Parenthood Federation and now Executive Director of the Sex Information and Education Council of the United States) predicts:

. . . as the discrimination implicit in the differential availability of contraceptive services as between private and public facilities becomes more widely publicized, and as the social and medical consequences of this discrimination become more apparent, increased pressures for corrective action will result in increased contraceptive services in tax-supported medical facilities—hospitals, welfare agencies, and health departments.[9]

Most medical care for mothers and children is provided by private physicians, and the majority of babies are born in voluntary hospitals. However, any of a number of services in support of the physician and the hospital can be made available by the health department. Public health nursing service is sometimes provided for private physicians' patients, and health department prenatal classes may be open to all expectant parents. Both services encourage patients to keep scheduled appointments with their physicians and to follow medical recommendations.

Health officials should participate in medical society or hospital committees concerned with maternal mortality or perinatal[10] mortality and morbidity, which have been found to be effective in improving standards of obstetrical care. Control of hospital staphylococcal infections, which endanger mothers and infants and can

---

[8] U.S. Department of the Army, Office of the Surgeon General, RESULTS OF THE EXAMINATION OF YOUTHS FOR MILITARY SERVICE, SUPPLEMENT TO THE HEALTH OF THE ARMY (Washington: The Department, 1965), p. 9.

[9] "Planned Parenthood." in Harry L. Lurie (ed.), ENCYCLOPEDIA OF SOCIAL WORK (New York: National Association of Social Workers, 1965), p. 558.

[10] The term "perinatal" is used to define a period before, during, and soon after birth.

be taken from the hospital to other family members, calls for health department participation, and in some states maternity units are under health department regulation.

As medical research uncovers new means of protecting newborns, such as the simple PKU test that may indicate a metabolic defect associated with mental retardation, the health department should make every effort to see that they are applied. Materials or services such as blood tests for syphilis or treatment of newborns to prevent blindness due to gonorrhea are often supplied by the health department, as well as biological materials for immunization. Some state and local health departments provide special services—hospital centers, transportation, nursing service, incubators and other equipment—for the care of premature babies.

Although some communities do not apply means tests (tests of ability to pay) for maternity clinics and child health conferences, these services are mainly used by persons who cannot pay for private care. Maternity clinics operated by health departments, teaching hospitals, or public hospitals provide care both before and after the baby is born. Patients may attend such a clinic of their own volition, but many are referred by public health nurses, physicians, or other clinics. A successful community maternal health service includes not only provision of prenatal care but also efforts to encourage expectant mothers to seek care early in their pregnancies.

In many areas, a significant proportion of mothers receive inadequate prenatal medical care, or none. Reports of recent years from a number of municipal hospitals show that 23 to 45 per cent of women delivered had no prenatal care, either because it was not available or because for various reasons they did not use the service.

The deterrents to good maternity care found in several studies of the problem, which Lesser has summarized,[11] include the expense and difficulty of transportation to a distant clinic and excessively restrictive financial or residence requirements for eligibility. Some mothers are unable to find anyone to stay with their other

children while they go to the clinic; others work during the hours clinics are open.

Among other factors cited are dissatisfaction with the clinic. "Patients spend long hours waiting to be seen in the clinic. Impersonal attitudes on the part of the staff, abrupt and hurried treatment, and the general climate of many overcrowded public clinics depreciates the value of the services provided." If infant mortality and the incidence of low birth weight are to be reduced, prenatal care of high quality must be provided conveniently and in a climate that will make it acceptable to women in the lower socioeconomic groups.

Public health nursing service for expectant mothers has always been an important part of MCH activities. The nurse not only refers many patients for medical and dental care, but in periodic visits helps them prepare for delivery and gives instructions in such matters as nutrition and child care. After the child is born, a nursing visit is usually scheduled within a day or two after the mother goes home, at least for patients under public medical care. Periodic nursing service should be continued until the baby is a year old or even longer if needed.

For families who cannot afford private health supervision, health departments conduct child health conferences, sometimes called "well-baby clinics," where children receive health appraisals and immunizations and are referred to physicians, clinics, or other agencies for needed treatment.

Most children seen in child health conferences are under a year old. A large proportion of children aged one to five receive no health supervision. In some communities, well-child services for this age group are not available, although it is a critical period for the discovery and correction of such problems as sight and hearing defects. Recognition that care in these often-neglected preschool years may be crucial to the child's future physical and emotional health and intellectual development is the basis for the Project Headstart program of the Office of Economic Opportunity and for grants from the Children's Bureau provided under the 1965 Social Security Amendments.

When most children are ill, they receive medical care from the family physician or pediatri-

---

[11] Loc. cit.

cian. Medical care for indigent children is usually provided in pediatric outpatient clinics or hospital services, and a few health departments conduct pediatric clinics as well as child health conferences. The advantages of combining or associating well-child services with services for sick children are apparent, and experiments are being made in some communities to accomplish this.

Childhood is a very important period for the establishment of dental health. In areas with fluoridated water, dental caries in children is reduced by about two-thirds. In other communities, somewhat less effective protection can be obtained by the topical application of fluoride, beginning when the child is three and repeated several times until he is 13. For children whose families cannot afford private dental care, dental clinics are sometimes conducted by the health department or under the auspices of a dental college.

Many preschool children are cared for, either full-time or during the working day, in places other than their own homes. The responsibility to determine that child-care centers provide a healthful environment for children usually rests with either the welfare or the health department. The health department may provide child health services, including health examinations and immunizations, for centers under public auspices. Wherever the responsibility is placed, the health department must be concerned with such children's health needs.

Child guidance resources, used to help overcome the emotional and adjustment problems of either preschool or older children, are scarce in most communities. As mental health programs become oriented to the community rather than the hospital, this gap in services for children may be closed (see Chapter 11).

Services for School-age Children

During the years from five to seventeen, children not only should have treatment for illnesses and injuries but also should receive periodic medical and dental examinations, including screening for conditions that should be corrected, and services to achieve correction. Children in families under private medical care may receive such services from the family doc-

tor, or pediatrician, and dentist. However, even parents who can afford to pay do not always seek health appraisals for their children when they are apparently well, and health defects may go unnoticed until they become serious. The Children's Bureau estimates that over 10 million school children have visual defects and about a million and a half have hearing impairments—problems that can easily interfere with their learning and their success as productive adults, but usually can be corrected or alleviated if they are diagnosed early.

The school provides access to almost all members of a population group whose health maintenance and improvement are exceedingly important both for their own future and for long-term community goals. Habits and attitudes developed in the school years, as well as services received, have lifelong influence on health. Although it is only one of the many goals of education, health has long been recognized as a proper concern of schools, and most schools have some kind of health program.

The recommended health concerns of schools are:

. . . to assure every pupil of (1) healthful school living conditions, (2) appropriate health and safety education, (3) effective school health services, (4) healthful physical education, and (5) teachers and other school personnel who are themselves healthy and who have up-to-date preparation for their special health responsibilities.[12]

This broad charge calls for participation of all school officials and personnel and of students and parents. Effective coordination with many other community agencies, both official and voluntary, is essential.

The potential of school health programs for contributing to comprehensive health services is often incompletely realized, and a major cause of failure is poor coordination with the mainstream of community health services. Although schools are in an excellent position to initiate detection of defects that should be corrected, they cannot undertake the services needed for correction. If the school health pro-

---

[12] National Committee on School Health Policies, Suggested School Health Policies (Washington and Chicago: The Joint Committee on Health Problems in Education of the National Education Association and the American Medical Association, 1962), p. 1.

gram is conducted as an isolated operation, not as an integral part of a coordinated system of community health services, its efforts are likely to be unproductive.

Children are screened for vision or hearing or other defects, sometimes as often as annually during their school years, but a large proportion of those found to have defects never receive follow-up service to correct them. This may be because the school has failed to communicate to parents the urgency of care for the children; but it is often because the school is not prepared to refer families who cannot afford to pay for care to agencies providing it.

Screening is futile if resources are not available for follow-up, or if planning for follow-up is not built into the screening program. This applies to the school health program as much as to any other.

The problem of coordination that vexes community health programs generally is compounded in school health by the multiplicity of agencies. There are over 35,000 public school districts in the nation's 3,071 counties, and the majority of school health programs are administered by boards of education. Some public school health programs are jointly conducted by health departments and school boards, and a smaller number are the sole responsibility of the health department. In the latter situation, or when a health department provides some service to the schools, it may have to work with as many as 10 or 12 boards of education, as well as with parochial schools.

Coordination with other health efforts in the community has additional value in helping school board health personnel continually refresh their professional expertise. The school nurse, for instance, has a much greater opportunity to keep current professionally if she has continual professional relationships with health department and other nurses, as well as with the staff of many agencies. She is more likely to feel the need and request opportunities for frequent refresher training in workshops and short courses that will help her keep up to date. Without such stimulation, her work becomes routine repetition of tasks that may have lost their meaning long ago.

Adequate health teaching in the schools is also greatly improved by established relationships with health agencies. Very few classroom teachers acquire a background of health information in their formal preparation for teaching, and even those who teach biology may have difficulty in relating the subject to the health needs of children and adolescents.

Ideally, health is included as an aspect of many parts of the curriculum—social studies, home economics, as a subject for reading and writing—and not just left to biology and physical education. If this is to be accomplished, the school health staff must be qualified to consult with teachers, and the faculty and school board must have sufficient rapport with community health interests to accept health as a part of the general educational background the school aims to give to students.

Boards of education employ almost 40 per cent of all public health nurses, and school health services use considerable amounts of physician time. Direct expenditures for these purposes are estimated to exceed $100 million a year in the country as a whole, chiefly from local sources.

SERVICES FOR CRIPPLED CHILDREN

One of the aims of all programs to promote maternal and child health is prevention of handicapping conditions, both physical and mental. Accident prevention programs, discussed in Chapter 12, also serve this purpose. The objective of crippled children's programs is to identify the children who do have crippling conditions and provide corrective services that will enable handicapped children to live lives that are as normal as possible.

All states except Arizona participate in the federal crippled children's program instituted under the Social Security Act of 1935, which provides grants (that must be partially matched by the states) for medical, surgical, and other care services for children with handicapping conditions (as defined by the states). All states include orthopedic and plastic defects and cerebral palsy in their definitions; many include rheumatic fever and cardiac conditions; some include epilepsy, cystic fibrosis, and serious eye and ear problems.

There is growing interest in the problems of

mentally retarded children[13] and those with multiple handicaps. As appropriations are increased, the Children's Bureau encourages states to broaden their definitions of crippling conditions and to remove such restrictions on eligibility as residence requirements.

Services are administered through networks of traveling or regional diagnostic clinics and centers providing medical and rehabilitative care. Children are referred by physicians, health departments, schools, hospitals, and welfare and voluntary agencies. Community organizations, such as Elks Clubs and crippled children's societies, often help in seeing that children receive care.

Services to handicapped children are to a very large extent motivated by compassion, but they also have economic importance. The extended care usually required for complete treatment and rehabilitation is expensive, but since it reduces dependency and the need for prolonged institutionalization, it results in a considerable long-term saving. Services for mothers and children that prevent handicapping conditions are also both humanitarian and economical in the long run.

Health of Workers

In the ancient civilizations of Egypt, Greece, and Rome, slaves performed work such as mining, metallurgy, and pottery making. Although the hazards associated with these occupations were known, they were not considered a subject for medical attention. Indeed, such work was probably given to slaves because it was hazardous and therefore not fit for citizens. It was many centuries before protection of workers from dangers associated with their work would become accepted practice.

Occupational diseases were studied by scientists from the early Renaissance through the eighteenth century, but little action was taken until the period of great social reforms in England in the nineteenth century. Then the conditions of workers were the subject of a series of laws, first establishing requirements for the protection of apprentices and women workers, and later setting up a system of factory inspections.

In the United States, where industrialization came later than in England, little was done to protect the health and safety of workers before 1900. Early in the twentieth century, however, the increasing social protest against hardship and misery, together with the growing strength of organized labor, resulted in enactment of a number of state laws for regulating working conditions. These early laws were generally poorly enforced and ineffective. But their very ineffectiveness led to official surveys and investigations that uncovered facts about the large number of industrial poisonings and high accident rates in industry.

By 1913, 23 states had enacted workmen's compensation laws. Most of the early laws compensated workers only for accidents on the job, but in later decades the courts began to interpret compensation laws as covering occupational disease. Today the workmen's compensation law of one state, Wyoming, covers accidents only; in 19 states, specified occupational diseases are covered, and the remainder of the states have full coverage.[14]

INDUSTRY AND OCCUPATIONAL HEALTH

The premiums paid by a company for workmen's compensation usually depend on its experience record—that is, a company with few claims pays a lower rate than one with many. This matter of dollars and cents has motivated industries to undertake safety programs and to improve working conditions of their employees.

Originally, the health services provided by industry were for occupational conditions or nonoccupational emergencies, but as the additional economic factor of the cost of absenteeism has come to be recognized, many companies have found it good management to offer health services aimed at preventing all illness. For instance, McKiever and Siegel cite an instance in which the operation of an employee health service not only reduced the number of work-

---

[13] See Chapter 11.

[14] U.S. Department of Labor, Bureau of Labor Standards, STATE WORKMEN'S COMPENSATION LAWS: A COMPARISON OF MAJOR PROVISIONS WITH RECOMMENDED STANDARDS (Washington: Government Printing Office, 1964), p. 8.

men's compensation claims by 73 per cent but cut absenteeism by half, at an average saving in production of over $800 per employee per year.[15] Other benefits cannot be measured as easily but are generally acknowledged: increased efficiency, better morale, and reduced turnover.

Employee fringe benefits increasingly include company-paid medical and hospital insurance. Some companies have found that costs in this area can also be reduced through employee health services. A large company whose premiums for this type of coverage are related to experience, as in workmen's compensation, actually effected a considerable saving through employee health services resulting in greater numbers of claims but smaller dollar amounts, since employees more often sought care for their ailments at a time when they could be corrected easily and inexpensively.[16] The practical implications of such experience for the community as a whole are exceedingly important.

Large organizations with many employees are able to provide occupational health services under their own auspices at a reasonable cost per employee, and indeed at an overall saving to the employer. Those with fewer than a thousand employees may find the cost of full-time industrial health service greater than the total saving effected.

A number of attempts have been made to solve this problem—cooperative arrangements covering several concerns, purchase of service from medical practice groups, or industrial medical groups. Even with these efforts a large number of workers employed in small companies receive only minimum and perhaps infrequent inspection and consultation services from state or local health departments and, in some cases, screening and health education services offered by voluntary agencies.

---

[15] Margaret F. McKiever and Gordon S. Siegel, OCCUPATIONAL HEALTH SERVICES FOR EMPLOYEES, A GUIDE FOR STATE AND LOCAL GOVERNMENTS (PHS Publication No. 1041 [Washington: Government Printing Office, 1963]) , pp. 39–40.

[16] N. H. Collisson, "Preventive Medicine in Industry," PUBLIC HEALTH REPORTS, November, 1964, pp. 949–50.

GOVERNMENT AND OCCUPATIONAL HEALTH

The first governmental program for preventive aspects of occupational health in the United States was the Division of Industrial Hygiene established in the New York State Department of Labor in 1913. In the following year, the Public Health Service created an Office of Industrial Hygiene and Sanitation, the predecessor of the present Division of Occupational Health. Growth of state government programs was very slow until the midthirties, when acceleration was stimulated by federal grants. The number of official industrial hygiene units reached an all-time high in the years from 1947 to 1950 again under the stimulus of federal grants.

In 1966, 42 states had occupational health units. In four states they are located in the department of labor; three states have units in both health and labor or industrial departments; in 38 states, the units are in the health department. Forty local governmental programs in industrial hygiene or occupational health are carried on by health departments.

Federal Program. The federal program of the Public Health Service division in occupational health includes extensive studies to identify occupational hazards and provide for their control. During the years since its work began, many occupational diseases or hazards have been eliminated or brought under control, but new problems continually arise.

Today, research is directed at such varied problems as health hazards in soft coal and uranium mines and in the asbestos and beryllium industries, the effects of industrial heat and noise, and skin diseases caused by the new synthetic resins. Investigations are made not only of the presence of toxic or damaging materials but of their actual effect on the human body— the effect, for instance, of mineral dust on the physiology of the lung.

The prolific invention of new materials for industry requires continual assessment of possible toxic or allergenic effects, either alone or in combination with other substances in the environment. Studies of this kind, which are also conducted by industry and by some state occupational health units, are exceedingly important for protecting workers from occupational exposure and preventing the production and marketing of toxic materials.

The Service also develops techniques and instruments for evaluating environmental safety; conducts epidemiologic studies on the incidence of occupational diseases and unidentified hazards in the working environment; and recommends appropriate controls. Its consultative and technical services are available to government agencies at all levels, industries, labor organizations, and universities and research groups. Although major assistance is given for administrative aspects of occupational health programs, many requests are answered for help in investigating occupational diseases and suspected health hazards in industry.

State Programs. State government programs in occupational health and industrial hygiene vary widely. The scope of activities is influenced to some extent by the location of units in the structure of state government and by the nature of professional direction. Industrial hygiene units in departments of labor tend to work more on accident prevention and safe working conditions; those in health departments put more emphasis on disease prevention and sanitation. Within a health department, a unit that is part of an engineering or other environmental health division may provide extensive services to industries in plant inspection and control of environmental hazards, whereas a unit located in a division of preventive medical services will give more attention to employee health services.

Generally accepted governmental services are field surveys and investigations of environmental hazards; collection of data on occupational illnesses and accidents and on absenteeism; research and development on detection, prevention, control, and treatment of occupational disease; advice and consultation; and health education.

Local Programs. The local health departments that have identifiable occupational health units carry on programs similar to those at the state level. Although a number of the activities of health officers, sanitarians, public health nurses, and other health department staff members inevitably relate to occupational health, in most communities no specific pro-

gram directed toward workers has been developed. According to Siegel, there has been a failure "in realizing the potential of a good occupational health program as a means of improving, strengthening, and focusing a community's attention on its general public health problems."[17]

The benefits of occupational health services are not unique to workers in large industry but apply to all workers, including employees of government, a large and growing component of the working population. The government, as an employer, has the same investment in the health of its employees as does any other industry, and experience has shown the management wisdom of providing occupational health services. The need in government is emphasized by data from the National Health Survey that show government employees to have higher-than-average illness-absence rates (except in educational services).[18] Occupational accidents among government employees also are in need of attention.

At the President's Conference on Occupational Safety in 1962, the Commissioner of Labor Statistics of the U.S. Department of Labor reported that the number of disabling work injuries in state and local government establishments had increased by 76 per cent from 1950 to 1961, while employment had increased 60 per cent.[19] Yet a very large proportion of local governments do not have employee safety or occupational health programs.

The health of school employees is a matter of concern to school officials because of their potential for influencing the health of children. However, service to help teachers and others who work in education to maintain their own health, and thus prevent absence and disability costly to school systems, is often neglected. And paradoxically, even people who work in health

[17] Gordon S. Siegel, "Neglect of Occupational Health in Public Health Planning," PUBLIC HEALTH REPORTS, November, 1964, p. 966.

[18] Philip E. Enterline, "Work Loss Due to Illness in Selected Occupations and Industries," JOURNAL OF OCCUPATIONAL MEDICINE, September, 1961, p. 407.

[19] Ewan Clague, "Work Injuries in the Public Service," PROCEEDINGS OF THE PRESIDENT'S CONFERENCE ON OCCUPATIONAL SAFETY, March 6–8, 1962 (Washington: Government Printing Office, 1962), p. 217.

departments and hospitals frequently do not have employee health services available to them.

The need for maintaining employee morale, which affects government's ability to compete for personnel and to reduce job turnover, has made occupational health an urgent concern of leadership. It is equally important to economical management of public funds.

CONTENT OF OCCUPATIONAL
HEALTH PROGRAMS

Even when industrial occupational health programs are motivated by desire to reduce costs and improve production, their objective, like that of public health, is prevention of disease, disability, and premature death. Such programs require two types of activities: (1) protecting workers from the hazards of their employment; and (2) promoting the health of workers so that they may be more efficient and productive employees.

Environmental protection involves protecting employees from exposure to toxic or irritating substances and to physical hazards such as noise, excessive heat, and ionizing radiation. This requires recognition, evaluation, and control of environmental factors that may cause sickness, impaired health, significant discomfort, or inefficiency.

Environmental surveys should be conducted at regular intervals, the length of which depends upon the nature of operations and other factors. Standards for the working environment have been set by a number of agencies, both governmental and professional—the U.S. Department of Labor, various state and local codes, American Standards Association, American Industrial Hygiene Association, Manufacturing Chemists Association, National Committee on Radiation Protection, American Conference of Governmental Industrial Hygienists, and the American Public Health Association.

Evaluation of the working environment and institution of control methods are functions of the industrial hygienist or industrial hygiene engineer. He may be assigned to the health unit or, more often, to the plant manager; he may work independently or in association with the plant safety engineer or the engineering department. He is responsible for making plant surveys, evaluating new chemicals and processes used in plant operations, and for recommending, as well as designing and evaluating, hazard controls such as personnel protective devices or improvements in plant ventilation.

Services directed to employees personally begin with preplacement physical examinations stressing physical requirements of jobs and measuring the medical fitness of applicants to perform required work. Any conditions needing medical attention, whether they would affect his work directly or not, should be reported to the applicant, or to his personal physician if he wishes. Once on the job, workers in some occupations that involve hazards to themselves or to others are required to have periodic examinations. For other employees these may be voluntary, although some firms especially emphasize routine checkups for executives.

Emergency care for minor illness or injuries is an important part of a health unit's function, and employees located in various parts of the plant should have first-aid training.

The preventive work of occupational health includes counseling employees both when they are examined and when they come for emergency care. By encouraging a worker to seek medical care when he first needs it, and by explaining his health needs in his own terms, the physician and nurse contribute to the maintenance of health. Some large companies provide counseling and referral services for employees with alcoholism problems, or with other emotional disturbances. Immunizations may be provided, or employees are at least advised to keep their immunization status current. In some services, injections or physical therapy is given on prescription of the employee's physician. Multiple screening programs are sometimes conducted or arranged for. In many industries, health education literature is made available to employees, and is most effective if it is used to follow up and emphasize information given in person.

Employee health service units are staffed by physicians and nurses who should be completely familiar with the work done and the working environment and should be trained in occupational health.[20] Ratios of one physician for 2,000 to 3,000 employees and one nurse for 500 employees are considered suitable. Other professional staff—therapists and X-ray or laboratory technicians—are sometimes employed.

As in any health program, records are necessary, and a number of guides have been prepared for developing record systems.[21] Occupational medical records should be the responsibility of professional personnel, and their confidentiality should be strictly maintained.

RELATIONSHIPS IN OCCUPATIONAL HEALTH

The field of occupational health concerns industry, labor, government, the medical profession, and many other community groups whose established attitudes and interests may not be in agreement. Clarification of roles and objectives, and dialogue between the various interests, is necessary for productive effort. For example, the industrial physician should be considered an impartial expert who is neither the tool of management nor the employees' advocate; he should have access to top management and have continuing associations with employees. He must maintain professional relationships with private practitioners, encourage their awareness of and interest in occupational diseases, and resolve misunder-

standings about the effect of occupational health services on their practice.

In many communities, if the health department starts an occupational health program, it must be willing to be exposed to what have been called "the interactions of the economics of private enterprise, labor-management disputes, professional unrest, and community power struggles."[22] The health department's role in occupational health must be one of representing the total health interests of the entire community. To play such a role requires understanding of the community, including the dynamics of its economy, and ability to converse knowledgeably and dispassionately with management, labor, and the professions on issues related to health.

Nearly half the people of the United States over 14 years old are employed workers, and their health needs deserve important consideration in planning for comprehensive community health services. Occupational health services can serve in two ways toward meeting such needs: (1) by protecting workers from possible threats to their health that exist in the environment in which they spend a considerable proportion of their lives, and (2) by early identification of conditions requiring medical care and referral at the time when it is the most effective.

If all employed workers—most of whom can pay for, or are insured for, medical care—were to receive it at the most advantageous point, the effect on long-term needs, to themselves and to their communities, would be appreciable. The potential of the occupational health program as an element of the total community system for preventive services deserves greater exploration.

---

[20] Qualifications for industrial physicians have been set by the Committee on Industrial Practices of the Industrial Medical Association; for industrial nurses, by the American Nurses' Association, Occupational Health Nurses Section.

[21] See American Conference of Government Industrial Hygienists, GUIDE TO RECORDS FOR HEALTH SERVICES IN SMALL INDUSTRIES (Cincinnati, Ohio: The Conference, 1960) ; and American Medical Association, Committee on Industrial Records of the Council on Industrial Health, A GUIDE TO THE DEVELOPMENT OF AN INDUSTRIAL MEDICAL RECORDS SYSTEM (Chicago: The Association, 1962) .

[22] Siegel, *op. cit.,* p. 964.

Part Three

Progress Toward
Comprehensive Health Services

Introduction

THE CROWDED HISTORY of the past half century has brought conspicuous changes in the nation's health. The composition of the population has altered along with the nature of its health needs. As scientific knowledge has extended ability to alleviate human ills, the attitudes, expectations, and demands of the public in regard to health have taken a new and broader form.

In 1900, the life expectancy of Americans at birth was about 47 years; in 1964, it was over 70 years. At the turn of the century, only 66 per cent of the people born 40 years before were still alive. In 1964, about 93 per cent of the 40-year-old group and more than 70 per cent of the people born 65 years before were still living. Nearly 30 per cent of the population in 1965 was in the age groups over 44 years old, compared with about 18 per cent in 1900.

This change in age distribution is attributed mostly to advances in control of acute and communicable illnesses. But in a population that includes a large proportion of older people, the chronic diseases become increasingly significant health problems. The data in Figure 14 show how trends in death rates since 1900 have reflected this development. As death rates from tuberculosis have been reduced by 97 per cent and from influenza and pneumonia by 82 per cent, cardiovascular disease death rates, always the highest, have almost doubled, and rates of deaths due to malignant neoplasms are two and one-third times what they were in 1900. Cardiovascular diseases and cancer now cause more than half of all deaths in this country. When death rates are adjusted to take account of the changing age composition of the population, death rates for cardiovascular disease show a decline since 1900, but those for cancer a substantial increase.

The chronic diseases also have an important effect on the nation's health and economy, as causes of illness and disability. In 1961–63, the National Health Survey by the U.S. Public Health Service found that more than 22 million people, 70 per cent of them over 44 years of age, had chronic conditions that limited their activities to some degree. For more than four million (87 per cent of them over 44), the limitation imposed was sufficient to prevent their carrying on major activities.[1] The leading causes of disability were heart conditions and arthritis and rheumatism; together they accounted for 40 per cent of the cases in which normal activities could not be continued.

Mental illness has also assumed great proportions as a national health problem. In the 1961–63 National Health Survey, 1.7 million people were reported to have mental and nervous conditions of sufficient severity to limit their activities. About two-thirds of them were over 44 years old. Inasmuch as these data were obtained through household interviews, they can be assumed to represent underreporting of conditions that family members may have been reluctant to report to strangers.

Although the health of young people generally has been greatly improved, many of them still suffer from the communicable diseases and the health hazards of infancy, as was pointed

---

[1] U.S. Department of Health, Education, and Welfare, Public Health Service, VITAL AND HEALTH STATISTICS, DATA FROM THE U.S. NATIONAL HEALTH SURVEY, SERIES 10, No. 17, CHRONIC CONDITIONS AND ACTIVITY LIMITATION, UNITED STATES—JULY 1961–JUNE 1963 (Washington: Government Printing Office, 1965), pp. 13 and 14.

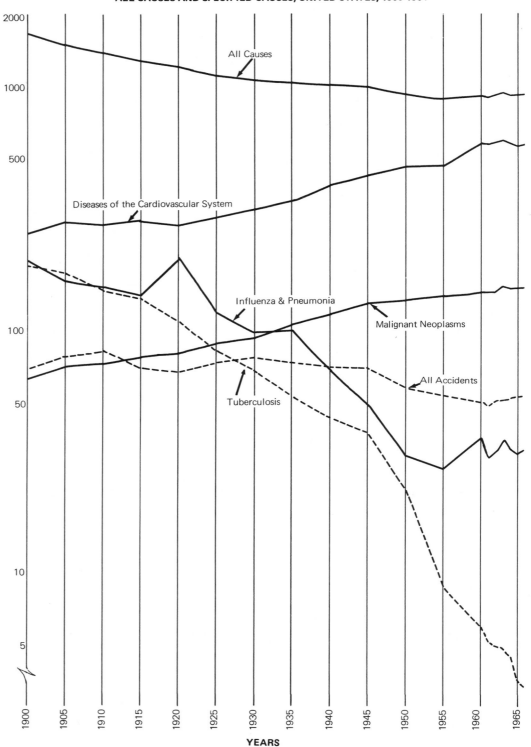

CRUDE DEATH RATES PER 100,000 POPULATION   log scale

ALL CAUSES AND SPECIFIED CAUSES, UNITED STATES, 1900-1964

All Causes

Diseases of the Cardiovascular System

Influenza & Pneumonia

Malignant Neoplasms

Tuberculosis

All Accidents

YEARS

FIGURE 14. *Crude death rates per 100,000 population*

out in earlier chapters. Today, however, accidents are the major cause of death in people of from one to 35 years old; in 1964, over 40,000 people in this age group were killed by accidents. In the population as a whole, accidents cause over 100,000 deaths each year and some 10 million injuries involving at least a day of disability. Unlike other special threats to young people, accidents have not been reduced dramatically since 1900.

Chronic diseases, mental illness, and accidents are problems as ancient as the communicable diseases, but they have only much more recently become the object of community action. Success in preventing environmental exposure to infection and in controlling communicable diseases through immunization and treatment have not only revealed the importance of other threats to human health but suggested that these, too, could be made less damaging to man. In the past two decades, programs in chronic disease control, mental health, and accident prevention have become an important part of community health service.

Although knowledge about these disorders has expanded enormously, their cause or causes are not yet fully understood. Therefore, ability to prevent them, in the sense of avoiding their occurrence, is limited. However, treatment of most of these conditions can now not only prevent or postpone death, but can also lessen the amount of illness and disability that usually results. As the proportion of older people in the population increases, and as general living standards increase, society looks upon old age more as a time of continued fulfillment than just an extension of existence. To enable older people to live out their years fully and productively, they must have within their reach services that can help to minimize the disability caused by certain disorders. The past pattern of community concern with prevention of disease has now extended to prevention of its consequences.

Many of the new programs have required new techniques of community health action. Procedures must be individualized to a much greater extent than is necessary for control of communicable diseases. The problems affect a great many people, but solutions must be found for each person in terms of his particular condition, his life situation, and his personal characteristics. Greater cooperation and more active participation are needed from patients and other individuals, since "one-shot" prevention or treatment is not possible. Inasmuch as care and service over a long period of time are frequently indicated, the cost to both the individual and the community of preserving life and preventing disability is a matter for public as well as private concern.

The social and economic aspects of many of today's major health problems are of such significance that it is obvious they cannot be considered exclusively health problems. Social disorders such as poverty, crime, or family disruption can be a cause, result, or complication of illness and disability. The economic effect of illness, with regard to both costs of care and treatment and loss of economic productivity, makes health a matter of economic as well as social policy. Neither prevention nor treatment of disease can be effected without regard to the surrounding social and economic conditions and needs, and indeed solution of some health problems will be found only through broad community action for development and improvement.

10

Chronic Diseases

CHRONIC DISEASE is defined by the American Public Health Association as including:

> . . . all impairments or deviations from normal which have one or more of the following characteristics: are presumably permanent; leave residual disability; are caused by a nonreversible pathologic alteration; require special measures for the patient's rehabilitation; may be expected to require a long period of supervision, observation or care.[1]

The definition covers conditions due to disease processes such as diabetes, cancer, or heart disease; residual damage due to either disease or trauma, such as the paralysis that may follow polio, a stroke, or an accidental injury; and conditions due to congenital defects.

The extent of disability ranges from minor to extreme. A great many people have chronic defects that, when properly cared for, do not hinder their activities—defects of sight corrected by glasses, for instance, and malocclusion of the teeth remedied by orthodontia. However, more than one person in 10 in the noninstitutionalized civilian population is limited to some extent in normal activities by chronic disease; three-quarters of these people are limited in their major activity—work, school, or keeping house—and one-fifth of them are unable to continue it at all.[2]

Chronic diseases affect people of all ages but are more prevalent in each successively older age group. In 1961–63, the National Health Survey found that 20 per cent of youngsters under 17 had some chronic conditions, as did 47 per cent of people from 17 to 44, 64 per cent of those from 45 to 64, and 81 per cent of those 65 and older. Furthermore, a much larger proportion of elderly people were limited in activity by their chronic illnesses: 49 per cent of those over 65, compared to 2 per cent of the under 17 group.[3]

Characteristics of Chronic Disease

Among the large variety of human ills covered in the general term "chronic disease" are some of the communicable diseases that cause long-term illness, notably tuberculosis, as well as mental illness and retardation. Since these conditions are considered in other chapters, they will not be discussed here. Accidents causing possible permanent injury are also discussed in another chapter.

CAUSES OF CHRONIC DISEASE

A few chronic diseases result from a previous episode of communicable disease. Although such chronic conditions are not themselves communicable, they result from infection. Rheumatic heart disease, for instance, is always preceded by, but does not necessarily follow, rheumatic fever, which in turn is always preceded by infection with a certain strain of streptococci, although such infections do not always result in rheumatic fever. Untreated syphilis

---

[1] CONTROL OF CHRONIC DISEASES IN MAN (in preparation). Adapted from the definition of the Commission on Chronic Illness.

[2] U.S. Department of Health, Education, and Welfare, Public Health Service, CHRONIC CONDITIONS AND ACTIVITY LIMITATION, UNITED STATES JULY 1961–JUNE 1963, HEALTH STATISTICS FROM THE U.S. NATIONAL HEALTH SURVEY, SERIES 10, NO. 17 (Washington: Government Printing Office, 1965).

[3] *Ibid.*

may result in syphilitic heart disease; poliomyelitis may cause irreversible paralysis; and in rare instances the acute childhood infectious diseases leave chronic sequelae such as deafness or mental retardation. When a mother has rubella (German measles) during the first trimester of her pregnancy, her child is at very high risk of congenital defects such as cataract, heart disease, or deafness. The total effect of acute communicable diseases in causing chronic conditions is not known, but their control and proper treatment are unquestionably important to the prevention of chronic defects.

In general, causes of chronic diseases are unknown. Even the specific conditions that bring about chronic diseases of infectious origin are not understood. But the epidemiologic study of chronic diseases—that is, the study of how they occur in populations—has revealed circumstances associated with higher-than-average incidence of many of them. Genetic factors are recognized as influencing the occurrence of certain chronic diseases. For instance, people who come from families in which there have been cases of diabetes or glaucoma are several times more likely to develop those diseases than are people whose families do not have them. Heredity is also believed to play a part in other diseases such as certain forms of heart disease and cancer, but its relative importance is not clear.

Premature birth increases the risk of congenital defects, both physical and mental. Injury at birth sometimes causes permanent damage to an infant, resulting in such conditions as cerebral palsy, although this neurological disorder may have other causes.

The incidence of some chronic diseases differs with sex or race. Women have higher rates of rheumatoid arthritis, diabetes, and hypertensive heart disease, whereas men have higher rates of coronary heart disease and chronic respiratory disease. A significantly larger proportion of nonwhites have hypertensive heart disease, and one type of anemia (sickle cell) occurs almost exclusively in Negroes.

Intensive investigation of environmental factors is producing growing evidence that they are often decisive in the occurrence of chronic disease. Studies of smoking habits and mortality experience have shown that deaths from cancer of the lung, throat, and mouth, as well as from a number of other causes including some forms of heart disease, occurred at significantly higher rates in persons who were heavy cigarette smokers than among those who were not.[4] Both cigarette smoking and air pollution have been found to be related to high rates of chronic respiratory diseases. Excessive exposure to ionizing radiation increases risk of various forms of cancer. Occupational exposure to certain substances or conditions has been linked with a number of chronic diseases—dust with respiratory diseases, and prolonged exposure to excessive noise with hearing loss, for example.

Nutrition also appears to have a bearing on the occurrence and development of some chronic diseases. A child's health and ability to survive are dependent to a great extent on the nutritional state of his mother, not just during her pregnancy but also at the time she becomes pregnant. Throughout life, adequate diet is known to promote health. Although its complete role in preventing susceptibility to most diseases is not clear, some deficiencies of diet are known to cause specific diseases. For instance, insufficient iodine results in thyroid disease and insufficient thiamine, in beri-beri; both conditions can in turn result in heart disease. However, in this country the most common nutritional problem that has been clearly identified as contributing to chronic disease is obesity. People who are overweight have significantly higher rates of diabetes and cardiovascular-renal diseases, and obesity increases disability from arthritis and paralysis.

Diet plays an important part in dental health, from conception and throughout life. Another factor of the environment that affects the soundness of teeth is the amount of fluoride contained in drinking water. People who drink water that contains adequate amounts of fluoride either naturally or as an additive have much lower rates of dental decay than those who drink water with less fluoride or none.

The chronic diseases as a group, like most of

---

[4] U.S. Department of Health, Education, and Welfare, Public Health Service, SUMMARY OF THE REPORT OF THE SURGEON GENERAL'S ADVISORY COMMITTEE ON SMOKING AND HEALTH (PHS Publication No. 1103, D [Washington: Government Printing Office, 1964]).

the communicable diseases, are more frequent causes of death and disability among persons at the lower end of the socioeconomic scale. The effect of socioeconomic status on chronic disease prevalence undoubtedly has a number of aspects—medical care, diet, and occupation, for instance. The role of stress, either physical or emotional, has not been clearly defined. The probability that it contributes to the development of disease when other causative factors are present is widely accepted.

The notion was once common that the chronic diseases were the all-but-inevitable effect of aging. Today, the higher rates of most chronic diseases among older people are increasingly considered to be due to their longer experience with elements of risk, both environmental and hereditary, rather than to the physical fact of aging itself. As information continues to be brought to light about the elements of heredity and environment combined in those who have a chronic condition, the possibility of increasing the proportion of people who maintain health and vigor through their old age is constantly improved. The application of presently available knowledge about risk factors can already accomplish a good deal toward that end. For instance, if the relatives of people with diabetes, perhaps the women especially, controlled their weight effectively and had periodic tests for diabetes, many cases of the disease could be forestalled or discovered at an early and therefore treatable stage.

EFFECTS OF CHRONIC DISEASE

Although some chronic conditions have relatively rapid onset, the usual pattern is rather slow development without recognizable symptoms. During the presymptomatic stages, however, the changes that take place in the body as a result of disease can often be discovered by various clinical tests. Diabetes causes an increase in sugar in the blood; high blood pressure precedes the development of hypertensive heart disease; in glaucoma, there is measurable excess fluid pressure in the eye; malignant tumors give off cells that are characteristically abnormal. All of these changes will produce positive findings on rather simple tests.

Furthermore, the first symptoms of some chronic diseases, although they may not seem serious or cause great discomfort, provide a clue for the competent physician. The early danger signs of cancer have been widely publicized by the American Cancer Society, and the National Tuberculosis Association urges recognition of cough and shortness of breath as signs of possible chronic respiratory disease. The President's Commission on Heart, Cancer, and Stroke reported that three-fourths of patients who have strokes are forewarned by brief symptoms such as loss of speech, weakness of limbs, staggering, and loss of consciousness,[5] and coronary heart disease sometimes causes attacks of chest pain long before a dramatic heart attack forces diagnosis.

When chronic diseases are diagnosed early, modern medical science enables treatment that can in most instances minimize their effects and allow patients to live normally, although usually with certain changes of living habits as concessions to their chronic condition.

If diagnosis is not made early, or if effective medical care is not available to a chronic disease patient, his condition may progress to an irremediable point before it receives proper medical attention. Unfortunately, chronic disease does not always respond to even the best available treatment, and many patients have more than one chronic disease, in combinations that increase the difficulties of managing their condition. Such patients, if they survive, may be seriously disabled. At one time, the plight of these people was considered hopeless, and as long as they lived they were expected to be helpless. Today, if a full range of medical and care services, including early and persistent rehabilitative efforts, is applied, many patients can be restored to a degree of self-sufficiency that makes the difference in their remaining years between living and simply existing.

Chronic Disease Services

Chronic disease services are generally considered to comprise three types of activities: (1) primary prevention, which precludes the oc-

---

[5] A NATIONAL PROGRAM TO CONQUER HEART DISEASE, CANCER AND STROKE, VOL. 1 (Washington: Government Printing Office, 1965), p. 14.

currence of disease; (2) secondary prevention, which detects disease and leads to treatment so as to discourage its development and lessen its damage; and (3) prevention of disability and dependency by helping the victims of chronic disease to achieve the best level of living competence that is possible within the limitations imposed by their disease.

PRIMARY PREVENTION

Many of the community health activities described in other chapters contribute to the primary prevention of chronic diseases. Environmental health services prevent exposure to biological and physical contaminates and unwholesome conditions that might cause, or contribute to the cause of, chronic conditions. Communicable disease control is directly responsible for preventing the chronic disabilities that might follow infections. Medical care for mothers during pregnancy and childbirth reduces the incidence of congenital heart disease and other defects. Regular health appraisal and care for infants and preschool and school children help to check diseases that might result in chronic illness and also promote positive health and establish habits favorable to physical and mental well-being. Occupational health services are directly preventive of illness and injury that could leave workers chronically disabled. Services to prevent accidental injury and adequate emergency services help to reduce the number of chronically disabled. Although these activities are not usually considered chronic disease control services, their importance in this reference should not be overlooked.

In the specific control of some chronic diseases, primary prevention depends on changes in individual behavior. The evidence that cigarette smoking plays a significant role in causing lung cancer and in contributing to other chronic diseases indicates that people who smoke cigarettes should relinquish this habit in the interest of their health and survival. The findings of research into the effects of smoking have led some people to think that "there ought to be a law" against cigarettes. Regulation of some kinds of unhealthful behavior— reckless driving or psychotic violence, for instance—is considered necessary because it directly threatens the interests of others. However, although behavior that jeopardizes a person's health, even when it does not immediately harm others, can almost never be truly said to "hurt no one but himself," regulation is usually neither an acceptable nor a successful method of changing it. In general, the individual is considered responsible for his own habits, and the community responsible for providing information about potential hazards and service to help people abandon or shun harmful behavior.

The American Cancer Society, the American Heart Association, and the National Tuberculosis Association, through their local affiliates, engage in continuing campaigns to discourage cigarette smoking. The PHS promotes dissemination of information on the subject and supports both research and service programs aimed at discouraging cigarette smoking. In some communities, interagency groups, health departments, and other community agencies not only provide information but conduct classes or groups for people trying to withdraw from their habit. A coordinating force in many of these activities is the National Interagency Council on Smoking and Health.

A great amount of effort has gone into programs, conducted by official and voluntary agencies in many parts of the country, that are aimed at discouraging young people from smoking. Such programs have had only limited success, according to a number of reports. Some of the difficulties that must be overcome are suggested by the report of a statewide study in New Jersey, which stated that among high school students "awareness of the fact that smoking has negative effects on health appears not of itself to result in significant reductions in smoking."[6] In the data presented, the smoking habits both of best friends and of parents are shown to influence students, best friends appearing to be somewhat more influential than parents.

Another study, made of a group of college students during a three-month period begin-

---

[6] Lillian Bajda, "Health Education Challenges in the Area of Cigarette Smoking and Health," presented at the Annual Meeting of the APHA, October 19, 1965, mimeographed.

ning shortly after the *Report of the Surgeon General's Advisory Committee on Smoking and Health* was issued, also found that knowledge of the facts set forth in the Report had relatively little effect on smoking habits.[7] (However, smokers tended to forget more of the facts during the three-month period than did nonsmokers.) Unfortunately, the number of people in the group who stopped smoking when the Report appeared and were still not smoking after three months was slightly less than the number of nonsmokers at the beginning who had begun to smoke by that time. The author suggests the possibility that frequent repetition of a threatening message may have an effect opposite to the one desired.

In both these examples, personal habits are clearly shown to be based on something other than information and reason. The populations studied were young, and the rewards or dangers of their behavior may have seemed remote to them. On the other hand, in older people, to whom presumably the possible unfortunate consequences are more immediate, habits are usually more firmly established; changing them, is therefore, equally difficult. The man in his forties who has been smoking two packs of cigarettes a day for two decades, customarily eating more than he needs, and getting little regular exercise, is not likely to change his ways simply because he learns that they are conducive to various serious disorders. In fact he probably does know that they are dangerous and would agree that he should change but doesn't, saying that after all it is his own responsibility. But the community has a responsibility to prevent the need for either complex and expensive health services or dependency or both and to develop in its citizens behavior patterns that will foster good health.

EARLY DIAGNOSIS

Inasmuch as knowledge about the cause of most chronic disease is limited, and therefore the present possibility of specific primary prevention is also limited, early detection enabling

prompt treatment is the principal tool for secondary prevention of chronic disease. Surgery for cancer; drugs and surgery for congenital heart disease; insulin and diet for diabetes; drugs to reduce hypertension; the combination of rest, corrective exercise, physical therapy, and aspirin that relieves rheumatoid arthritis—all these tools of modern medicine are most effective when they are applied before disease has progressed too far.

If most people received a thorough health appraisal at regular intervals, including a careful history, physical examination, and tests to screen for the chronic diseases, the presence of chronic disease could be detected and early treatment undertaken to limit such conditions. However, regular health appraisals are not usual except in pediatric practice, in some group medical care plans, and in a few employee or executive health services. In spite of the urging of health agencies and insurance companies, few people present themselves to a physician for a complete examination unless they have symptoms of illness. A thorough examination, including all appropriate tests and a sufficient period of the physician's time, is expensive and is not usually covered by health insurance except in some prepaid group medical care plans. A further reason for the lack of frequency of complete medical examinations was pointed out by Breslow:

Examinations are frequently superficial because most physicians today are oriented more toward caring for the sick than toward maintaining health. The pressure of caring for the sick in the home, office, clinic, and hospital precludes any substantial amount of time being devoted to health maintenance examinations. Obstetricians and pediatricians have succeeded to a considerable extent in directing their efforts toward health maintenance. However, it will probably be many years before this is typical of medical practice as a whole. Even though all other difficulties were overcome, at the present time there are not enough physicians in the United States to provide this type of examination for the majority of the American people. Hence, the discovery of chronic disease in the general population through periodic health examinations has distinct limitations.[8]

---

[7] James W. Swinehart, "Changes Over Time in Some Reactions to the Surgeon General's Report on Smoking and Health," presented at the Annual Meeting of the APHA, October 19, 1965, mimeographed.

[8] Lester Breslow, "Chronic Disease and Disability in Adults," in Philip E. Sartwell (ed.), MAXCY-ROSENAU PREVENTIVE MEDICINE AND PUBLIC HEALTH (New York: Appleton-Century-Crofts, 9th ed., 1965), p. 534.

Most people go to a doctor only when they have symptoms of illness, and probably the majority of cases of chronic disease are diagnosed as a result of such action. Unfortunately, patients often allow symptoms to persist for a considerable length of time before seeking medical care. Furthermore, when a patient comes for treatment of an acute illness, the physician often fails to use the opportunity to examine him for asymptomatic chronic conditions or even to question him about symptoms he may not have recognized or thought important. As pointed out in Chapter 8, neither outpatient nor emergency departments of hospitals ordinarily take full advantage of a patient's visit, and even inpatient hospital admission does not always involve routine screening tests.

In many areas, medical organizations, voluntary health agencies, and health departments carry on professional education programs aimed at encouraging the use by physicians of opportunities to examine patients for chronic diseases, improving the physician's skill in applying screening tests, and heightening their level of suspicion of chronic disease in patients with certain symptoms that also may accompany minor illness. At the federal level, the PHS both supports local continuing education for physicians and develops and tests new techniques of presenting information to busy practitioners. A few medical schools are placing increased emphasis on health maintenance, giving students a better background for early diagnosis than the usual almost complete orientation toward treatment of overt illness. However, such action has not yet had a significant effect on medical practice as a whole.

A major device used by community agencies to accomplish early diagnosis of chronic disease is the mass screening survey, in which tests are applied to selected people at high risk of certain diseases. Screening tests are administered by technicians to groups of people, usually under the auspices of a health department or voluntary health agency. Surveys may be directed to special population groups, such as hospital patients or residents of nursing homes, or to neighborhoods or industries. They may be continuing services offered by the health department at specified locations. Well-child con-ferences and school health programs usually include screening for chronic diseases or defects. The periodic health examinations given to members of some group medical care plans begin with a series of screening tests, the results of which the physician has when he makes his examination.

Such programs had their beginning in mass chest X-ray surveys for tuberculosis and mass blood-testing for syphilis. Now, in addition to single-disease screening, multiple or multiphasic screening programs frequently include any or all of a number of other tests such as blood-sugar tests for diabetes, vision and hearing tests, blood pressure readings, and in some programs tonometry (a test of pressure in the eye to screen for glaucoma), or cytological tests (especially the Pap smear to screen for cervical cancer). The tests are not diagnostic, but they do select the persons with the greatest probability of having various diseases. The advantages of screening are in its relative quickness and ease of testing, economical use of professional time, and low unit costs; it is becoming more and more feasible as instrumentation and automation increase the efficiency of the clinical laboratory.

The screening procedure itself is only one step toward the program's goal of identifying persons with chronic disease and treating them to minimize disability. The next steps—definite diagnosis and indicated therapy—are largely the responsibility of the medical practitioners in the community. In the most successful screening programs a medical advisory committee of local physicians is organized (or appointed by the medical society) to take part in planning the program and to interpret it to their colleagues, alerting them to expect referrals and encouraging their concern with early diagnosis.

The success of a screening program also depends on the response to it (the proportion of the people to whom it is directed who are actually screened) and the extent to which suspicious findings are followed through to diagnosis and medical care if it is necessary. If a program is jointly sponsored by all the community agencies concerned with either the diseases for which tests will be given or the population to be tested, it can call upon their combined efforts to publicize and explain the testing and stimulate participation. Publicity should emphasize that persons who have "positive" reports on screening should go to their doctors or a clinic for diagnostic check up, and it should not be either unduly frightening or so reassuring that it plays down the need for action.

When actual referrals are made by a screening program and participants are notified that their physicians or a clinic will be expecting them, the urgency is more apparent than if "suspects" are simply told they should see their doctors. For those who do not respond within a reasonable time, a special effort to encourage follow-up should be made through letters, telephone calls, or public health nursing visits if necessary. These procedures should be planned for in advance of the screening. Experience in screening programs has shown that even though they participate in the testing, people who do not feel ill sometimes fail to pursue a referral or to follow through with diagnostic procedure or treatment.

Perhaps the most crucial need in achieving the earliest possible diagnosis of chronic disease is to create public demand for it. Many common feelings and attitudes, in addition to failure in understanding the implications of untreated chronic disease, discourage this demand. Optimism that makes a person believe he could not possibly have a disease, fear that makes him reject the possibility, preoccupation with other matters, concern about expense of diagnosis and treatment, and, especially for people receiving public medical care, the inconvenience and difficulty of obtaining medical care—all these may discourage rational behavior in seeking, accepting, or following through on services to diagnose and prevent the progression of chronic conditions. A considerable part of the need is for health education in its broadest sense to inform the public and to help individuals perceive the value of early diagnosis to their own aims and interests. At the same time, there is great need for devising ways of providing diagnostic and treatment services in a reasonably convenient manner, so that the obstacles to obtaining them will not outweigh their value in the eyes of those who need them.

TREATMENT AND CARE TO PREVENT DISABILITY AND DEPENDENCY

The division between secondary prevention, through early diagnosis, and care of chronic diseases is arbitrary, because treatment is the objective of early diagnosis. Furthermore, the object of all treatment and care programs should be to prevent or lessen disability from chronic disease.

The care needed by any chronic disease patient is highly individual. It depends on his disease and response to treatment; the degree and nature of disability, which may change from one time to another; and on his usual work, his family, and other aspects of his life situation, as well as his feelings and personal characteristics.

Some patients remain essentially well under medication or other measures prescribed by the doctor in his office. In some cases, these patients must also adapt their diet, increase their exercise, or otherwise change their daily living habits, and some of them need professional help and encouragement in accepting the need for such measures or in learning how to accomplish them.

A great many people spend some time in a hospital for surgery or acute illness, from which they may recover almost completely. But they all need continuing medical supervision. Their condition is not usually cured; it is under control or its progression has been slowed down or halted. But chronic disease is unhappily likely to reappear or become resistant to the particular measures being taken to hold it in check. Although people who are under the care of private physicians usually receive regular medical review of their condition, those who do not fully understand their situation may neglect taking care of themselves or may discontinue regular visits to the doctor. Patients receiving their medical care from clinics and hospital outpatient departments often miss the full benefits of modern medicine until they become seriously ill.

For another group of patients, experience with treatment of chronic disease begins in general hospitals, with acute illness that subsides fairly soon but requires long convalescence and rehabilitation. Sometimes further hospitalization is indicated, in a chronic disease hospital or a general hospital that will provide the special care and rehabilitation necessary to bring the patient back as close to normal as possible.

After their initial illness, chronic disease patients frequently have ups and downs—times when they can manage quite satisfactorily under a home care program and times when they need hospital care, either in a general hospital for acute illness or in an extended care facility or nursing home for longer periods. Care should be provided that fits the patient's conditions at a particular time, but with the expectation that hospital or other institutional care will not necessarily be required indefinitely.

Rehabilitation. The aim of rehabilitation in the management of chronic disease and disability should be to maintain or restore the highest potential function that can be achieved for each patient. Through the application of modern rehabilitation techniques, many people who have suffered strokes have been restored to self-care, and others with arthritis have been able to postpone the progression of the disease and keep moving. Going far beyond vocational goals, rehabilitation is concerned with helping people to whatever degree of self-sufficiency they can reach, whether it makes work possible or not. Even if a person is too severely disabled or too old to work, he profits physically and emotionally from doing what he can for himself. Furthermore, activity, even if it is limited, helps to prevent the increasing infirmity that results from inaction.

Rehabilitation measures should begin early in the treatment of chronically ill patients and at diagnosis for persons with handicapping conditions and should continue until optimum potential is reached, after which follow-up for maintenance of function should continue indefinitely. Such measures should be part of the service provided in acute general hospitals, chronic disease facilities, home care programs, and nursing homes. All staff who care for chronically ill and disabled patients should be well grounded in the principles of care to prevent disability and maintain function and should be imbued with the concept of total rehabilitation.

Rehabilitation in its broad sense includes a number of services in addition to care and treatment for a particular disease or disability or physical restoration and improvement of a particular function. For example, a patient's care would be incomplete if a dental evaluation were omitted. Dental care should not be limited to emergency procedures for the relief of pain or the elimination of infection but should include procedures that improve the patient's ability to chew and to speak clearly and restore facial contours. If the disabling effects of chronic illness make a visit to the dental office difficult or impossible, transportation should be provided or arranged, or the dentist should provide care in the home using the recently developed portable dental equipment.

Advice on diet may also be important, whether it must be adapted to the patient's chronic illness or simply be adequate to keep him in good general health and forestall deficiencies that could make him weaker or otherwise complicate his condition.

The social and psychological implications of chronic illness must also be dealt with. Serious chronic illness is understandably discouraging, and few patients are able to accept it and the limitations it imposes with complete equanimity. The success of treatment and rehabilitative measures may very well depend on the help patients and sometimes their families receive in adjusting to disease, in resolving emotional problems it may arouse, and in fostering optimism and a desire for recovery. There is frequently need for help in understanding and accepting the physician's recommendations, as well as in obtaining the services recommended. Such personal problems are the special province of the medical social worker, but her efforts need the support and assistance of not only professional and nonprofessional staff, but of families, friends, and volunteers as well.

The economic burden of chronic illness is often serious. Even families whose incomes are sufficient for other needs are frequently unable to meet the costs of health care. Thus, they may do without preventive services that could forestall or reduce the severity of illness, and when illness does occur, it may bring them to complete dependency. Recognition that it is shortsighted to allow families to lose their independence before they can qualify for help with the costs of illness has led to the broadening of definitions of eligibility for such help in the 1965 amendments to the Social Security Act (Title XIX), discussed in Chapter 14. People who are already dependent or become so because of chronic illness must also receive whatever assistance is necessary for their support and necessary to keep their families together, in addition to treatment and care services for their illness.

Home Health Services.[9]   A large number of people with varying degrees of chronic illness or disability cannot readily use outpatient services but do not require 24-hour institutional care if certain services can be made available in the home in addition to physician's care, and under his direction. A person who is homebound may have a family who could learn to give him most of the care he needs if they had some professional help and guidance from a nurse, or perhaps a physical therapist. Even a person who lives alone can often manage if he has help at strategic points in his daily life—getting out of bed or in and out of the bath tub, for instance, or preparing his meals. Others may need a wide range of services in order to stay at home.

Being able to be at home and still receive necessary care improves the morale of chronically ill patients who have lived through long periods of hospitalization and helps to make them less dependent. It can postpone or obviate the need for eventual hospitalization of those whose illness or disability would worsen without adequate health service.

The extent and nature of home health services vary in different communities. However, the potential of coordinated home care programs for extending the benefits of modern medical care outside the hospital is increasingly recognized as an advantage not only to programs for the chronically ill, but to the total complex of comprehensive medical care as well.

Nursing Homes.[10]   For patients who do not need hospital care but for whom care at home is not feasible, the nursing home may be the practical solution. Nursing home care, however, should not be simply custodial, but should include medical supervision and rehabilitation. Although for some patients the nursing home will be a permanent residence for the rest of their lives, they should be helped to reach as a high a level of health and strength as possible. Patients who can become sufficiently rehabilitated so that nursing home care is no longer necessary should, on achieving this goal, move to their own home, a foster home, or to a home for the aged.

A high proportion of patients in nursing homes are very elderly people whose advanced age contributes to their disability from chronic disease. In addition to needing intensive personal care, frequently the reason for their admission to the nursing home, they need skilled nursing care, regular medical and dental care, and other restorative services. If the nursing home cannot provide these, it should seek them from other community agencies.

Community Programs for Chronic Disease

The manner in which services for chronic disease are provided differs so greatly from one community to another that no pattern is representative. In all areas, a complex of institutions and agencies—public, private, and voluntary—are concerned with various aspects of the problem. Their number and variety are in some instances so great, and their interrelationships so tenuous, that it would be impossible to say whether the community has an adequate chronic disease program, as such. The need for a coordinated approach to comprehensive community health services is most apparent in the field of chronic disease.

INFORMATION, REFERRAL, AND COUNSELING

An important step toward coordination in the community is to establish central information and referral services. Such services are not as a rule concerned only with chronic diseases, but it was the needs of chronic disease patients that stimulated their establishment.

In any sizeable community, there may very well be hundreds of different sources of service for chronic disease patients, each with its own definition of persons eligible for service and of services offered. Physicians and other profes-

---

[9] See also Chapter 8.
[10] See also Chapter 8.

sional people may not have full knowledge of all available services, and agencies are often unfamiliar with each other's functions. It is obviously impossible for a layman to be informed about the variety of agencies and services available. Information and referral services are an effort to bring physicians and their patients and community resources together.

The simplest type is an answering service based on a roster of agencies and facilities, maintained by a hospital or council of social agencies or health department, that gives information on request of physicians or other professional persons. If the information service is staffed by a person professionally qualified to make judgments about the relative appropriateness of different agencies in a given situation, it is more useful.

In some communities, the staff of information and referral services is made up of medical social workers or public health nurses, who participate in long-term patient care by evaluating the patient's needs and arranging for him to receive services accordingly, perhaps from several agencies. Contact with the patient and his physician continues as long as it is necessary, and changes are made in referral to fit the patient's changing situation.

The most complete programs also include counseling and consultation to help patients accept and adjust to the services recommended by the physician. They also help in obtaining the necessary services, thus contributing to the adequacy of follow-up important to the control of many chronic diseases. Such assistance not only helps to make illness less burdensome to the individual or family, but also cuts the red tape that sometimes interferes with the community's efforts on behalf of the ill.

In addition to its primary concerns, a well-run information, referral, and counseling agency that has current acquaintance with community resources and can document the needs for service not available can provide information that is absolutely necessary for establishing wise priorities in community health planning.

LEADERSHIP

Recognition of the urgent need for orderly programs in chronic disease, and leadership in

seeking solutions to present problems, have come at the local level from various sources. In some cases, the movement toward coordination of activities begins with a health council or council of social agencies, but the spark may come from an individual agency such as a hospital or visiting nurse society. In its work with many communities over the country to help them in such efforts, the PHS has found that the *sine qua non* is an imaginative instigator, devoted to the idea that the community's miscellaneous and unrelated resources must be drawn together into a smooth-running system that will serve people who need help when they need it.

Health departments have often taken leadership in coordinative efforts. However, comprehensive chronic disease programs include many treatment and care services that have not been considered the concern of health departments until recently. Some departments, of course, are responsible for indigent medical care but are not expected to be involved in private care except in such matters as hospital and nursing home licensure.

In the past decade or two, many health departments have engaged in chronic disease activities, but these activities have consisted chiefly of screening programs, public health nursing (often for indigent patients), and public and professional education—in a sense extensions of earlier programs, modified to fit new needs. A growing number of local health departments now provide additional home care services and sponsor information and referral services. But coordination of all services for the total community is not a function that the public or the medical profession usually expects of the health department. To take the leadership that concern for the whole community demands, most health departments not only will have to inform the public of the need for coordinated services but also must enlist the medical profession in this effort to improve facilities for the practice of modern medicine.

State health departments are an important source of help and support to local communities in chronic disease programs. In addition to financial aid, they usually provide consultation and training. Many states have nurse consultants in rehabilitation, for instance, who provide training to nurses throughout the state, and an increasing number have occupational therapy consultants. The state health department may offer direct services for such undertakings as screening, including health education consultation. In some states, long-term care or rehabilitation facilities are operated under state auspices.

At the federal level, the PHS conducts a variety of programs in the interest of chronic disease control. The National Institutes of Health support and engage in research aimed at improving scientific understanding of such diseases. Elsewhere in the PHS, many programs are concerned with promoting the application of present knowledge, both in activities such as communicable disease control and accident prevention that help to prevent chronic disability, and in efforts directed toward specific chronic conditions and the improvement of community health services. Grants are made to states and communities, and technical assistance directed toward chronic disease problems is offered.

In any local community, the interests of chronic disease control could best be served through an orderly and complete area plan for comprehensive health services. The plan should be part of the community's long-range plans for its future and should take into consideration all present and anticipated health needs and resources. Community planning for health, discussed in a later chapter, is in large part community planning for chronic disease control.

11

Promotion of Mental Health

THE DISORDERS that interfere with positive mental health are considered here as two broad and distinct classes of diseases and conditions —mental illness or disease (emotional disturbance), and mental retardation or deficiency (subnormal intellectual development). In general, mental illness interferes with the individual's ability to use skills acquired for living in his social and physical environment, and mental retardation represents limitation of intellectual ability to acquire those skills. Mental illness is often temporary or reversible; mental retardation is often permanent, although its effect can be alleviated in the majority of cases. Both mental illness and retardation can occur in one person, and either condition can contribute to the other. That is, a child's emotional disturbance can seriously limit his ability to learn, or limited intellectual capacity can place undue stress on an individual, resulting in emotional disturbance.

Until relatively recently, both kinds of mental disorders were considered hopeless, incurable, and usually a cause of shame for the families of the victims. This attitude has not altogether disappeared, but today a growing number of people are coming to recognize that these conditions represent illness and disability, rather than disgrace.

In the past, people were generally presumed to be mentally healthy if they were not "insane." Now there is increasing recognition that mental illness has many manifestations of varying severity. The association of mental illness with social problems—delinquency, drug addiction, alcoholism, or family disruption, for instance—and the personal discomfort accompanying it are beginning to be understood. As a result, there is growing demand for services to treat mental illness of all kinds—a demand that at present cannot be met in most communities.

Recent progress toward understanding mental retardation has been even more notable, and facilities for training and rehabilitating the mentally retarded are being established in many communities. Discovery of some of the causes of mental deficiency, such as the inborn error of metabolism called phenylketonuria (PKU), in some instances offers means to prevent the condition by testing to detect such abnormalities and treatment to correct them. New emphasis on determining the actual capacity of the mentally retarded child and providing education or training up to his limits helps reduce the extent of dependency in many cases.

Society's slowness in responding to the needs of the mentally ill and mentally retarded is perhaps not surprising in view of the nature of these conditions. By reason of his illness, the mentally ill person behaves in a manner that may repel those around him rather than inspire sympathy, as physical illness usually does.[1] The behavior of mental patients, though rarely violent, is frequently troublesome and without reference to the demands of the world around them. Even a friend or relative who recognizes the patient's sickness as a sickness may find it difficult to accept his lack of response to offered help and be frustrated if unable to reach the patient with rational suggestions. For those with less insight into the situation, the only so-

[1] Joint Commission on Mental Illness and Health, ACTION FOR MENTAL HEALTH (New York: Basic Books, Inc., 1961), p. 18.

lution may be to get him out of harm's way in a remote institution.

The behavior of the mentally retarded is also different from that of other people. The incapacity of mentally retarded children is frequently a source of distress to their parents and may be an object of ridicule, or even of fear, to others. However, the inability of a mentally deficient person to behave as others do is more often considered "not his fault" than the similar inability of the mentally ill.

Improvement of the lot of the mentally ill is coming about through broadened understanding of their situation and through extension of the American sense of social justice and belief in the worth and rights of the individual. As measures are successful in reintroducing the mentally ill and handicapped into the ordinary life of the community, understanding and acceptance will become more general.

Nature and Causes of Mental Illness

Mental and emotional disturbances are usually classified under four major headings: psychoses, neuroses, character or personality disorders, and psychosomatic disorders. *Psychosis,* the condition usually meant by the term "insanity," results in odd behavior and severe distortion of reality in the mind of the sufferer. *Neurosis* is less severe than psychosis. Although neurotic persons may be very uncomfortable, have difficulty in their relationships with others, and have their energy depleted by irrational anxiety, most of them are able to carry on ordinary activities after a fashion in spite of their misery. *Character or personality disorders* may cause such antisocial behavior as drug addiction, chronic lying or cheating, stealing, chronic alcoholism, or sexual deviation, unaccompanied by anxiety or guilt. However, such disorders may cause less socially damaging behavior such as compulsive cleanliness or emotional aloofness. In *psychosomatic disorders,* emotional distress has physical effects on the body, causing actual organic illness. These disorders are not to be confused with hypochondria, a neurosis in which the patient is convinced he is ill but actually has no organic disease.

SIGNS AND SYMPTOMS

Signs and symptoms that occur in a wide variety of mental disorders, both rather mild and disablingly severe, are listed in the American Public Health Association's *Mental Disorders, A Guide to Control Methods,*[2] as the following seven syndromes, or groups of symptoms occurring together: (1) depression, (2) severe anxiety (panic), (3) chronic tension, (4) paranoia (delusions of persecution or grandeur), (5) mania, (6) confusion, and (7) retardation. Obviously, perfectly healthy people can have most of these symptoms at some time to some degree, in response to life situations. That is, a man may be depressed at the end of a day when things have gone wrong, but he will be more optimistic the next day. A mother may be anxious when her child is ill, but she will get over it when he recovers. Depression or anxiety symptomatic of mental illness is unrelated to immediate situations and is not eased as they change.

The *Guide* also points out:

. . . many mental disorders, particularly the psychoses (both "functional" and "organic"), are frequently accompanied by distortions of personality function which are associated with more or less severe destruction of the affected person's social relationships.[3]

Such behavior takes one of three forms: withdrawal, or loss of interest in the surroundings, and sometimes concentration on a personal life of fantasy; anger, hostility, and quarrelsomeness; or a combination of the two. The term "social breakdown syndrome" has been coined to refer to these patterns of behavior.

Mental illness, even severe psychosis, is not illness of the whole mind or personality, and the patient continues to be healthy in some ways just as the patient with a physical disease continues to function normally in some ways. Furthermore, "normal and abnormal behavior, mental health and mental illness are not entities, but relative terms, with no clear line of demarcation between them; indeed, they mean different things to different people"[4] (even

---

[2] (New York: APHA, 1962), pp. 25–30.
[3] *Ibid.,* p. 1.
[4] ACTION FOR MENTAL HEALTH, *op. cit.,* p. 59.

among psychiatrists). This is perhaps more true of mental health, the definition of which appears to be exceedingly difficult even for experts to agree upon,[5] than of mental illness, although the latter presents problems to laymen, too. One team of researchers found that the people in a town they studied "regarded as 'normal' a much wider range of behavior than psychiatrists would." However, they also found that once a person had been hospitalized for mental illness, behavior on his part might be considered abnormal, although in others it would be judged normal.[6]

CAUSES OF MENTAL ILLNESS

The cause of some mental illness is known to be physical. Some conditions can be directly attributed to infection, such as the general paresis caused by syphilis. Others are due to injury (sometimes before birth) or to exposure to certain toxic substances. Still others are caused by circulatory disturbances, metabolic diseases, or other physiological disorders. But even when these causes are present, mental illness is not inevitable; and when it occurs, its extent may not be in direct relation to the extent of physical damage. In arteriosclerosis, for instance, "there is not a direct correlation between the extent of brain deterioration as seen on autopsy examination and the extent of functional impairment."[7] However, these conditions are called organic because of their known association with organic disorder.

Many of the most common mental illnesses are not known to have a physical cause. They are usually classified as psychogenic—arising in the mind or emotions—and are also called functional, in distinction from the organic conditions. But authorities believe that there is multiple causation of these conditions, as well as of those in which physical factors have been implicated. Biochemical abnormalities are under investigation as contributing to certain mental illnesses, notably schizophrenia. Genetic factors are considered to have a role in this group of illnesses, but

. . . the causal responsibility of heredity has not been fixed with any certainty, and the most that can be said is that genetically determined characteristics probably make their contribution to mental illness in an infinitely subtle and complex manner.[8]

Environmental aspects, which in mental health parlance include everything in the individual's life experience, are believed to have a major part in bringing about psychogenic illnesses. They are unsatisfactory as a total explanation because under similar circumstances of stress some people develop mental illness but others remain essentially healthy. However, severe or prolonged stress in the living situation is undoubtedly a contributing cause, and both prevention and treatment of mental illness involve easing unnecessary stresses as well as helping individuals to withstand those that cannot be avoided.

Research in the behavioral sciences has uncovered common patterns in life experience, especially in the early years, that appear to affect the risk of mental illness. Certain periods in a child's life have been found to be critical in the development of a normal personality; for instance, the capacity to establish healthy human relationships, known to be one of the attributes of mental health, develops in infancy in "a setting of maternal care," and "when maternal care is not present in sufficient quantity, the capacity to love and to care about the feelings of others may be damaged."[9] Certain events occurring at some time in most people's lives evoke strong emotions—death of someone loved, for example—and when they occur, they are sometimes emotionally overwhelming unless the sufferer has help in dealing with his feelings.

---

[5] See Marie Johoda, CURRENT CONCEPTS OF POSITIVE MENTAL HEALTH, Joint Commission on Mental Health and Illness (Monograph No. 1 [New York: Basic Books, Inc., 1958]).

[6] John Cumming and Elaine Cumming, "Mental Health Education in a Canadian Community," in Benjamin D. Paul, (ed.), HEALTH, CULTURE AND COMMUNITY (New York: Russell Sage Foundation, 1955), pp. 58–59.

[7] APHA, op. cit., p. 51.

[8] Richard J. Plunkett and John E. Gordon, EPIDEMIOLOGY AND MENTAL ILLNESS (Joint Commission on Mental Illness and Health, Monograph No. 6 [New York: Basic Books, Inc., 1960]), p. 30.

[9] Paul V. Lemkau, "Mental Health Services," in Philip E. Sartwell (ed.), MAXCY-ROSENAU PREVENTIVE MEDICINE AND PUBLIC HEALTH (New York: Appleton-Century-Crofts, 9th ed., 1965), pp. 605–06.

Nature and Causes of Mental Retardation

Mental retardation is classified according to degree of intellectual disability: profound, severe, moderate, and mild.[10] Profound mental retardation involves "gross impairment in physical coordination and sensory development" and requires constant care. The severely retarded have limitations in motor development, speech, and language, but they are not completely dependent. The moderately retarded can learn to care for themselves and can be trained, but they need a sheltered environment even when they become adults. Mild retardation involves slowness in development, but the mildly retarded can be educated up to certain limits and even become independent, although they may need guidance under certain circumstances.

The term "mental retardation" thus covers a broad range of conditions, characterized by differences in both mental ability or potential and in adaptive behavior. Estimates made of the distribution of mental retardates by degree of retardation indicate that almost 90 per cent are only mildly retarded. The profoundly and severely retarded are considered to comprise only 5 per cent of the estimated total.[11]

Mental retardation, like mental illness, is not a single disease or condition but has various causes. In the majority of cases, especially of the mildly retarded, there is no recognizable brain damage. Most of these cases occur in the lower socioeconomic groups, where retardation is believed to represent stunting of intellectual growth in childhood through lack of opportunity and encouragement to learn, as well as the many adverse conditions surrounding their early lives.[12]

Some cases of mental retardation are caused by infection either before or after birth. German measles occurring during the first three months of pregnancy may cause retardation or other defects. In some cases, brain damage results from the infectious diseases of childhood.

It also may be due to injury or to poisoning from drugs, either before or after birth, or associated with metabolic or nutritional disorders. Although much progress has been made in recent years in extending knowledge about the causes of mental retardation, there is still much to learn.

Extent of the Problem

The actual number of people who suffer significant mental illness is not known. Recent estimates indicate that about three million people are under care for mental illness during a year. This figure includes persons hospitalized in psychiatric and general hospitals—local, state, and federal; public, voluntary, and private—as well as those receiving outpatient service in clinics or from private practitioners. It does not include people with psychosomatic illness treated by physicians other than psychiatrists.[13]

Obviously, many people not under treatment have emotional disturbances sufficiently severe or chronic to call for professional help. A number of different community surveys have been made in efforts to determine the prevalence of mental illness; but because of the differences among them in populations studied, their objectives, and techniques, the findings have shown a range of rates so wide that no reasonable application could be made to the general population.[14] However, the frequently quoted estimate that one person in ten in the noninstitutionalized urban population suffers from recognizable emotional disturbance or mental illness is probably no exaggeration.

Factual information on the prevalence of mental retardation is also unavailable. Probably 1 per cent of the population is known to public and private agencies as mentally retarded, and experts estimate that the actual total is three times that number.[15]

---

[10] U.S. Department of Health, Education, and Welfare, the Secretary's Committee on Mental Retardation, An Introduction to Mental Retardation, Problems, Plans, and Programs, June 1965 (Washington: Government Printing Office, 1965), p. 2.

[11] Ibid., p. 11.

[12] Ibid., p. 7.

---

[13] U.S. Department of Health, Education, and Welfare, Public Health Service, What Is Mental Illness? (PHS Publication No. 505 [Washington: Government Printing Office, 1965]).

[14] Plunkett and Gordon, op. cit., p. 91.

[15] An Introduction to Mental Retardation, op. cit., p. 10.

Prevention

The prevention of either mental illness or mental retardation having a physical cause is a function of community health services in general rather than mental health services specifically. Prevention and treatment of communicable diseases, protection of workers and of the public from toxic materials in the environment, appropriate medical care to postpone mental deterioration due to cerebral arteriosclerosis and senility, programs for the control of alcoholism, prevention of accidents—all of these activities can serve to reduce the incidence of mental illness or mental retardation. Perhaps the most directly important public health measure to prevent mental retardation is the adequacy of maternal health services to promote health during pregnancy, reduce rates of premature birth, and prevent injury at birth.

In addition, general measures that encourage people's well-being are believed to contribute to the prevention of mental illness. According to the APHA *Guide,*

These include the provision of medical care, adequate nutrition, housing, environmental sanitation, social welfare for the underprivileged, educational facilities to foster self-realization, special help for the handicapped, health education, and programs for the rehabilitation of disintegrating communities.[16]

More specific efforts to prevent or relieve undue emotional stress are considered an important aspect of mental health promotion. To a great extent these must be individual rather than community efforts, but the community's interest can be expressed in several ways. Health education about emotional stress during certain periods of life as well as in crises can help people to accept their own emotional storms and to apply their sympathy intelligently when relatives and associates are distressed. Educating parents and prospective parents about personality development, the child's needs for healthy personal growth, and sound principles of child rearing is an important part of prenatal and well-child services.

The application of mental hygiene concepts

in schools is both important and difficult. According to Lemkau, the problem is attacked by:

. . . first, the selection of teachers whose sound mental health will serve as an example and will help to set the ideals of the child; second, by training these teachers to have an understanding of the emotional and developmental life of the child so that he can be led toward the most sound development.[17]

Dr. Lemkau comments that the methods of accomplishing these tasks are by no means fully known or standardized. However, the school environment, where children spend so large a portion of their growing years, should foster their progress toward emotional maturity, and the community's interests are served when whatever expertise is available is used toward accomplishing this goal.

For children who are mentally retarded, an important aspect of preventing mental illness lies in determining their level of intellectual skill and limiting as much as possible demands upon them, inasmuch as mental illness is related to the excess pressures of life. Doyle and Seidenfeld have said:

These pressures that create frustration for all people are many times magnified for the retarded where the threshold of frustration tolerance is at times depressed when the individual has fewer ways of coping with demands of his environment.[18]

Many community agencies and individuals engaged in health or social work can help in various ways to prevent the type of mental illness associated with social and emotional stress. The health professions have continuous associations with people experiencing the stresses that may accompany the birth of a child, illness or accident, or the death of a relative, and they have many opportunities to provide the emotional support needed in these circumstances. An important part of the family doctor's traditional role is to console the bereaved and to ease the sorrow of families troubled by illness and misfortune. In their services to families, public health nurses with training in mental

---

[16] *op. cit.,* p. 57.

[17] Lemkau, *op. cit.,* p. 613.

[18] Patrick J. Doyle and Morton A. Seidenfeld, "Mental Retardation," in Julian S. Myers (ed.) , AN ORIENTATION TO CHRONIC DISEASE AND DISABILITY (New York: The Macmillan Company, 1965) , p. 420.

health can guide parents in matters of child rearing and can give or obtain help for them in meeting crises in family life.

For some social agencies, such as family service societies, prevention of emotional illness is a major objective. In keeping families together and contributing to their adjustment, such agencies help to ensure an emotional environment conducive to healthy personality development. And, of course, child welfare and adoption agencies have the major responsibility for preventing the stress that infants suffer from maternal deprivation.

The administration of welfare and other forms of financial assistance has obvious mental health implications. People who need such public aid are already living under difficult conditions. The manner in which aid is given can alleviate the conditions, or it can intensify them, and result in emotional problems that prevent a return to independence.

Many areas of community service less directly related to the problem still affect mental health. The effect of the physical environment has already been discussed in Chapter 5. Certainly the courts, the police, and youth workers can influence the mental health of a great many people; and although mental health cannot be their major focus, it does deserve their attention in order to minimize problems of mental illness.

EARLY DIAGNOSIS

Early diagnosis of both mental illness and mental retardation is important to secondary prevention, that is, the minimizing of disability. For mental illness, casefinding in the usual sense is not appropriate, but the American Public Health Association emphasizes the importance of orienting professional persons or groups in the community so that they can recognize psychiatric symptoms and make proper referrals. "The major referring professions which need to be given understanding of symptoms and knowledge about referral," the *Guide* says, "are the clergy, school teachers, staff of social agencies, general physicians, public health nurses, and personnel counselors."[19] Such orien-

tation is futile in a community where services are not available or accessible to all who need them for psychiatric diagnosis, which must be accomplished through personal interview and requires the skill of trained specialists.

When a child is severely or profoundly retarded, his condition is usually recognizable; at least it is soon apparent that the child is not entirely normal. Unfortunately, however, many such children do not receive the diagnosis, evaluation, or other services that might reduce the extent of their lifelong disability. Some parents may be unable or unwilling to recognize that their child is different from others, sheltering even a profoundly retarded child from medical or other help. Service is often not sought for moderate or even severe retardation until the child goes to school and his inability to carry on schoolwork becomes obvious.

Mild retardation is less easily distinguished from normal intellectual growth in young children. It may appear as the slowness in learning sometimes experienced by normal children and may go unrecognized, especially in families whose standards and expectations for their children are not high. Furthermore, this type of retardation may result from an infancy spent in an environment of neglect and deprivation. Therefore, except when children receive some kind of preschool training, mild retardation is usually not detected until the school years. A program such as Operation Head Start allows for early identification of children who are actually retarded and "should help bring many thousands of prospective mentally retarded persons over the border into normal intelligence ranges."[20]

Procedures for diagnosis of mental retardation include physical and neurological examination, laboratory procedures, and various psychological tests. They should also include an appraisal of the family and environment so that realistic recommendations for services can be made. A number of different professional skills are required for comprehensive diagnosis and evaluation.

Ideally, all community services for both the

---

[19] APHA, *op. cit.,* p. 9.

[20] AN INTRODUCTION TO MENTAL RETARDATION, *op. cit.,* p. 7.

mentally ill and the mentally retarded should be concerned with secondary prevention. As better ways of treating and managing these conditions are developed and success dissipates some of the hopelessness that once was felt about both of them, the object of services will more often be prevention than it has been in the past.

Services for the Mentally Ill

A number of different methods of treating mental illness are used, separately or in combination, depending on the nature of the patient's illness and, sometimes, on the background and training of the therapist.

METHODS OF TREATMENT

Somatic treatment, directed at the body rather than the emotions, is effective in relieving symptoms and making possible other forms of therapy. It includes the use of drugs, such as the tranquilizers that have been dramatically successful in tempering the extreme behavior of mental patients, as well as various forms of shock therapy. The latter are less common since the advent of drugs.

Psychotherapy, considered necessary for all mental patients, is defined by the Joint Commission on Mental Illness and Health follows:

. . . an attempt by a professionally trained therapist to gain cooperation and insight through verbal or non-verbal communication with the patient at regular intervals over some extended period of time. The object of psychotherapy is to find psychologically and socially acceptable solutions for the patient's troubled or trouble-making ways of thinking and doing.[21]

Psychotherapy takes many forms and may be provided by psychiatrists, psychologists, or psychiatric social workers. In its simplest form, it may consist of a number of sessions conducted by a social worker or general practitioner; in some areas, laymen are being trained to give simple therapy to troubled people.

The most complex form of psychotherapy is the process of psychoanalysis, in which a specially trained psychiatrist works with a patient in frequent, sometimes daily, sessions over a period of years, with the objective of enabling the patient to recall and resolve the distressing events in his life that have obstructed his personality development. Psychoanalysis is used to treat neurosis and is not adapted to the treatment of psychosis nor to mass application. Less than a tenth of the nation's trained psychiatrists are qualified psychoanalysts, and of course such long and intensive treatment is expensive. For all these reasons, psychoanalysis, although it has contributed significantly to understanding the human mind and emotions, is not suitable therapy for the majority of the mentally ill.[22]

Group therapy, in which a number of patients participate under the guidance of a trained therapist, is believed to have a particular usefulness in helping patients back to satisfactory personal relationships. In addition, it has the practical advantage of using professional time economically.

Sometimes the approach is through drama or dance, in which the mentally ill attempt to relieve their distress by acting out their feelings. Occupational or work therapy is another means of helping patients toward normal behavior.

Inasmuch as a great many cases of mental illness are related to environmental situations, it is sometimes possible for a caseworker or agency to help a patient recover by altering his environment to remove the special stress that has upset him. In all forms of treatment for mental illness, work with the patient's family is considered essential in order to improve relationships and reduce emotional strain for the patient, as well as to deal with the anxiety in other family members that may be caused by the patient's illness. Social casework is thus an indispensable element in psychotherapy.

THE PLACE OF THE HOSPITAL IN MENTAL ILLNESS

Many cases of mental illness, even severe psychosis, can be treated satisfactorily outside the hospital if community resources are available

---

21 ACTION FOR MENTAL HEALTH, *op. cit.,* pp. 35–36.

22 *Ibid.,* pp. 79–80.

for outpatient treatment and supportive services. However, even under these circumstances, patients sometimes need to be hospitalized not only to protect the community if their behavior is extreme, but also to protect them from public reaction to their strange behavior and to give them respite from the pressures of living in the normal world. The hospital is often the best place for application of modern intensive treatment.

Until recent years, general hospitals as a rule accepted psychiatric cases only for diagnosis and referral to mental hospitals. Today, an increasing number of general hospitals have psychiatric services that provide therapy, and they have several advantages over the state mental hospital. Such hospitals are located in the community so that the patient is not drastically removed from his normal life situation. The legal procedures involved in admission to state mental hospitals and release from them do not usually apply in general hospitals, and patients who enter are expected to return relatively soon with improved health. As a result, treatment for mental illness in a general hospital does not carry the stigma of a stay in a mental hospital.

A modern mental hospital, however, is very different from the traditional institution that had as its main purpose the custody of "crazy people" who had to be "put away." It is conceived as a "therapeutic community," in which all the circumstances of the patient's life, as well as specific treatment, will contribute to his recovery. Patients are relatively free to come and go and may be encouraged to participate in outside activities such as recreation and church services—a situation that serves to reinforce their sense of personal dignity and worth that a locked ward easily destroys. Under these circumstances, and with the aid of drugs, an appropriate atmosphere for psychotherapy can be provided.

Many mental hospitals unfortunately have not reached such a desirable state. The frightful conditions that aroused public indignation in the late 1940s have been corrected to a great extent, but in the majority of state mental hospitals, more emphasis is given to custodial than to restorative functions. Hunt points out that patients are usually treated kindly:

Overt cruelty is probably less common in a well-run state hospital than in the average neighborhood outside. However, when based upon false premises, well-meaning kindness can itself be a cause of disability. The certified mental patient in our culture is traditionally regarded as one who has lost all capacity for managing his own affairs. For his own protection and welfare and for the safety of the public his every move must be directed and supervised. He is ordered to get out of bed, is told what clothing to put on, when and where he may smoke a cigarette. He is ordered to take part in occupational therapy, to toss a medicine ball, or watch a movie. He takes a bath only at the prescribed time and under the immediate supervision of an attendant. To make sure that no patient can escape from this well-intentioned coddling, all but a tiny minority spend their lives behind locked doors and barred windows with their occasional airing strictly guarded by watchful attendants.[23]

Dr. Hunt goes on to point out that this highly sheltered and guarded situation is not often necessary for the protection of either the patients or the public. Experiences in hospitals without locked doors and barred windows "have shown beyond question that much of the aggressive, disturbed, suicidal, and regressive behavior of the mentally ill is not necessarily or inherently part of the illness as such but is very largely an artificial by-product of the way of life imposed upon them."[24] As the Joint Commission puts it, mentally ill patients share the general attitude of normal people that being locked up is punishment; and when they are acutely ill, they are usually hypersensitive to the insult of forcible detention:

To be rejected by one's family, removed by police, and placed behind locked doors can only be interpreted, sanely, as punishment and imprisonment, rather than hospitalization. Anger begets anger; force invites counterforce.[25]

The imposition of restrictions that aggravate mental illness cannot justly be blamed entirely on the mental hospital. The community turns over its mental patients to the hospital and

---

[23] Robert C. Hunt, "Rehabilitation Potential of the Mentally Ill," in Milton Greenblatt and Benjamin Simon (eds.), REHABILITATION OF THE MENTALLY ILL (Publication No. 58 [Washington: American Association for the Advancement of Science, 1959]), p. 29.

[24] Ibid.

[25] ACTION FOR MENTAL HEALTH, op. cit., pp. 53–54.

holds it responsible for keeping them. Many state hospitals are overcrowded and have many times the 1,000 patients considered the largest number that should be cared for in one facility. They are frequently understaffed and underfinanced and often isolated from population centers so that opportunities to encourage public understanding are limited. In spite of these handicaps, however, a number of state hospitals have pioneered in new treatment and in extending service into communities. They recognize that they cannot wait for public attitudes to change, but must demonstrate that a therapeutic community rather than a custodial institution for mental patients benefits both patients and communities.

OTHER TREATMENT FACILITIES

Until recent decades, the majority of people with diagnosed mental illness were cared for in mental hospitals, chiefly those operated by the states. After World War II, a number of communities began to establish outpatient psychiatric clinics, which had previously existed in only a few places.

When the National Institute of Mental Health of the U.S. Public Health Service was authorized by the National Mental Health Act of 1946 and began in subsequent years to provide financial support for mental health programs outside the hospital, it gave impetus to the growing movement toward outpatient treatment. The advent of tranquilizing and antidepressant drugs in the late 1950's enabled early hospital discharge of large numbers of patients and encouraged the development of resources for their care in communities.

In addition to clinics, part-time hospitalization has been found to be suitable for many patients. Day care allows the patient to continue intensive treatment and to be relieved from daily pressures while still living at home; night care permits patients who are able to work to continue to have the service and security of the hospital.

REHABILITATION

Recovery from mental illness is often a slow process, and patients who have been hospitalized over a period of years usually need rehabil-itation before they are ready to take up independent lives. Many have lost their working skills through disuse and need vocational retraining; almost all need help in acquiring or retrieving the social skills important in every aspect of normal life. Vocational rehabilitation service, in addition to evaluation, counseling, and training, should in some cases include sheltered work. However, although there are several hundred rehabilitation centers under both voluntary and public auspices and an even larger number of sheltered workshops, most of these facilities are reluctant to accept former mental patients.

For social rehabilitation, halfway houses have been established where convalescent mental patients can live under less demanding conditions than if they returned to the community completely on their own. Foster homes are sometimes found for patients who do not have their own homes or whose homes are unsuitable for their needs. These living arrangements help to prevent or counteract the damage caused by institutional living. Social clubs for ex-patients provide a comfortable setting for recreation and the security of social contacts with people whose understanding can be taken for granted.

All the various resources that communities offer to the unhospitalized mental patient, at whatever stage of his illness, help to prevent the need for hospital care.[26] When such resources are coordinated in such a way that patients can return to a hospital for short periods when they need its special services, they do much to refute the concept that mental illness means hopeless, permanent disability.

THE COMMUNITY MENTAL HEALTH CENTER

As new possibilities in treating mental illness emerged, the established idea of the state mental hospital being the major facility became outmoded. As early as 1954, the state of New York enacted a community mental health serv-

---

[26] For an account of one program aimed specifically at preventing the need for hospital care, see Milton Greenblatt et al., THE PREVENTION OF HOSPITALIZATION, TREATMENT WITHOUT ADMISSION FOR PSYCHIATRIC PATIENTS (New York and London: Grune and Stratton, 1963).

ices act under which assistance could be given to local areas for a variety of mental health facilities. After psychiatric drugs became available, many other states passed similar laws.

In spite of these developments, change was slow. The drugs, as wonderfully effective as they are in relieving the distressing symptoms of mental illness, do not cure it; in or out of the hospital, patients on drug therapy still need other treatment. Mental hospitals, on which the states were spending more than $800 million a year by the late 1950s,[27] were still occupied almost to capacity. With such a burden to carry, state and local governments were not in a position to embark on the kind of extensive new programs that could have an impact on the problem.

In 1961, the report of the Joint Commission on Mental Illness and Health was published. The Commission, created by the Mental Health Study Act of 1955, recommended an aggressive attack on several fronts.[28] On this basis, President Kennedy asked for a "bold new approach," and in 1963, the Community Mental Health Centers Act (Public Law 88–164) was passed by the Congress, authorizing appropriation of up to $150 million to finance up to two-thirds of the cost of constructing community mental health centers. Funds were to be allotted to the states according to their respective populations and needs.

Under the regulations for administration of the act, a community mental health center must provide at least five types of service: inpatient, outpatient, partial hospitalization (at least day care), emergency service around the clock, and consultation to community agencies and professional personnel. Consultation and education services are especially important, for it is through them that a center will become a part of the community. In addition, adequate services include diagnostic service, rehabilitation, precare and aftercare, training and research, and evaluation. The requirements do not mean that all services must be housed under one roof, but they must be coordinated in such a way that patients eligible for one serv-

ice will be eligible for the others and can be transferred from one to another. Clinical records must be transferred with the patient, and wherever possible the same staff should continue to care for him. Construction grants were to cover new or expanded facilities, not to duplicate those existing.

The act required a community mental health center construction plan for each state, based on an inventory of existing facilities and comprehensive mental health planning, coordinated with related state and local planning. It required that an advisory council, representing all mental health interests in the state, be formed to consult with the designated state agency carrying out the plan. On the basis of the planning, each state was to set priorities for defined areas, according to need and existing resources.

Responsibility for administration of state mental health services is centered in a department of welfare or of institutions in a few states. About half the remaining states have a special department or board, and in the other half mental health is a specific concern of the state health department. At the local level, patterns vary more widely. Under the federal program, a community is defined as an area of not less than 75,000 nor more than 200,000 people, so that for these purposes a community may be only a part of the area covered by a local government jurisdiction, or it may include more than one such area. Where more than one such "community" exists in an urban area, their efforts should be coordinated.

Sponsors of community mental health centers in various localities can be health departments, general hospitals, state or local mental hospitals, mental health associations, or other agencies or combinations of agencies determined by the community to be best able to coordinate its resources for mental health to provide a comprehensive program. Under the regulations, special consideration is given to projects that propose affiliation with general hospitals, enabling mental health to be returned to the mainstream of community medical services.

Further federal legislation, enacted in 1965 (Public Law 89–105), provides additional as-

---

27 ACTION FOR MENTAL HEALTH, *op. cit.*, p. 6.
28 *Ibid.*

sistance to community mental health centers by making grants available for initial staffing of both those receiving construction grants and those providing new mental health services.

Services for the Mentally Retarded

Although mental retardation cannot be "cured," modern treatment and rehabilitation can help many of the mentally retarded to increase their abilities. The services needed are medical, social, educational, and vocational.

DIAGNOSIS AND TREATMENT

A child thought to be retarded should have a complete diagnostic evaluation. (See p. 146.) It is necessary to determine whether his condition is indeed mental retardation or another condition that may give the same impression—hearing defect or emotional disturbance, for instance—and to assess the extent of his disability and his potential. If the child has defects such as impaired vision or epilepsy in addition to mental deficiency, these should also be evaluated and considered in recommendations for his future.

In the past 10 years, under federal grants for maternal and child health services, many states have established diagnostic centers where children can receive such thorough study. However, although there are about 150 special clinics for the mentally retarded, many related to university medical centers, they are able to meet only a small fraction of the need.[29]

Almost as important as the diagnosis itself is the counseling given to parents when their child has been determined to be retarded. Parents must be helped to deal with the feelings that this life crisis may arouse—sense of guilt, fear of the future, anxiety or hostility—if the child is to have the loving care he needs even more than a normal child. Parents also need assistance in learning to care for the child in such a way as to encourage his potential for development as well as help in finding and using community resources in his behalf.

One of the recommendations of the President's Panel on Mental Retardation, reported in 1963, was that:

> There be available to every retarded person whether in his community or at a reasonable distance: a person, committee, or organization to whom parents and others can turn for advice and counsel; life counseling services; and a sufficient number of qualified professional and informed nonprofessional people willing to assist in developing a program for an individual . . . .[30]

After diagnosis, a retarded child should have whatever medical care is indicated. This may be only the care that all children need, but it may include drug treatment for related conditions or symptoms caused by his disability. Surgery is indicated in a few cases, and psychiatric treatment in many.[31]

RESIDENTIAL CARE

Although the present trend in work with the mentally retarded is toward care in the community, in their own homes or foster homes, residential care is necessary in some cases. At present, almost 200,000 people are resident in institutions for the mentally retarded, all but about 4 per cent in state institutions.[32] Many of these institutions are overcrowded, poorly staffed and financed, providing only custodial care. In addition, a number of mentally retarded persons are residents of mental hospitals, which are not equipped to provide appropriate care for them. Without the kind of comprehensive service that will bring out and make usable whatever capacity the retarded person has, his institutionalization is likely to be lifelong. A large number of people now in institutions for the mentally retarded are adults, who will have to remain there for the rest of their lives because at the time when their potential for community living could have been developed, they did not receive the necessary help.

SPECIAL EDUCATION

The need for special education opportunities for the large proportion of mentally retarded

---

[29] AN INTRODUCTION TO MENTAL RETARDATION, *op. cit.*, p. 5.

[30] *Ibid.*, p. 23.

[31] See Doyle and Seidenfeld, *op. cit.*, p. 435.

[32] U.S. Department of Commerce, Bureau of the Census, STATISTICAL ABSTRACTS OF THE UNITED STATES, 1965 (Washington: Government Printing Office, 87th annual ed., 1966), p. 77, Table 101.

children able to profit by them is obvious, yet the majority of such children do not have access to special education. There is a great shortage of teachers professionally trained to work with the mentally deficient, although fellowship grants made by the federal Office of Education for training in this field are helping to increase their number. In the meantime, retarded children without the benefit of special classes, if they go to school at all, may simply be exposed to the same education provided for other children, at which they cannot succeed. They are allowed to advance from grade to grade without accomplishment, and their school years do not help them toward any degree of independence as adults.

Another need, emphasized by the National Association for Retarded Children, is for recreation opportunities:

For the mentally retarded—children and adults—recreation is of utmost importance. Normal youngsters usually have many opportunities to learn to play and become outgoing and friendly. The mentally retarded—because they're generally shunned as being "different"—may never have these opportunities.[33]

The socializing influence of play can help to prepare a retarded child to get along with other people—a capacity he must have if he is to enter any working situation.

VOCATIONAL REHABILITATION

Vocational training is an aspect of the program of any retarded person whose disability will allow him to profit by it. His specific abilities must be determined early and developed. He must learn not only to do particular work, but also to get to and from work, to recognize its importance and his obligations to it—and the many other requirements for holding a job. Normally competent people take for granted the business of getting on a bus to go to work, getting off at the right stop, being on time, and working until quitting time; and they soon learn what is expected of them by superiors and other employees. But these abilities are all hurdles for the mentally retarded that must

sometimes be learned by long and laborious practice. And they are as much a part of rehabilitating the retarded to self-sufficiency as is training in a job skill.

In the states, vocational rehabilitation programs may include any of several services for the mentally retarded: diagnosis, physical restoration, counseling and testing, prevocational and vocational training, maintenance and transportation during rehabilitation, assistance in job placement, and follow-up.[34] In some areas, sheltered workshops, occupational training centers, or even halfway houses have been established.

Finding jobs for mentally deficient workers requires interpretation of their abilities to employers, as well as ensuring their adequate training. Unfortunately, many mental retardates who have been prepared for work have not been able to find it.

In the federal government, the Civil Service Commission and the Vocational Rehabilitation Administration jointly sponsor a program to place mental retardates in suitable jobs, such as routine clerical worker, food service worker, mail handler, laborer, laundry worker, and many others. The several state departments of vocational rehabilitation have responsibility for evaluating and certifying retarded clients for placement in suitable federal job openings. After a slow beginning, the program grew when employers found that retarded workers excelled in the kinds of jobs that are difficult to keep filled because the work is routine and repetitive. The economic soundness of programs to hire the mentally retarded, as well as other handicapped persons, should recommend them to state and local governments.

COMPREHENSIVE SERVICES FOR THE MENTALLY RETARDED

As services for the mentally retarded have grown up in the states, they have been established in a variety of agencies according to the kind of service. Departments of health, welfare,

---

[33] HOW TO BRING NEW HOPE TO THE MENTALLY RETARDED (New York: The Association, undated).

[34] U.S. Department of Health, Education, and Welfare, MENTAL RETARDATION ACTIVITIES OF THE DEPARTMENT OF HEALTH, EDUCATION, AND WELFARE (Washington: Government Printing Office, 1965), p. 48.

education, and labor, crippled children's services, divisions of vocational rehabilitation, institutions, and sometimes mental health agencies have had separate, often unrelated and uncoordinated programs. In the late 1950s, a national conference on mental retardation called by the Council of State Governments made strong recommendations for interdepartmental cooperation in a coordinated attack on the problem, and in 1962 the President's Panel on Mental Retardation concurred with the conference recommendations.

Coordination proved exceedingly difficult to achieve in most states, however, until federal legislation in 1963 (Public Law 88–156) provided grants to the states for planning coordinated action to combat mental retardation. At the same time, other legislation provided for grants for construction of various types of mental retardation facilities, including formula grants to the states, requiring a state plan. The plan must designate a single agency with authority to administer the plan; provide for a state advisory council representing all agencies, public and private, concerned with mental retardation; set forth a construction program based on a statewide inventory of facilities and needs, conforming to federal regulations regarding adequate service, and including provisions for services for persons unable to pay; and establish priorities for proposed projects. All these requirements, as well as others concerning administration of plans, help to ensure coordination of effort within states in behalf of the mentally retarded. Furthermore, the act makes specific provision for sharing among states when facilities can more effectively be combined.

The federal regulations define adequate services for the mentally retarded as including diagnostic, treatment, educational, training, personal care, and sheltered workshop services. Facilities constructed under the grants may be clinics, day facilities (for treatment, education, training, custodial care, sheltered work) , or residential facilities.

Promotion of Mental Health

Promotion of mental health reaches into many areas of community life and is not the concern of only the community mental health center. Some agencies actually deal with manifestations of mental illness and may be a part of the center or closely related to it (alcoholism clinics, programs to rehabilitate drug addicts, organized efforts to prevent suicide) . Much of the emphasis of work done with juvenile delinquents or adult criminals, in prison or on probation, is similarly directed toward people whose ability to cope with life in our society is impaired.

The new programs aimed at reducing the stresses of poverty are clearly in the interest of mental health. Operation Head Start repairs damage done to children's intellectual and emotional development by deprivation in infancy. The Job Corps, Vista, and the various community action programs seek not only to remove or lessen some of the burdens of the poor but also to help people strengthen their ability to manage life and its unavoidable crises.

In the work of most of the community agencies, public and private, concerned with the people's health, security, welfare, education, safety, religion, and recreation, the mental health component is readily apparent. There is growing recognition, however, that the relief of stress is a community function that cannot be left solely to social agencies.

A community that aspires to health cannot wisely ignore the effect upon people's lives of the crises created by slum clearance and relocation, for instance, or by routing of commercial traffic through residential neighborhoods. In matters such as these the consultation and education services of community mental health centers can make a unique contribution. The promotion of mental health is more than the treatment of mental illness; it is an important consideration in the administration of all community affairs.

12

Accidental Injury

PROGRAMS for accident prevention are based on the recognition that accidental injury, like other human ills, has causes that can be removed or counteracted. In other words, accidental injuries are not a matter of chance and should be subject to control. Although most people accept this idea intellectually, the feeling that "accidents will happen" persists, perhaps because people learned this attitude in childhood. Furthermore, ours is a culture with strong ties to a pioneering past when a certain amount of danger was unavoidable and indifference to danger was necessary for success. In spite of the greatly changed circumstances of our present-day lives, therefore, caution is still likely to be considered a sign of weakness, and lack of caution lies behind many accidents. The success of accident prevention programs thus depends to a great extent upon overcoming the influence of long-held attitudes that tend to negate the facts.

Accidental Deaths and Injuries

In each recent year, more than 100,000 people have met accidental death in the United States. Only cardiovascular diseases and cancer have caused more deaths than accidents have.[1] In young people 1 through 34 years old, accidents are the first cause of death, but more than half of all accidental deaths occur in persons 35 and over; the highest rates are among infants under a year old and the elderly. Accidental death rates are more than twice as high among men as among women, but rates for men have declined faster since 1910 than those for women, which have gone down very little.[2] Accidental death rates for nonwhites are higher than for whites; among American Indians, the accidental death rate is three times the rate for the total population. Geographically, the chances of fatal accidents are greatest in the Mountain States and Alaska and lowest in New England and the Middle Atlantic States. In general, accidental death rates are higher in rural than in urban areas.

National Health Survey data on accidental injuries that do not result in death indicate that annually more than one person in four in the total population suffers injury requiring medical attention or at least a day of restricted activity; about 2 million of these people require hospitalization. More general hospital days are needed for injuries than for deliveries of babies, and the American Medical Association estimates that accidents require 50,000 hospital beds and 68,000 hospital personnel at an annual expense of $500 million.[3]

Many accidental injuries result in permanent impairment. They are the major cause of visual impairment in persons under 65 years old; they cause one-fifth of the cases of paralysis in those

[1] See Figure 14.

[2] A. Joan Klebba, "Accidental Deaths in the United States," in "Accidents" reprinted from HEALTH, EDUCATION, AND WELFARE INDICATORS for December 1964–January 1965, p. 23.

[3] U.S. Department of Health, Education, and Welfare, Public Health Service, ACCIDENTAL DEATH AND INJURY STATISTICS (PHS Publication No. 1111 [Washington: Government Printing Office, 1963]), p. 10.

under 45 and 75 per cent of all cases of loss of limbs.[4]

More males than females are injured in accidents, although the difference is not so great as it is for accidental death. Rates of accidental injury, like those for accidental death, are higher in rural than in urban areas.

Causes of Accidents

Although factors in the causation of accidents can be generally divided between human and environmental factors, in most instances the two are probably combined. If a man's foot is cut by a power lawn mower, for instance, the mower may be considered the cause, and it is true that some mowers have better safety design than others. However, the cause may actually have been the man's failure to read the instruction manual or to heed the safety precautions therein.[5]

HUMAN FACTORS

Some of the human factors relating to accident causation are physical. Failing sight, hearing, and other senses, slowing of reaction time, and loss of strength and ease of motion that may come with age certainly account for many accidental deaths and injuries in the elderly. Fatigue or drugs or alcohol will affect the function of the senses, slow down reactions, and interfere with coordination in people at any age, increasing the likelihood of accidents.

A person's intelligence, knowledge, and judgment affect his risk of accidents. Until he is taught about danger and acquires the judgment to guide his explorations, the bright child's inquisitiveness puts him in the way of mishaps. Attention, time and space orientation, and perception are other pertinent cognitive aspects.

The role of individual emotion in accidents is somewhat difficult to pinpoint, but a person who is angry or upset has his attention distracted and both his judgment and his physical

functioning disturbed. His chance of trouble under these conditions is certainly increased.

In any discussion of human factors in accidents, the influence of drinking cannot be omitted. Alcohol affects not only physical function but judgment and other intellectual abilities as well. Drinking has had most attention in relation to drunken driving as a cause of traffic accidents, since it is associated with a considerable proportion of them; but alcohol is undoubtedly a factor in many other kinds of accidents. From review of studies of alcohol and highway accidents, Haddon concludes that even moderate alcohol consumption appears to increase risk but that the risk is multiplied with excessive use or addiction.[6]

The human characteristics that may contribute to accidents do not lend themselves to simple and completely dependable preventive measures. Any individual differs from one time to another in the characteristics that dispose him to mischance. Even if a person is habitually careful, has no physical impairments, and is well acquainted with rules of safety, temporary circumstances of stress or illness may lessen his control of situations. However, his attitudes, physical adequacy, and knowledge protect him even then and may well either prevent an accident or minimize its severity. Community efforts to develop attitudes of realistic caution, to correct or compensate for physical deficiencies, and to instill knowledge about safety can contribute significantly to reducing accidental injuries.

ENVIRONMENTAL FACTORS

Accidents occur as people use the environment or objects in it, and removal of unnecessary hazards is vital to prevention. The safety of an environment depends on who uses it for what activities. Safety may involve such things as lighting and temperature control in a workshop to decrease the strain for men working with machinery. In planning streets and roads for safety, the amount of traffic and its speed must be considered. In homes where there are chil-

[4] *Ibid.*, p. 13.
[5] See William V. White, ACCIDENTAL INJURIES ASSOCIATED WITH ROTARY LAWN MOWERS (Washington: The Outdoor Equipment Institute and the National Safety Council, no date).

[6] W. Haddon, Jr., "Alcohol and Highway Accidents," reprinted from the PROCEEDINGS OF THE THIRD INTERNATIONAL CONFERENCE ON ALCOHOL AND ROAD TRAFFIC, London, September, 1962.

dren, their curiosity and ubiquity must be considered; for older people, adjustments may be needed to compensate for less acute senses, unsteadiness, or weakness.

Technological progress has furnished the world we live in with an enormous number and variety of objects and has made our population remarkably mobile. The potential for accidents in such a complex environment can be reduced by engineering for safety in manufacturing and building. But it is human behavior on the part of industry and community, as well as by individuals—concern and awareness about hazards, action to remove them, and caution to avoid them—that makes the environment safe.

Some Current National Approaches

Because of the involvement of human characteristics and behavior, the underlying causes of many accidents are similar, no matter where they happen. Environmental factors had major emphasis in early safety programs, however, and it is still common to classify accidents and direct programs of prevention according to the place they occur. The precedent was set, perhaps, by the early industrial safety programs, which concentrated on the work place. It is worth noting, however, that some industrial safety programs aimed at reducing the economic cost in loss of working time because of accidental injury are turning their attention to safety in the home, in traffic, and elsewhere off the job, where most accidental deaths and injuries of workers now occur.

Automobile Accidents

Automobile accidents now cause about 45 per cent of all accidental deaths and a considerable, though smaller, proportion of disabling injuries. Concern about the problem is nationwide, and solutions are being sought to make cars, highways, and drivers safer.

In 1966, the Congress passed major legislation in the interest of automotive safety: The National Traffic and Motor Vehicle Safety Act (Public Law 89–563) and the Highway Safety Act (Public Law 89–564) . Under the first act, the Department of Transportation[7] is directed to establish safety standards for motor vehicles and vehicle equipment, with consultation from a National Motor Vehicle Safety Advisory Committee, most of whose members represent the public. Safety information is to be required on tire labels, and a grading system is prescribed "to eliminate deceptive and confusing tire nomenclature and marketing practices."

The Highway Safety Act provides for federal assistance to the states in carrying out comprehensive highway safety programs for which standards will be set by the Department of Transportation. It also authorizes research on highway safety and establishes a National Highway Safety Advisory Committee.

The Public Health Service of the Department of Health, Education, and Welfare carries on various activities to promote motor vehicle safety as a part of its overall program to reduce accidental injuries. It cooperates with other agencies in the aggressive national campaign to encourage the use of seat belts,[8] for instance, and has encouraged and supported crash injury research resulting in safety devices such as door locks, padded instrument panels, and recessed steering wheels. These devices have been incorporated in many new cars.

The human factors in traffic safety have long been the focus of driver education and safe driving campaigns aimed at improving the competence of drivers. Recently, interest in the physical and mental condition of drivers has been increasing. The American Association of Motor Vehicle Administrators has joined with the American Medical Association and the PHS in examining the place of licensure in preventing accidents due to impairments. As a result, some 30 states now have a formal mechanism for providing advice on medical aspects of driver licensing to their state licensing authorities.

The American Public Health Association, in

---

[7] The two acts designated the Department of Commerce to administer the laws. Responsibility was transferred to the Department of Transportation when it was established in October, 1966.

[8] See You Can Help to "Belt America" U.S. Department of Health, Education, and Welfare, Public Health Service (PHS Publication No. 1214 [Washington: Government Printing Office, 1964]) , a manual on development of seat-belt programs.

a resolution passed at its 1965 annual meeting, emphasized the importance of sound medical criteria for driver licensing and at the same time warned about the limitations of present understanding about medical factors related to accidents. The Association pointed out particularly that advanced age in itself, in the absence of specific impairments, has not been scientifically documented as a cause of accidents.[9]

The AMA, through its Committee on Medical Aspects of Automotive Safety, provides continuing information to the profession on such matters as determining fitness to drive and the effects of drugs on driving ability, as well as the physician's responsibility in these matters. As one paper specifically concerned with drugs has put it:

Physicians do not want to act as enforcers of social policy but by assuming the responsibility of educating their patients about drugs and driving safety, they can serve the patient and the community in a realistic way.[10]

MOTORCYCLE ACCIDENTS

The number of motorcycles registered in the United States was doubled between 1961 and 1965, and the increase was accompanied by significant increases in deaths and injuries due to motorcycle accidents.[11] Adequate training in controlling the vehicle and realization of the dangers involved could prevent many motorcycle accidents. Risk of fatality or serious injury can be reduced by the use of safety helmets and other protective equipment. However, few of the states require special driver licenses for motorcyclists, and in even fewer are they required to wear safety helmets. Community programs of information and training in motorcycling are urged by the PHS and other interested organizations.

HOME ACCIDENTS

Over one-fourth of accidental deaths and nearly half of accidental injuries that require medical

attention or restrict activity occur in or around the home. Opportunities for home accidents are manifold, and action to make homes safer takes many approaches.

Because the average home contains a variety of chemical products used for washing and cleaning, eliminating insects, relieving headache, and a variety of other purposes, accidental poisoning has become a major problem. The Federal Hazardous Substances Labeling Act of 1960 requires that products whose toxicity has been determined must be labeled with proper warnings. However, labeling is not always effective, and the Child Protection Act of 1966 went further to authorize the Secretary of Health, Education, and Welfare to ban from interstate commerce hazardous substances intended for use in households when the hazard involved is such that cautionary labeling would not be an adequate safeguard. The act also bans from interstate commerce toys and other articles used by children if they contain hazardous substances.

A continuing campaign of education is directed by local and state health departments and safety councils, backed by national agencies, to parents, children, and the public to promote care in handling and storing chemicals in the household. To deal with accidental ingestion of harmful substances when it does occur, more than 500 poison control centers in every part of the country provide information on the ingredients and toxicity of thousands of medicines and household products and the symptoms and treatment of poisoning.

Most poison control centers began under the auspices of local medical groups, and they are now usually operated through cooperation of several agencies, both official and voluntary. The states coordinate the activities of poison centers and set standards for their operation. The National Clearinghouse for Poison Control Centers, a function of the PHS, not only provides the centers with index cards on thousands of household products and medicines, but reviews and processes accidental poisoning case reports for study and use both by government agencies such as the Food and Drug Administration and by manufacturers.

Children not only like to put things in their

[9] JOURNAL OF THE AMERICAN PUBLIC HEALTH ASSOCIATION, December, 1965, p. 2010.
[10] Carlos J. G. Perry and Alan L. Morgenstern, "Drugs and Driving," JOURNAL OF THE AMERICAN MEDICAL ASSOCIATION, January 31, 1966, p. 379.
[11] See U.S. Department of Health, Education, and Welfare, Public Health Service, MOTORCYCLES IN THE UNITED STATES (Washington: The Service, 1966).

mouths when they are playing; they also like to hide—and the hiding place they choose is sometimes unfortunate. A refrigerator that is discarded or out of use seems ideal to a youngster, but it is built to be airtight, and a child trapped in it cannot survive more than 10 or 15 minutes. In the 1950s, the tragic deaths of children trapped in this manner led to action by a number of national organizations. The National Safety Council launched an education campaign, and three organizations—the Refrigeration Service Engineers Society, the Boys Clubs of America, and The Associated Locksmiths of America—offered free service to remove doors from abandoned and out-of-service refrigerators. A federal law passed in 1956 prohibits interstate shipment of refrigerators without safety devices, but even with these, additional protection may be necessary.

A conference sponsored in 1963 by the PHS was attended by representatives of the Federal Safety Council (U.S. Department of Labor), the Refrigeration Engineers Society, the Children's Bureau, the American Academy of Pediatrics, and the National Electrical Manufacturers Association. Most of these organizations have developed plans for programs to be carried out by their local affiliates, and the PHS has published guides for state and local health departments.[12]

Another hazard in the home that has been the subject of the cooperative attention of several government agencies, representatives of industry, and the National Safety Council is the glass door, frequently a feature of modern houses. In the early 1960s, reports of injuries resulting when people, frequently children in a hurry, crashed into or through glass began to concern both industry and the health agencies. Some results of cooperative efforts have been the development of standards on safety for architectural glazing material by the United States of America Standards Institute (formerly American Standards Association) and several

building code organizations, a requirement by the Federal Housing Administration for the use of safety glass, and a jointly sponsored continuing information program. State and local governments in many areas have passed code restrictions concerning architectural glass.

RECREATION ACCIDENTS

As their standard of living has improved, many Americans have become outdoor-sport enthusiasts. They take up skiing and scuba diving, build swimming pools in their back yards, go boating on rivers and lakes and oceans, and go hunting. Sometimes their enthusiasm is greater than their skill, and the number of accidental injuries and deaths associated with recreational activities is mounting.

Drowning is the greatest of all recreational accident problems and results in more than 6,000 deaths each year. Studies by the PHS have shown that important factors in the growing number of child drownings, especially in residential pools, are temporary lapses in adult supervision, as when a mother goes into the house to answer the telephone, and inadequate means of keeping unsupervised youngsters out of pools. The sooner that children learn to swim, the safer their pleasure in the water will be. Some state and local health departments have demonstrated the feasibility of teaching children to swim by the time they are in fourth grade. When elementary schools do not have pools, portable pools can be used. Programs of this type can be carried on in cooperation with groups affiliated with the National Council for Cooperation in Aquatics, such as the American Red Cross, the National Safety Council, and the National Swimming Pool Institute.

EMERGENCY MEDICAL SERVICE

When someone is seriously injured, his life or the extent of his injury often depends on the immediate care he receives and on his immediate transportation to a hospital. As early as 1949, the American College of Surgeons began investigating the adequacy of ambulance service and often found it lacking. Concerned about the training of ambulance drivers, the College has cooperated with state health de-

---

[12] See U.S. Department of Health, Education, and Welfare, Public Health Service, CHILDREN AND REFRIGERATOR ENTRAPMENT (PHS Publication No. 1259 [Washington: Government Printing Office, 1965]). Contains bibliography.

partments, medical schools, and medical societies in providing courses for them. More recently, the Association of State and Territorial Health Officers has recommended that state health departments help communities to survey their existing emergency medical services and develop coordinated and adequate systems to provide them. The PHS has sponsored several state studies and is developing a model survey schedule for use in other states. It is also working with medical and hospital agencies in developing standards for personnel training and licensing, design and required numbers of ambulances, type and quality of equipment, communication systems among ambulance, hospitals, and police, and staffing of hospital emergency departments. It must be remembered that ambulance service is primarily a method of transportation; it is a link in a chain that culminates in the availability and utilization of a facility that provides needed medical services. (For a discussion of hospital emergency departments, see Chapter 8.)

In spite of the fact that the ambulance is thought of as part of hospital service, this is no longer usually the case.[13] Throughout the country, many ambulance services are operated either as private businesses or by volunteer organizations. In smaller communities, where they cannot support themselves independently, they are usually provided by funeral directors.

Tax-supported ambulance service exists in many large cities. It may be operated by the police or fire department, the health department, or a public hospital. In some cities where most ambulances are privately owned, the fire department provides and operates resuscitation equipment.

Ideally, an emergency medical service should have ambulances available around the clock, properly equipped for all types of first aid and with such devices as safety belts for patients and attendants; they should be staffed by able drivers and attendants trained in first aid and res-

cue work; they should have a communication system that enables prompt response when and where they are needed and the ability to alert hospital personnel to be waiting for the patient. Such a service is not inexpensive, and frequently the reason given for inadequacy is an economic one. As one author put it:

> The economic problems can be summarized briefly by noting that rural ambulance finances are hampered by there being too few patients or population at risk to support even one ambulance, and that urban ambulance finances are a problem frequently because there may be too many companies in competition to provide any single one with an adequate economic base of operation. Add to this the additional burden and economic waste inherent in excessively frequent turnover of personnel which is due primarily to very low wages, but which then leads to further costs for constant rehiring and retraining of ambulance personnel.[14]

It is essential that each community have a detailed plan providing rapid and efficient emergency treatment. The plan should provide adequate means of communication and transportation so that people requiring emergency service can be moved as quickly as possible to suitable facilities for care and treatment. Development of a plan for emergency medical service must begin with careful evaluation of each community's needs and existing services, involving all those concerned. On the basis of such a study, a planned program including an ordinance governing ambulance systems operations and standards may be reasonably proposed. A Joint Action Committee of the American College of Surgeons, the American Association for the Surgery of Trauma, and the National Safety Council, with Public Health Service assistance, has prepared a model ordinance for the guidance of local communities.[15]

Public education is an essential part of any community emergency medical services program. This should include first-aid or medical self-help training, universal tetanus toxoid immunization, and emergency medical identification for those with medical conditions that could create or aggravate emergencies.

---

[13] See Howard W. Mitchell, "Ambulances and Emergency Medical Care," JOURNAL OF THE AMERICAN PUBLIC HEALTH ASSOCIATION, November 1965, pp. 1717–24; and Julian A. Waller, "Ambulance Service, Transportation or Medical Care," PUBLIC HEALTH REPORTS, October, 1965, pp. 847–53.

[14] Howard W. Mitchell, op. cit., p. 1722.
[15] Available from the Public Health Service.

Local Programs

Accidental-injury prevention is a function of a variety of organizations in the community, both public and private. The police department is responsible for enforcing traffic regulations and investigating accidents, and in many cities it has a special division concerned with preventing accidents. The fire department is concerned not only with preventing or minimizing injury when fires occur but also with preventing fires. Various agencies concerned with housing have obvious responsibility for home safety. The schools not only should ensure a safe environment in buildings and playgrounds, but also should provide safety education by both instruction and example, in school buildings and on grounds and playing fields. Driver education in schools has been recognized by insurance carriers to be of such value as to affect insurance rates. Public utilities and transportation facilities, publicly or privately owned, must guarantee safe as well as efficient and economical service, and recreation and public works departments have similar obligations.

In the private sector, medical and allied professions and hospitals are obviously concerned; industries may be interested either in preventing accidental injury of their employees both at work and in the community or in preventing injury in connection with their products or services. Voluntary organizations such as Red Cross Chapters, service clubs, and scout organizations often engage in specific accident-prevention programs.

Coordination of all these interests and activities is essential, and this is one of the functions of a local safety council with widely representative membership. However, whether in the absence of a safety council or in cooperation with it, health departments can make significant contributions to community programs. They are in the best position to analyze the local problem of accidental injury and death, using epide-miologic techniques to determine both human and environmental factors so that workable preventive measures can be developed. In the course of their daily work, members of the health department staff have numerous opportunities to promote safe conditions and behavior—engineers and sanitarians, by considering the safety of environment as well as its freedom from contaminants; public health nurses, as a part of their help and instruction to families in homes and clinics; and health educators in their work with other staff members and community groups. If such effort is to be a continuing part of the health department's functions, it requires not only leadership from the health officer but assignment of such responsibility to a particular staff member.

Many health departments engage in specific program activities in accidental injury prevention. They may take leadership in improving emergency medical services or in developing laws or ordinances concerned with safety. Some health departments offer courses for safety chairmen of civic or other community groups, and many carry on special campaigns to reduce injuries caused by such common equipment as power lawnmowers and bicycles.[16]

No single agency at the local, state, or national level can undertake full responsibility for preventing accidental injury. Prevention requires the attention and active participation of government, industry, professions, organizations, and private individuals. But the tragic number of deaths and injuries affecting a large part of the population each year and the cost in suffering as well as in dollars clearly call for community leadership to ensure that in this matter everyone's responsibility does not become no one's responsibility.

---

[16] See U.S. Department of Health, Education, and Welfare, Public Health Service, A GUIDE TO THE DEVELOPMENT OF ACCIDENTAL INJURY CONTROL PROGRAMS (PHS Publication No. 1368 [Washington: Government Printing Office, 1965]) .

13

Health Services in Disasters

SINCE the Federal Disaster Act was passed in 1950, the authority it gives the President to declare an affected area a "major disaster area," thus making it eligible to receive federal financial assistance, has been used about 250 times. Hundreds of lesser disasters for which federal funds or assistance were not requested have occurred throughout the country. Some disasters are phenomena of nature—hurricanes, tornadoes, floods, blizzards, and earthquakes. Others are unforeseen consequences of man's activities—fires, explosions, airplane crashes, and railroad accidents. A strike of essential workers, a riot, or widespread power failure may also produce disaster conditions.

Almost all disasters engender an immediate need for organized medical services to care for the injured, the exhausted, and the frightened. Many also disrupt normal services and controls that protect against the spread of disease, such as sewer systems and sewage treatment plants, and inspection of water and food supplies. If garbage and other solid waste cannot be removed over a period of days or weeks, or if stagnant water collects, insects and rodents become a serious threat. If people must be evacuated from their homes and stay crowded together in temporary shelters with improvised food and sanitary provisions, danger of epidemic is inevitable. The aftermath of a disaster may thus multiply the injury incurred by the event itself.

A community can do very little to prevent most disasters,[1] but it can do much to alleviate their effects and prevent consequent health

problems. Through experience in situations that have arisen and through efforts to reduce the potential damage of the most grim disaster of all, war, techniques have been developed to prepare communities to deal with such crises. The federal government and the states are ready to assist in various ways, but the major need is for action at the community level.

National Programs

In the federal government, a number of different agencies are resources for various types of assistance when disasters occur. Among these resources are the Office of Emergency Planning in the Executive Office of the President; the Office of Civil Defense, the Army Corps of Engineers, and other constituents of the Department of Defense; and the Office of Emergency Transportation in the Department of Transportation. In the Department of Health, Education, and Welfare, the Public Health Service is the major source of federal support in providing emergency health services. It is prepared to make material and personnel available when needed, to advise communities on health problems, and to provide liaison with other sources of aid as well as help in obtaining it. PHS's activities related to disasters include continuing aid for planning and training. Health mobilization representatives are assigned to state health departments and some metropolitan areas, as well as to regional offices of the De-

---

[1] In communities located where earthquakes or floods are possible, municipal leadership should ensure that codes and regulations regarding such matters as flood

plains and earthquake-sensitive buildings are adequate for protection of the public from disaster.

partment of Health, Education, and Welfare. As is the case with other forms of federal help in regard to health, requests for disaster aid for local communities are routed through the state health department to the DHEW Regional Office.

CONTINUING AID

Working with other government and professional organizations, the PHS has prepared a series of publications for the guidance of local communities in planning emergency medical and public health services.[2] In step-by-step order, procedures are spelled out for the most effective use of available health resources in a disaster. Each of several professional groups—nurses, pharmacists, dentists, veterinarians—has prepared a manual on the role of its members in emergency situations, included in the series. In order to promote local programs, the PHS has developed and assisted in presenting training courses for all types of health workers.

When a disaster occurs, people are sometimes stranded for a period of time without needed medical services. To help them help themselves in such an emergency, the PHS in cooperation with the Office of Civil Defense has prepared the Medical Self-Help Training course, which is provided through state health departments and civil defense offices.[3] Going beyond first aid —usually based on the assumption that a doctor will take over fairly soon—the course presents procedures for longer term emergency care such as nursing care of the sick and injured and emergency childbirth, as well as radioactive fallout protection and sanitary living under disaster conditions. At the local level, the 16-hour course is presented by volunteer instructors on the basis of filmstrips, lesson books, and other materials supplied with instructors' kits. A series of motion pictures is also available. The

American Medical Association assisted in developing the program and endorses it, and a number of other professional organizations both endorse and help promote it. The American National Red Cross has asked instructors of its standard first aid course to add an additional six hours of instruction to include medical self-help content.

A number of national nongovernmental agencies provide assistance and information about various aspects of emergency health service. The American Hospital Association, for instance, produces two basic documents for the guidance of hospitals, *Principles of Disaster Planning for Hospitals,* and *Readings in Disaster Planning for Hospitals.*[4] Disaster committees of the American Medical Association and the American Hospital Association work closely with the PHS in developing emergency health programs. Both the National League for Nursing and the American Nurses' Association issue publications on disaster nursing for members of their profession.

EMERGENCY AID

All health mobilization representatives are prepared to act quickly, if a disaster occurs and help is requested, to expedite federal action in meeting health needs. Such help may take the form of people or supplies or both. Within hours of the Alaska earthquake in 1964, for instance, PHS physicians, nurses, and engineers had arrived in Anchorage in response to the state health officer's request; typhoid vaccine with injection equipment, and hypochlorinators to protect the water supply, followed shortly. The situation may be less dramatic but nevertheless threatening, as it was in New Mexico in 1965, when some 75,000 acres of flooded land presented the possibility of an epidemic of mosquito-borne encephalitis. In that episode PHS arranged for pilots, aircraft, and spraying material. Floods often endanger water supplies and immediately necessitate inspection, testing, and often treatment of water. During the midwest spring floods in 1965, 28 PHS sanitary engineers were sent to help in cities along the Mississippi.

---

[2] See U.S. Department of Health, Education, and Welfare, Public Health Service, EMERGENCY HEALTH PREPAREDNESS PUBLICATIONS CATALOGUE and COMMUNITY EMERGENCY HEALTH PREPAREDNESS, ("Health Mobilization Series," A-1 and A-2 [Washington: Government Printing Office, 1964]).

[3] See U.S. Department of Health, Education, and Welfare, Public Health Service, MEDICAL SELF-HELP TRAINING FOR YOU AND YOUR COMMUNITY (PHS Publication No. 1042 [Washington: Government Printing Office, 1965]).

---

[4] The Association, 1963 and 1956.

To meet the need for medical facilities in case of overwhelming disaster, the PHS stores Packaged Disaster Hospitals in communities throughout the country for use if local resources become inadequate. In most cases a PDH is affiliated with an existing local hospital. Packed in over 600 boxes, each PDH contains equipment and supplies to set up a complete 200-bed hospital for 30 days' operation. They are inspected regularly to ensure their readiness for use. Permission to open and use all or part of a PDH may be granted by the PHS at the request of the state. Accepting responsibility for a PDH means assuring its safety in storage and also developing a plan for its disaster use, including designating a staff. Detailed guidance on the utilization of the PDH is available.[5] When adequate plans and preparations have been made, the PDH can be activated very quickly. During Hurricane Hilda in 1964, the PDH at Raceland, Louisiana, was ready to treat patients within an hour after authorization was given to set it up. Public Health Service permission was given in less than 30 minutes, and a local veterans' group, which had prearranged responsibility for setting it up, had been alerted and was standing by when permission was received.

Most often the entire PDH is not needed, but permission is requested to use some of the equipment or supplies contained in it. Generators, stored with each PDH, have been used during community power failures, for instance; and cots and blankets have been used in shelters provided for victims of floods, tornadoes, and a variety of other community crises.

The American National Red Cross, under its congressional charter, provides services including food, clothing, and shelter to victims of disaster, and its work is coordinated with community emergency health services. In Raceland, for example, the food for patients and staff of the PDH, supplied by a local supermarket and prepared by volunteers, was paid for by the American Red Cross. That organization also continues to give assistance after the immediate emergency is over.

State Programs

When a disaster occurs that overtaxes a community's capacity to fend for itself, the state is the first source of aid appealed to. Some states have special civil defense agencies, but help for emergency health services is the responsibility of the state health department. The role of the state health department, according to the Association of State and Territorial Health Officers, is to develop state plans and organizations for postdisaster services, to prepare staff of operating programs to assist communities in emergency health planning, and to encourage training and PDH programs.[6] The states vary considerably in their health department provisions for emergencies; in some of them a special unit of the department is devoted to such work, and in others the responsibility is placed in another operating unit.

Local Programs

In local areas, initiation of planning for dealing with disasters may come from a civil defense agency, but disaster preparedness is a responsibility of all agencies of local government as well as of certain nongovernmental groups and facilities. They must prepare to provide a number of necessary services—fire, rescue, public works, police, welfare, radiological defense, communications, transportation, supply, and manpower, as well as health. A single city or county may plan to operate self-sufficiently in disaster; or a combined city and county, or even several counties, may be covered by one plan.[7]

The health department is considered the most suitable agency to base local emergency

[5] U.S. Department of Health, Education, and Welfare, Public Health Service, ESTABLISHING THE PACKAGED DISASTER HOSPITAL (PHS Publication 1071-F-1 [Washington: Government Printing Office, 1966]).

[6] PROCEEDINGS, 1963 ANNUAL MEETING OF THE ASSOCIATION OF STATE AND TERRITORIAL HEALTH OFFICERS (Lansing, Michigan: The Association, 1964), p. 15.

[7] For details on planning and organizing local programs, see COMMUNITY EMERGENCY HEALTH PREPAREDNESS, op. cit.

health service plans on,[8] and the health officer usually becomes chief of the service. Because participation of all health professionals in the community is needed, an emergency health advisory committee is recommended, with representation from all the health professions and local hospitals, the Red Cross chapter, and other health-related facilities.

WRITTEN PLAN AND ORGANIZATION

In developing a written plan for emergency health services, advisory committees should be guided by the state's plans and methods regarding civil defense and disaster preparedness. They may be able to obtain help from the state in their preparations. The plan should be based on consideration of the most probable situations that may have to be met. Geographic location, for instance, will often determine the

---

[8] See American Public Health Association Program Area Committee on Health Services in Disaster, "The Role of State and Local Health Departments in Planning for Community Health Emergencies," AMERICAN JOURNAL OF PUBLIC HEALTH, January, 1963, pp. 109–10.

likelihood of a certain kind of natural disaster, such as a flood or hurricane; and location, extent, and nature of industry will affect a community's danger in case of attack on the nation. Analysis of the possible situations in terms of probable emergency health service requirements, compared with an estimate of key resources available in the community—physicians, nurses, hospital beds, and the like—allows for a realistic decision about the maximum scope of the plan.

On the basis of an organization designed by the committee, leaders can be chosen for various activities and given the assignment of writing the respective parts of the plan. Each section should present sufficient detail to make it useful in emergency. When the sections have been written and edited for consistency, and the written plan has been reviewed by community and state health and civil defense leaders, it should be printed and made available to everyone who has a role in the plan or is otherwise interested.

The details of organization for emergency

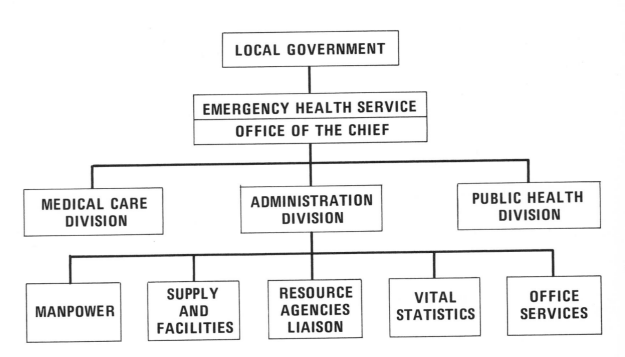

FIGURE 15. *Basic organizations: community emergency health service*

health services vary among communities, but their basic pattern is usually similar to that presented in Figure 15. In case of disaster, all community health resources become a part of the organization, according to arrangements set forth in the plan.

PUTTING THE PLAN INTO EFFECT

The written plan, important as it is, is only the first step of preparation. A manpower schedule must be developed and people with appropriate skills recruited. Since some people may be called on to perform services that go beyond their normal work, they will have to become familiar with the special needs of a disaster situation. This applies, for example, not only to the pharmacist who may be assigned to the laboratory of a PDH, but also to the physician whose specialty practice does not call for skill in emergency care and to persons not in the health professions who will be needed as aides and supporting manpower. After a roster is completed, it must be continually checked and kept up-to-date.

Health facilities must develop plans for special procedures in case of disaster and tie them in with manpower assignments. General hospitals will need to have means of expanding bed capacity and increasing the capacity of services such as X-ray and operating rooms. Specialty hospitals can often plan to care for casualties, and the extent to which they can do so should be determined. Hospitals with contractual responsibility for a PDH should indicate in their disaster plan how its components are to be utilized to expand operating capability. Hospitals accredited by the Joint Commission on Accreditation of Hospitals[9] are required to have a written plan for the care of mass casualties that is rehearsed twice a year, and it is important that this plan be consistent with overall community plans.

Many physicians serve on the staff of more than one hospital, and care must be taken that they are not depended on in more than one place in case of all-out emergency. If a PDH is to be affiliated with a local hospital, its staffing must be taken into consideration; and the staff-

ing needs for first-aid stations and emergency outpatient services must not be overlooked. It is usually easier to provide the material and space for expanding health facilities than to provide the necessary additional staff, even when medical care standards are to be very "austere."

Health supplies and equipment are also essential to emergency care, and planning for their use requires determining the average amounts normally on hand in the area. Community hospitals seldom maintain large inventories of expandables because resupply is easily accomplished. In a large-scale disaster, however, a greatly increased patient load, plus the disruption of normal lines of resupply, would face the hospital with an acute need for critical medical items for disaster care. Thus, in addition to its PDH program the Public Health Service is undertaking a program to place a 30-day supply of such items in the nation's hospitals. Priority will be based primarily on the hospital's location and the availability of staff and supporting services.

Assistance from civil defense officials may be available for acquiring and storing additional materials for disaster. Requirements for items not exclusively used for health purposes but nevertheless indispensable must be taken into consideration. Generators are a prime example, and two-way radios that keep emergency health units in communication with each other and with the community.

If a plan for emergency health services is to be made into an effective resource, it must continually mesh with other emergency plans. In planning and assigning manpower, for instance, agreements must be made with local manpower officials not only to refer available health workers to the emergency health service for assignment to emergency health duties but also to help in recruiting supporting manpower. If a disaster occurs and the emergency health service goes into operation, it will require help from those responsible for communications, transportation, food service, and other emergency services, and advance planning is necessary to ensure that they can provide what will be needed. Communications must receive particular attention since health services can neither provide nor receive support from other

---

[9] See Chapter 8.

emergency operations if they are out of touch, and effectiveness often depends on prompt awareness of events as they happen.

Testing under simulated disaster conditions is a way to determine the adequacy of emergency health services before a real disaster situation occurs. Some parts of the health plan, or certain facilities, may be subjected to periodic testing, or participation by several health units in a community civil defense exercise may bring health and other community emergency services into simultaneous practice operation.

PURPOSE OF PREPARATION

When a disaster occurs, the people of most communities rise to the occasion with amazing fortitude, and stories of generosity and willing helpfulness always come out of such events. If the community has planned for such an exigency and people have been assigned and trained to help, the severity of the catastrophe will be minimized. However, in situations of extreme danger or excitement, people's willingness to help does not necessarily tell them what to do nor provide them with ability to do what is needed. After the fact, the community's spirit cannot provide health facilities or materials that may be desperately needed. Being prepared helps to assure that people's altruistic inclinations can be directed most effectively toward relief of suffering and survival.

14

Financing Medical Care

EARLIER CHAPTERS have shown the extent to which the level of a community's health is affected by the quality and quantity of its medical care services. The occurrence or consequences of many of today's most insistent health problems can be prevented only by adequate medical care. The money spent on such care from either private or public resources comes, directly or indirectly, from the community. As it is spent, it adds to the community's total income and, at the same time, helps to preserve the earning capacity of those whose health is maintained. For economic as well as humanitarian reasons, the community's interests are served when the objective of providing adequate medical care for all is achieved.

When medical care consisted mostly of service given by a family physician to a patient in his office or the patient's home, with only rare recourse to hospitalization, the financial transactions involved were relatively simple. The patient paid the doctor and the hospital directly if he could. When he could not pay the doctor's bill, usually calculated in terms of the patient's financial situation, the doctor either treated him without charge or allowed him to pay a little at a time; in rural areas, the doctor accepted payment in kind. A chicken for the doctor's Sunday dinner often represented payment. In the hospital, the patient who could not afford to pay usually became a "ward patient,"[1] although in a large city he might go to a public hospital.

As medical science has grown, complex systems of providing medical care have developed. More than half of the physicians in private practice now specialize, so that most individuals receive their care from more than one physician. In addition to a spectacular array of therapeutic drugs, modern medical practice uses a variety of diagnostic tests and treatment procedures requiring expensive equipment and trained personnel. To take advantage of these procedures, doctors now often treat patients in a hospital.

Along with the changes in medical practice, there have been changes in people's desires and needs for personal health care. The success of medical care in itself has created increased demand for it. A larger proportion of the population is now in older age groups whose health problems demand more extended personal health services than do those of younger people.

These and other changes in the practice and cost of medical care increased the country's total expenditure for personal health services from $11 billion in 1950 to $31.2 billion in 1964. During this period, there was a corresponding modification in the method of paying personal health care bills. Whereas in 1950, 65 per cent of the total expenditure represented direct payment by consumers, in 1964 this proportion had gone down to 49 per cent. The share paid by government was reduced slightly, from 23 to 22 per cent; and that by philanthropy and other sources decreased from 2.9 to 2.1 per cent. But the part of the total bill paid by consumers through health insurance increased from 9 to 25 per cent.[2] The program of

---

[1] Chapter 8.

[2] Louis S. Reed and Ruth S. Hanft, "National Health Expenditures, 1950–64," SOCIAL SECURITY BULLETIN, January, 1966, p. 13.

health insurance for people over 65, established under the Social Security Amendments of 1965, will bring a further increase in the proportion of total personal health care expenditures financed by government insurance.

Methods of Consumer Financing

In 1964, 6 per cent of the money spent by individual consumers in the United States for all personal needs was spent on personal health care. This compares with 23 per cent of personal expenditures spent for food and 15 per cent for housing.[3]

Although two-thirds of individual expenditures for personal health services are still paid directly by consumers, it is becoming less usual for individuals and families to pay for all their personal health services in this way. Over 70 per cent of the population is estimated to have some private health insurance coverage,[4] and in 1964 payment of insurance claims met almost one-third of consumer expenditures for health.[5]

The proportion of people insured tends to be larger among families who would probably be able to pay for their medical care if they were not insured. Nearly 88 per cent of people living in families with annual incomes over $10,000 had some form of hospital insurance in 1962–63, and nearly 83 per cent had some form of surgical insurance. Those in lower income families and in older age groups less frequently had health insurance.[6]

People with insurance, nevertheless, customarily pay a considerable part of personal health bills directly. Health insurance coverage varies widely in completeness, but with few excep-

tions, it does not include dental care. Eyeglasses and other appliances are not often covered, nor are drugs that are prescribed outside the hospital. Treatment of mental illness outside the hospital is rarely included. In fact, although health insurance met 69 per cent of consumer expenditures for hospital care in 1964 and 35 per cent of those for physicians' services, it paid for only 2 per cent of other types of personal health service.[7]

Of the nearly $8 billion paid out in benefits by private health insurance organizations in 1964, 46 per cent came from Blue Cross or Blue Shield plans; 48 per cent was paid by commercial insurance companies, all but one-fifth of it on group policies; and the remaining 6 per cent came from independent plans.[8]

BLUE CROSS

The more than 75 Blue Cross plans covering states, parts of states, or local areas in the United States all provide hospital benefits, and a few provide surgical-medical benefits as well. They are coordinated in the Blue Cross Association, so that a member of a plan in one area is eligible for service benefits in another, and members may transfer from one plan to another without loss of status. However, each plan is a locally governed corporation, operating on a nonprofit and usually tax-exempt basis. It is subject to state review and regulation and is publicly accountable.

Although most Blue Cross plans originally charged all groups the same fees for the same coverage, now almost all of them charge each group over a given size according to its experience. According to Reed, "The plans, in general, came to this practice reluctantly; they were forced into it by the competition of insurance companies, which had always rated according to experience."[9]

Most members of Blue Cross plans come in under group policies; their health status there-

[3] Health Insurance Institute, SOURCE BOOK OF HEALTH INSURANCE DATA 1965 (New York: The Institute, 1965), p. 55.

[4] Louis S. Reed, THE EXTENT OF HEALTH INSURANCE COVERAGE IN THE UNITED STATES (Washington: Government Printing Office, 1965), p. 32.

[5] Reed and Hanft, *op. cit.*, p. 14, Table 10.

[6] U.S. Department of Health, Education, and Welfare, Public Health Service, VITAL AND HEALTH STATISTICS, DATA FROM THE NATIONAL HEALTH SURVEY, SERIES 10, No. 11, HEALTH INSURANCE COVERAGE, UNITED STATES, JULY 1962–JUNE 1963 (Washington: Government Printing Office, 1964), p. 12, Table 1.

[7] Reed and Hanft, *op. cit.*, p. 16.

[8] Louis S. Reed, "Private Health Insurance in the United States, An Overview," SOCIAL SECURITY BULLETIN, December, 1965, p. 20, Tables 8 and 9. This reference is the major source used for information on health insurance.

[9] *Ibid.*, p. 7.

fore does not determine their eligibility. All plans allow members who leave enrolled groups to convert to nongroup policies. In other enrollment of individuals, poor health risks are usually excluded, and benefits in connection with preexisting conditions may be excepted or postponed. Group and nongroup policies are written for both individuals and families, and dependents generally are entitled to the same benefits as the insured head of the family.

The benefits available vary considerably, not only among plans but according to different types of contracts, or options under single contracts, offered by each plan. However, all members are entitled to hospital room and board, usually in semiprivate rooms, for periods varying from 40 to 365 days a year and to services considered to be hospital, rather than medical, services. Care in nonparticipating hospitals is usually paid for at a set daily amount, lower than the payment for similar service to participating hospitals. Nearly all plans cover members for hospital outpatient service for emergencies or minor surgery, and some include certain diagnostic procedures as well. Mental illness and tuberculosis, formerly excluded by most plans, are now frequently covered for stipulated periods when care is given in a general hospital. At least part of the cost of nursing-home care is covered by some plans, although it is often a part of extended benefit or major medical coverage.[10]

An increasing number of plans now offer what are called extended benefits in supplementary contracts. Such benefits may include longer periods of hospitalization than provided in the basic contract, as well as physicians' services and sometimes drugs, diagnostic service, and private-duty or visiting-nurse service. Major medical benefits are offered by some plans and are administered similarly to those of the commercial insurance companies (discussed later in this chapter). A distinguishing characteristic of Blue Cross hospital insurance is that its benefits are chiefly in service rather than in cash. The plans contract with hospitals to provide care for members and reimburse hospitals according to an arranged schedule of allowable costs. The patient is charged only for items not covered by the plan. In most areas, all licensed hospitals participate, but some plans contract only with hospitals that meet standards higher than those required for licensure.

BLUE SHIELD

There are 74 Blue Shield plans in the United States, operating under legislation specifying which practitioners may participate and usually stipulating that a given proportion of board members must be physicians. Legislation generally exempts the plan from taxes, except local real estate taxes. All plans offer coverage for surgical, obstetrical, and anesthesiological services in or out of the hospital, and physician care in the hospital. Many plans cover hospital diagnostic services if they are not covered by Blue Cross, and a growing number include out-of-hospital diagnostic procedures.

A few Blue Shield plans provide full service benefits to all subscribers regardless of income. Others provide stipulated amounts toward payment for services, which physicians need not accept as full payment. In the majority of plans, however, participating physicians agree to accept specified amounts as full payment from patients with incomes under certain ceilings—usually $4,000 for a single person and $6,000 for a family. Other patients may be charged more.

All licensed physicians are usually eligible to participate in Blue Shield plans, and most of them do.

Blue Shield and Blue Cross plans customarily are affiliated when they serve the same area. In some places, the plans are combined; in others, where only one or the other exists, it serves both purposes. In seven states, however, the two are in competition.

INSURANCE COMPANIES

Nearly a thousand insurance companies in the United States write health insurance.[11] In 1964,

[10] Blue Cross Association, "The Availability and Financing of Nursing-Home Care," BLUE CROSS REPORTS, April–June 1964, pp. 13–14.

[11] SOURCE BOOK OF HEALTH INSURANCE DATA 1965, *op. cit.*, p. 51.

they paid almost half of the total benefits for hospital, surgical, and medical expenses, plus an additional amount for loss of income due to illness.[12] The majority of health insurance business is in group policies, and some companies offer health benefits as part of a package including life and other kinds of insurance that constitute fringe benefits to employee groups.

Insurance companies operate under state laws and regulations concerned mainly with their solvency and ability to meet their contractual obligations, and to some extent with protecting the interests of the policyholder. The state of New York, for instance, requires that a person insured under a group policy be allowed to convert to an individual policy when leaving the group and specifically prohibits refusal to renew individual policies because of deterioration in health. The laws vary considerably among the states, as does enforcement.

Commercial group hospital insurance usually provides for reimbursement of daily hospital room and board charges up to specified amounts for specified periods, and of charges for other hospital services also up to a specified amount. Group surgical coverage as a rule provides reimbursement for various procedures according to a schedule set forth in the policy, and "regular medical" coverage takes care of physician visits and other services up to a maximum set for each illness. Benefits for dependents may be at a lower level than for employed heads of families.

Major medical insurance usually covers almost all illness expense except for dental care, health appraisals, eye refractions and glasses, and hearing aids. Contracts provide that the policyholder will pay his own bills up to a stipulated "deductible" amount and also a certain percentage of subsequent expenses as coinsurance. That is, he pays the first $50 or $100 or a larger sum, and 20 or 25 per cent of further costs; maximum benefits are set for either any illness, a year, or life, usually at a high figure. Major medical policies may be either supplementary to or integrated with basic health insurance.

Although commercial policies provide for reimbursement to the insured person, usually he may assign benefits to the hospital or physician, who will then be paid directly by the company.

Individual health insurance written by insurance companies chiefly covers hospital and surgical expense only. Benefits are lower, there are usually restrictions regarding preexisting conditions, and policies may be refused to persons considered to be poor health risks. Although many policies can be cancelled if the company no longer considers the insured a good risk, some states prohibit cancellation within the term of the policy, and some companies offer policies that cannot be cancelled or are guaranteed renewable.

INDEPENDENT PLANS

In the country as a whole, some 800 independent plans provide for prepaid hospital or medical care or both for specified groups of people.[13] The largest total enrollment is in employee-employer-union plans, financed almost entirely by employers under agreements reached through collective bargaining. Other plans are sponsored by communities or consumer groups, and a few are private group clinics sponsored by physicians. In a small number of communities, dental societies conduct prepaid dental service plans.

A considerable number, but not all, of the independents are prepaid group practice plans. That is, services are given by one or several groups of physicians practicing together and are paid for, entirely or in major proportion, by prepaid fees of subscribers. Most of the people enrolled are in employee or other groups, although the plans usually provide for individual members as well.

Hospitalization in prepaid group plans is arranged in various ways. The largest independent, the four Kaiser Health Plans on the West Coast with over a million enrollment, operates its own hospitals. The Health Insurance Plan of Greater New York, also very large, does not itself provide hospitalization but requires that its members be covered by Blue Cross or other hospital insurance. Group Health Association

---

[12] *Ibid.*, p. 44.

[13] *Ibid.*, p. 50.

of Washington, D.C., provides hospital care by contract with Blue Cross.

COMPARISON OF PLANS

The variations in coverage among different plans within any one type are almost endless. Agnes Brewster points out that there are some 78 different provisions for maternity and infant care coverage in Blue Cross–Blue Shield plans, "and hosts of others among commercial policies —this for a nearly uniform health condition requiring quite standardized services."[14] Minimum coverage under insurance company policies can be much lower than under the Blue plans, but under both types of insurance, policies are written for broad coverage. However, neither of these major types provides for the amount of service outside the hospital that prepaid group practice plans do, and in most contracts such preventive services as health appraisal and immunization, encouraged in group practice, are specifically excluded. This difference affects relative rates of hospital utilization, perhaps because the ready availability of service outside the hospital makes some hospital care unnecessary, or because coverage of such service affects the physician's choice of where treatment will be given.

The Federal Employees Health Benefits Program offers an interesting comparison. The program covers over 6 million people under either (1) a governmentwide Blue Cross–Blue Shield service plan (high and low options), (2) a governmentwide insurance company indemnity plan (high and low options) and a number of other indemnity plans, or (3) any of several group practice plans. Enrollees in the Blue Cross–Blue Shield plan averaged 82 per cent more hospital (for nonmaternity care) days per 1,000 than did enrollees in group practice plans in the first three years of operation.[15]

The administrative costs of the three main types of health insurance vary considerably. Operating expense averages 5.9 per cent of premium income for the Blue plans, 22.4 per cent for the insurance companies, and 7.6 per cent for independent plans.[16]

An initial "deductible" amount and coinsurance, or a proportion of further covered costs, must be paid by the insured under many insurance company plans and under Blue Cross plans for major medical expense insurance (but not for basic hospital insurance). These provisions are the subject of considerable disagreement. Advocates of the deductible consider it a deterrent to unnecessary use of services, whereas opponents believe it discourages people from seeking medical care early when it can often be preventive. Coinsurance has been defended as requiring an indication of personal responsibility by the insured,[17] but it is sometimes criticized as not allowing him to anticipate the extent of his medical expenses.

Free choice of physician is believed by most of the medical profession to be important to the doctor-patient relationship. Whereas under plans of either the Blues or the insurance companies, the insured may select any licensed physician, under prepaid group practice he is limited to the physicians in the group. Many people who use group practice, however, feel that the choice of a family physician can be made more competently by his peers than by a layman and prefer the medical group's judgment to their own. The validity of this position depends, of course, on the group's ability to attract colleagues of high quality. In this regard, it has been pointed out that:

The most important consideration for physicians who take pride in practicing good medicine is the setting that prepaid group practice can offer. They can secure consultations with qualified specialists and laboratory tests for their patients, without concern about the financial burden imposed on the patient. And they can continue to extend their own knowledge of medicine through close association with qualified specialists who are not competitors. Physicians in solo practice can, and often do, sustain similar close working relationships with their colleagues. However, when such association occurs,

[14] Agnes W. Brewster, "Achievements of Voluntary HEALTH INSURANCE," BULLETIN OF THE NEW YORK ACADEMY OF MEDICINE, December 1965, p. 1293.

[15] George S. Perrott, "Federal Employees Health Benefits Program, III. Utilization of Hospital Services," AMERICAN JOURNAL OF PUBLIC HEALTH, January, 1966, p. 59.

[16] Reed, "Private Health Insurance in the United States," op. cit., p. 18.

[17] The Foundation on Employee Health, Medical Care and Welfare, Inc., FAMILY MEDICAL CARE UNDER THREE TYPES OF HEALTH INSURANCE (New York: The Foundation, 1962), p. 68.

it is usually through staff membership in a well-organized hospital—again an informal type of group practice through trustee appointment, although, financially, it is not structured as group practice, and for the patient access to the various physicians is tied to economic considerations at each move.[18]

Medical Care Financed by Government

The largest share of government expenditures for personal health services goes for medical assistance to the indigent. In many communities, such assistance is available only to persons who are eligible for other forms of public assistance; in a smaller number of areas, help in payment for personal health service is also given to the medically indigent—people who are able to pay for their other basic needs but cannot manage health bills too.

Medical Assistance Programs

Under the Social Security Act as it has been amended over the years, the federal government, using a matching formula based on the state's per capita income, contributes toward state programs of public assistance in four categories: Old Age Assistance, Aid to Families with Dependent Children, Aid to the Blind, and Aid to the Permanently and Totally Disabled. The legally established objectives of these programs are to help the elderly attain self-care, to help the blind and the disabled attain either self-support or self-care, and to help parents or relatives to attain "maximum self-support and personal independence consistent with the maintenance of continuing parental care and protection."[19] In terms of these purposes, aid for personal health care is an exceedingly important part of total assistance. Federal matching funds could always be used to increase payments to persons receiving assistance in order to permit them to pay for health services, but in 1950 the Social Security Act was amended to allow direct payment by government, in behalf of a recipient, to the vendor—physician, drug-gist, hospital, nursing home—who provided medical service. Since 1956, funds have been earmarked for this purpose in each of the four categories of assistance, and in 1965 vendor payments for medical care under these categories amounted to about $65 million a month.[20] Federal regulations require that statewide standards be established for these programs.

In addition to the categorical assistance programs, which are federally assisted, local areas provide general assistance or relief, financed from state or local funds or both, to persons not in the four federally aided categories. Although most of these programs theoretically provide medical aid for persons receiving maintenance assistance and even sometimes for the medically indigent, in many areas such help is very limited, and its availability varies from one community to another. Even the categorical programs with federal matching funds are often inadequate to meet needs.

Since 1960, federal aid has been available to states for programs of medical assistance to elderly people with low incomes but not eligible for Old Age Assistance. Under the Kerr–Mills bill, which established these provisions, the participating states have determined not only the services covered but the levels of income and assets permitted for eligibility. Restrictions on the basis of length of residence in a community (which are usual in assistance programs) are prohibited. Vendor payments for Medical Assistance to the Aged, in which most of the states now participate, were about $50 million a month in 1965.

At the local level, the various categories of medical assistance programs are usually administered by the welfare department, which not only determines eligibility but also makes fee-for-service arrangements for care. In a few states, such arrangements are made through contracts with Blue Cross and Blue Shield, or with the state medical society. In New York City, some Old Age Assistance recipients receive comprehensive medical care from the Health Insurance Plan of Greater New York under a contract with the welfare department. In some states, the health department adminis-

---

[18] *Ibid.*, p. 178.

[19] Pearl Bierman, "Meeting the Health Needs of Low-Income Families," THE ANNALS OF THE AMERICAN ACADEMY OF POLITICAL AND SOCIAL SCIENCE, September, 1961, p. 108.

[20] See monthly issues of WELFARE IN REVIEW, Table 12.

ters some part of the program, although for the federally supported programs this must be under agreement with the welfare department, because the federal government cannot legally deal with more than one state agency in a public assistance program.

In addition to care provided under vendor arrangements by private physicians, voluntary hospitals, nursing homes, and others, some state or local governments operate general hospitals or clinics for the indigent. Any one person may receive part of his care from a private physician under vendor payments, another part in a public clinic, and, if necessary, care in a public hospital.

The intent of the legislation in providing vendor payments for medical care was to keep medical service to the economically depressed within the mainstream of community medical services. However, the actual situation is often such that the objectives of medical assistance cannot possibly be met. In some areas, physicians are not paid for service, on the premise that they do not want to be paid; in these circumstances, hospitalized patients may receive good care, but outside the hospital it may be unavailable to them. It is common practice for welfare departments to reimburse hospitals at a set daily fee that is considerably short of actual cost, and the number of days a patient may be hospitalized is also often limited. When funds are short, medical assistance may be confined to instances of advanced or life-endangering illness, and conditions of lesser urgency go untreated until they become critical.

The Social Security Amendments of 1965, which established under Title XVIII, health insurance for the aged, or medicare, also provide under Title XIX the means for states to establish comprehensive medical assistance programs.[21] Under this program, which will replace all the vendor payment programs in the various assistance categories by January 1, 1970, the federal share of medical expenditures is increased, no maximum is set on the amount to be matched in each state, and extension of aid to the medically indigent is encouraged.

The program will include all persons now receiving maintenance assistance in the four categories. If a state provides medical assistance for the aged not receiving Old Age Assistance, it must also include the medically needy among the blind, families with dependent children, and the disabled who are not receiving assistance. Eligibility requirements must be consistent for all categories of recipients and may not exclude persons over 65 years old or, after July 1, 1967, persons under 21. Durational residence requirements are also prohibited. The income test must be flexible enough to take into account the effect of large medical bills. Deductible amounts and cost-sharing are prohibited with respect to inpatient hospital service, and for the elderly needy the deductible under the hospital insurance provisions will be paid. Payment for similar costs of other medical assistance will be related to each person's or family's income and resources.

Under previous legislation, states had to provide only some institutional and some noninstitutional care (the amount was not specified) as medical assistance to the aged, and minimum benefits under other vendor payment programs were not stipulated. Under Title XIX, in order to qualify for federal participation in medical vendor payments a state must have, by July 1, 1967, provided assistance for inpatient hospital services (and specifically reimbursement of "reasonable cost"), outpatient hospital services, other laboratory and X-ray services, skilled nursing-home services for persons over 20, and physician's service (in office, patient's home, hospital, or skilled nursing home). These benefits must be equally available to all individuals in the categories covered.

The new assistance provisions do not directly cover medical assistance for needy persons other than those in the four categories; but because the health insurance provisions will relieve the states of a considerable portion of the present expenditures for medical care of the elderly, they are expected to use these savings to work toward broad coverage of all the medically needy. The law specifically states:

The Secretary shall not make payments under the preceding provisions of this section to any State unless the State makes a satisfactory showing that it is

---

[21] See Wilbur J. Cohen and Robert M. Ball, "Social Security Amendments of 1965: Summary and Legislative History," SOCIAL SECURITY BULLETIN, September, 1965.

making efforts in the direction of broadening the scope of the care and services made available under the plan and in the direction of liberalizing the eligibility requirements for medical assistance, with a view toward furnishing by July 1, 1975, comprehensive care and services to substantially all individuals who meet the plan's eligibility standards with respect to income and resources, including services to enable such individuals to attain or retain independence or self-care.[22]

As Dr. Ellen Winston, Commissioner of the Welfare Administration, stated:

If States take full advantage of the new legislation, they can go a long way toward assuring that people who need but cannot afford health and medical care will receive it. They can do so in four stages: covering first all the people—and there are over 7 million of them in the nation—who depend upon the public assistance programs for all or some of their basic income; covering next the people in the same general categories who do not need financial assistance for daily maintenance but do need assistance with health and medical bills; then covering all children under 21 in any family with an income too low to allow for medical expenses, and finally picking up, at the States' own expense, any remaining medically needy persons aged 21–64.[23]

MEDICAL CARE UNDER PUBLIC HEALTH OR RELATED PROGRAMS

In earlier chapters, the medical care aspects of a number of public health and related programs were mentioned. Care may be provided in state hospitals, such as those for tuberculosis or mental illness, or in a general hospital run by local government. It may be included in the programs of local health departments—medical or dental clinics, public health nursing, and other field services—supported by state and local tax funds and often in part by federal grants.

Although some health department services traditionally classified as preventive aspects of medical care, such as screening or immunization, may be available to anyone in the community, persons who receive medical treatment are usually subject to a means test or residence requirements, or both. Furthermore, treatment is often limited to a particular disease or condition and is not available for the patient's continuing health problems. That is, in a venereal disease clinic he can receive treatment for syphilis, but not for glaucoma if he suffers from that, too.

Maternal and child health and crippled children's services, for which federal aid has long been available, were also the subject of provisions of the 1965 Social Security Amendments. The authorized amounts of federal grants for these purposes were increased, and a five-year program of project grants was instituted to provide comprehensive health care and services for children of school or preschool age, particularly in areas with a concentration of low-income families. The grants will be made to state health departments (or through them to local health departments), to state crippled children's agencies, to medical schools, or to teaching hospitals affiliated with medical schools and will cover up to 75 per cent of the cost of the projects. Services will include screening, diagnosis, and preventive services for all children in the area and treatment, correction of defects, and both medical and dental aftercare for children in low-income families.

Persons eligible for vocational rehabilitation services may receive medical care either in rehabilitation facilities operated by the state rehabilitation agency or in other facilities under contract with that agency.

Under the federal legislation in support of community mental health centers, the services must be available to the entire community, to both those who can afford to pay for them and those who cannot. Care of patients unable to pay will undoubtedly be financed from a number of sources, including aid available to persons on assistance and to the medically indigent, but special funds are being set up for this purpose in some areas. Centers receiving federal assistance may not impose residence requirements.

MEDICAL CARE FOR SPECIAL BENEFICIARIES

The federal government assumes responsibility for medical care of several groups of citizens and either provides it in government facilities or purchases it in behalf of these beneficiaries. Members of the Armed Forces, including the

---

[22] Public Law 89–97, 89th Congress, H.R. 6675, July 30, 1965, Title XIX, Section 1903 (e).

[23] "Medical Assistance Under Title XIX of the Social Security Act," WELFARE IN REVIEW, August, 1965, p. 15.

Commissioned Corps of the Public Health Service, are entitled to such care, as are their families. Some 400,000 American Indians and Alaskan natives, primarily those living on reservations, receive medical care from the PHS.

Veterans are entitled to medical care for any condition related to their service in the Armed Forces. It is provided to them chiefly in more than 150 VA hospitals (and on contract in other hospitals), in nearly 100 outpatient clinics, and in a number of homes where chronically disabled veterans receive domiciliary care. For conditions unrelated to service, veterans can receive care in veterans' hospitals if they are unable to pay for hospitalization.

Philanthropy and Other Resources

The pattern of philanthropic support of medical care has changed considerably with the increase in government support of service for the indigent and the growth of health insurance. The greatest proportion of care provided without charge by physicians is in fulfillment of their obligations as members of hospital staffs. Although many physicians still provide some care outside the hospital free or at reduced fees, this form of personal philanthropy is much less common than it used to be, especially in cities.

The philanthropy of a voluntary hospital can be measured in several ways. One, of course, is the free care given outright to inpatients who cannot pay. This is also less usual today, because much of what would once have been free care is now covered by insurance or is purchased under assistance. However, in areas where the welfare department pays a fee that covers only part of daily costs, the hospital perforce contributes the remainder. If the hospital is not endowed sufficiently, the difference becomes an unwitting philanthropy of the paying and insured patients, whose daily charges must be increased to make it up. A similar situation exists with regard to persons who enter the hospital as paying patients but who are unable to pay their bills—often because of inaccurate understanding of their insurance coverage. Mrs. Brewster points out that, since maternity benefits are often less complete than other insurance coverage, hospital accounts receivable are especially high for obstetrical cases.[24]

Outpatient service of hospitals may be provided without charge or for nominal fees when it is not financed by welfare payments. At least part of physician services are usually contributed by members of the staff, and other expenses are assumed by the hospital.

In many communities, voluntary health or social agencies provide or help to pay for personal health services for persons not able to finance them themselves and not eligible for government assistance. Some of these agencies direct their aid toward care for children or other special population groups. The visiting nurse associations provide a broader service, ordinarily free to those who cannot pay. Churches and fraternal groups may help their members to meet medical bills, and of course families and friends are sometimes able to give or lend the money needed.

Although employee health services provided in industry cannot be considered philanthropy, they are financed neither by the employees nor by government. As described in Chapter 9, such services are usually concerned with work-related conditions and with emergency care but occasionally include health examinations for some or all employees. Under state workmen's compensation laws, major employers are required to provide medical care for workers injured on the job or sometimes for those with illnesses found to have resulted from the job. Cost of such care is usually covered by insurance carried by the employer with a commercial company or a state insurance fund.

Health Insurance for the Aged

The provisions of Title XVIII of the Social Security Amendments of 1965, Health Insurance for the Aged, have many qualities of private insurance but are financed in part by the federal government. The hospital benefits under Part A are paid for through an additional tax on earnings (plus a contribution from the general fund of the Treasury to cover benefits for the

---

[24] Agnes W. Brewster, *op. cit.*, p. 1293.

Table 11

Hospital Insurance Benefits for Persons over 65 Under Social Security Amendments of 1965

Service Covered	Extent of Coverage	Deductible and Coinsurance Paid by Insured
Inpatient hospital services		
General hospital	90 days per spell of illness[1]	$40 per spell of illness; $10 a day for 61st through 90th day. First 3 pints of blood must be paid for
Mental hospital	90 days per spell of illness; lifetime limit of 190 days	
Tuberculosis hospital	90 days per spell of illness for services that will improve patient's condition or render it noncommunicable	
Care in extended care facility	100 days per spell of illness, if admitted within 14 days after discharge from hospital following at least 3 days' stay	$5 a day for 21st through 80th day
Diagnostic services in hospital outpatient departments	Unlimited, but each study confined to 20-day period	$20 per diagnostic study and 20% of remaining cost
Home health services	100 visits per year beginning within 14 days after discharge from hospital following at least 3 days' stay	None

[1] A spell of illness is defined as beginning on the first day of hospitalization and ending after 60 days spent outside a hospital or extended care facility.

uninsured) and therefore are, like Old Age and Survivors' Insurance, part of the Social Security program.

The supplementary medical benefits under Part B are financed through a premium paid by participants, set at $3 a month until 1968, and matched by an equal contribution from the general fund of the Treasury. The insured under this part pay a deductible of the first $50 of covered expenses incurred annually, and coinsurance of 20 per cent of other costs.

ELIGIBILITY

Almost everyone in the United States 65 years of age or over is eligible for hospital insurance (Part A). Persons covered by Social Security or Railroad Retirement are automatically included. Other citizens of the United States or resident aliens who have lived in the country more than five years and are 65 years old are entitled to hospital benefits if they apply for them. Persons covered by Federal Employees Health Benefits are excepted. Participation in

supplementary medical insurance (Part B) is open to any citizen or five-year resident alien who applies within specified enrollment periods.

BENEFITS

The services paid for under Part A, hospital insurance, and the costs to the insured, are summarized in Table 11. The deductible amounts will be subject to adjustment by the Secretary of Health, Education, and Welfare, beginning in 1968, according to a formula stated in the Act.

Payment for inpatient hospital services specifically excludes medical or surgical services and private-duty nursing. An extended care facility is a nursing home or rehabilitation center that provides skilled nursing care under medical guidance and fulfills a number of other requirements spelled out in the regulations.

To receive payment for home health services, a patient must be confined to his home and under a physician's care. The services must be furnished or arranged for by a qualified home health agency under a plan established and reviewed periodically by a physician. Home, in this context, need not be a private residence but can be a home for the aged, a boarding home, or a nursing home not classified as an extended care facility. Services covered may include part-time or intermittent care provided by or under the supervision of a registered professional nurse; physical, occupational, or speech therapy; medical social services under the direction of a physician; part-time or intermittent services of a home health aide; medical supplies (other than drugs and biologicals) and use of medical appliances. If the home health agency is affiliated with an approved teaching hospital, services of interns and residents may be included. Any of the services can be provided on an outpatient basis at a hospital or extended care facility, but transportation cost is not covered.

Under Part B, supplementary medical insurance, the benefits include payment for physicians' services[25] wherever they are furnished; diagnostic tests; X-ray or radioactive isotope therapy; ambulance service; various supplies and appliances and rental of equipment; and home health services under an approved plan (not necessarily following hospitalization). Specific limitations are placed on payment for psychiatrists' services outside the hospital, not to exceed $250 annually, and on home health services, limited to 100 visits in any calendar year.

ADMINISTRATION

The Act provides that reimbursement to providers of service under hospital insurance will be based on reasonable cost, and under medical insurance, on reasonable charges. For hospitals this will mean payment at daily rates based on actual expense, including such costs as depreciation and interest. For physicians, it will mean payment of usual charges for services in accordance with prevailing local charges.

---

[25] The Act defines a physician as a doctor of medicine or osteopathy licensed by the state, or a doctor of dentistry or dental or oral surgery, licensed by the state, but only with respect to surgery related to the jaw or any structure contiguous to the jaw or the reduction of any fracture of the jaw or any facial bone.

The Act also provides for arrangements between the Secretary of Health, Education, and Welfare and the states under which a state agency—the health department in all but two states—is designated to certify hospitals, extended care facilities, and home health agencies as providers of service according to federal standards and to give consultation to providers to help them maintain standards. The states are paid for these services.

The Secretary has an agreement with each hospital, extended care facility, and home health agency but works through state agencies and private organizations nominated by the providers as fiscal intermediaries in administering the hospital insurance program. The medical insurance part is administered through private insurance carriers who determine reasonable costs or charges, receive and disburse funds, determine compliance, and perform other administrative functions. Central records on each participant are kept by the Social Security Administration under conditions that permit eligibility to be checked promptly.

In order for many elderly people with low incomes to profit by these insurance plans, Title XIX of the law authorizes federal aid to states electing to pay the deductibles for eligible persons who qualify for Old Age Assistance or Medical Assistance for the Aged, as well as their premiums for medical insurance.

IMPLICATIONS OF MEDICARE

The 1965 health insurance legislation does not provide for complete financing of medical care for elderly people. The deductibles and coinsurance still constitute a considerable outlay of personal funds. However, the insurance does prevent catastrophic expense for most aged people. Various private insurance carriers have developed plans for supplementary insurance to help meet immediate costs, and participants have been urged not to cancel their private health insurance. For many older people who might have had to request assistance for their medical bills, the program means being able to manage independently. As the states take advantage of the opportunity to base medical assistance for the elderly on the insurance plan, people who cannot afford private insurance or would not be accepted for it can benefit fully from Medicare even if they cannot meet the personal costs.

The stipulation in the bill that reimbursement for hospital service both under assistance and under Medicare will be in terms of reasonable cost will undoubtedly have an effect on the quality of care services, both for the elderly and for the community. As Dr. William H. Stewart, Surgeon General of the Public Health Service, has said:

The community has the opportunity to develop a truly comprehensive system of quality medical services; for full-cost reimbursement means that the federal government is willing to pay for quality. In this sense, this legislation underwrites the development of quality services.[26]

The fact that services will have to be developed is an essential point. Neither the new health insurance nor the expanded medical assistance program, nor indeed most private health insurance plans actually provide personal health services. They help to pay for such services, but if a service is not available in the community, it cannot be purchased at any price.

In recognition of the general lack or inadequacy of home health services, Congress appropriated funds late in 1965 for formula grants to the states to help establish such services. The PHS is giving technical assistance and consultation in administering the grants. Under Medicare, hospitals and extended care facilities must have systems for utilization review, a means of assuring that these facilities are not wasted or used unwisely. Such general provisions will help, but every community that expects its citizens to profit from the new legislation will have to assess its own resources for medical care and undertake the readjustments and additions that are called for. In some areas, the role of public hospitals that in the past have been used solely for care of the indigent will have to be reevaluated if their occupancy rates are significantly affected by people's increased ability to pay for private care.

Elements of Good Medical Care

In its *Guide to Medical Care Administration,* the American Public Health Association[27] describes four basic elements of good medical care: accessibility, quality, continuity, and efficiency.

If good medical care is to be accessible to persons when they need it, they must be able with relative ease to go to a doctor, clinic, or hospital when they recognize their need. Further, the help they receive there must serve as what the APHA *Guide* calls a "portal" to a comprehensive range of services, which must therefore be available in sufficient quantity to meet needs.

Quality of care services cannot be measured only in terms of the professional competence of those who provide them but must include acceptability to the people needing service. Community leaders may not be able to make judgments about the competence of professional practitioners, but they can encourage the exercise of such judgment by those who are able, and they can help to ensure quality. They can also create the acceptability of, indeed the demand for, quality on the part of the consumer public by sharing their own understanding and bases of measurement.

Good medical care must have continuity; that is, it must be focused on persons, not diseases, and provide for all of the patient's health needs. And it must be available to him, if possible, through one source—family physician, group practice, or clinic—that takes responsibility for directing him through the complex of services he may need during his life. Patients who must start all over again in every encounter with medical care receive neither satisfaction for themselves nor the full benefit of professional skill.

Efficiency in medical care is important to consumers in terms of their own economic resources and to society in terms of total economic resources. Both individuals and society have many competing demands on their resources, and none, including medical care, has so high a value as to justify waste. Because the

---

[26] From address delivered at the Annual Conference of State and Territorial Health Officers, Washington, D.C., November 17, 1965.

[27] Volume I, CONCEPTS AND PRINCIPLES (New York: The Association, 1965) .

trained talents and skills of medical and related personnel are in short supply, any approach to services for all the population must be made through the most productive use of such talents and skills.

Although increasing support in financing medical care comes from the federal government, organization and administration of facilities are local functions and can be worked out in a variety of ways according to individual community preferences and patterns. But the responsibility of community leadership is clear. As W. J. McNerney, President of the Blue Cross Association, has said:

... the distribution of health services cannot be left to the interactions of a free market for many reasons. The nature of the services rendered, people's attitude toward, and knowledge about, them, and the essential lack of economic competition involved— all seriously compromise most, if not all, of the major elements of the market mechanism.

Controls, whether the result of competitive forces or of regulation, are a matter of degree. No one is calling for complete control or for none. The degree and method must be applied sensitively to the economic forces under discussion. The health field is in the throes now of making basic decisions in its area. Under rising costs and with increasing public unrest, planned controls must be substituted for competitive controls by someone.[28]

[28] "The Future of Voluntary Prepayment for Health Services," NEW ENGLAND JOURNAL OF MEDICINE, October 21, 1965, p. 911.

15

Some Health-related
Social Problems

HEALTH and social problems are profoundly interrelated. They occur together, and either can cause or result from the other. Poor health, illness, or disability affects a person's personal independence and often his economic status; it may alter his feeling about himself and his actions toward other people as well as theirs toward him. On the other hand, social disorganization or inadequacy not only exposes people to disease but also places them under stress that increases their vulnerability to illness and disability.

Modern concepts of the health and medical sciences increasingly include the social aspects of all health problems. In Chapter 1 and elsewhere a number of social and behavioral attitudes toward illness and death and toward smoking, for example, were cited for their effects on utilization of preventive and other health services and for their importance to the promotion of good health. Although social factors affect all health problems and programs, there are particular kinds of health problems that can be resolved only through intensive combined social and health activity; for example, the health problems related to poverty, aging, alcoholism, and drug addiction and abuse.

Poverty

The unusual incidence of disease and prevalence of ill health among the poor have been recognized for centuries, and some of the earliest organized health services were undertaken to alleviate the suffering of the "sick poor." Illness and early death were accepted as the lot of the poor, ameliorated only by charity. Early in the nineteenth century, factors in the physical environment of the poor—noisome sanitary conditions, extreme overcrowding, and wretched working circumstances—began to be blamed for poor health. The germ theory of disease, when it was developed, as well as increased understanding of nutrition, threw further light on the matter.

Today, there is growing realization that the reasons for higher rates of morbidity and mortality among the poor are not subject to simple explanation. Some conditions prevalent in lower income groups are not known to be communicable nor to result from inadequate nutrition—coronary heart disease and cancer, for instance—and this fact suggests at least a question about the role of psychological and social stress. Other health problems that have been significantly reduced in higher income groups through preventive care and treatment are still serious among the poor, both because services are not readily available to them and because the "culture of the poor" places relatively little value on prevention or early treatment.

Like everyone else, poor people have their own strengths and weaknesses, and their life situation affects them in different ways. However, social research has shown that although in the United States today people with continuously low incomes comprise a number of different culture groups, they have in common certain conditions of life that often affect their attitudes in similar ways.[1]

The lives of the poor are limited and without variety in experiences and associations. They do not habitually read newspapers or listen to news or educational programs. They rarely participate in civic or political organizations and are generally isolated from the social structure of the community through which services are developed and needs answered. For those who are poor and also belong to minority ethnic groups, the isolation may be greater.

Lack of skill and education among the poor makes them helpless to affect their working situations, sometimes prevents their working at all, and hinders them from finding ways to improve their ability. Living in a society that values and continually displays the material rewards of success that are largely unavailable to them, the poor strongly desire the material comforts of which they are deprived. They assume that people who have things look down on those who have not, and frequently they look down on themselves. With incomes that at best take care only of immediate needs and confronted more often than the prosperous with emergencies, the poor live in a continual state of insecurity.

Such conditions of life are bound to discourage positive efforts to preserve health and prevent illness. Not only lack of health education but a fatalistic feeling of powerlessness to change destiny—based on life experience—make poor people unresponsive to preventive health services. As Irelan has stated:

When a household is operating with a minimum of material necessities, first aspirations are for concrete, physical improvement—for a better place to live, for more and better household equipment, even for some luxuries.[2]

Before it becomes important to the poor, ill health must become serious illness, cause severe pain, or interfere with their ability to earn a living.

When people in low-income groups do become ill, they seek help only for the immediate problem, and this is what they usually receive. But because their lives are limited, poor people are uncomfortable with strangers and unable to accept impersonal relationships simply in terms of a function performed. Middle-class health workers are at least cultural strangers to the poor, and they expect to deal with them in terms of professional function. The detachment that professional people must maintain, perhaps for the sake of their own equanimity, does not suggest to the low-income patient a personal interest in or concern for him. The patient's faulty understanding of health and his lack of rapport with the advisor make him unresponsive. If the physician or other professional person refers him to another clinic or resource, such action strengthens his impression of professional indifference, or indeed rejection.

The geographic location of facilities often means expenditure of both time and money and may take the patient into an unfamiliar neighborhood where he is uneasy. Financial arrangements, even when assistance is available, are complicated. A person who qualifies for free care or payments for care while he is on maintenance assistance must often manage on his own when his income increases even slightly. He or members of his family may be eligible for some services in certain locations but not for others. And in any case, he must experience the process of eligibility determination, which is in itself a humiliation. There is little in the total situation that enables the person with low income to establish a continuing relationship with a physician or even a clinic that would encourage his acceptance of service.

The often uneasy relationships of professional people and the poor in long-established health services for the indigent have been understandably difficult for both. Because they believe in the powers of science and know the value of prevention, health professionals are frustrated by the fatalism and unresponsiveness of the poor. Referral and separation of services, which are difficult for even knowledgeable patients to cope with and baffling to the unsophis-

---

[1] See Lola M. Irelan and Arthur Besner, "Low-Income Outlook on Life," WELFARE IN REVIEW, September, 1965, pp. 13–17; and Lola M. Irelan, "Health Practices of the Poor," WELFARE IN REVIEW, October, 1965, pp. 1–9.

[2] *Ibid.*, October, 1965, p. 5.

ticated, are recognized by professionals as a sometimes necessary result of specialization. Inadequacy of service has been usual for so long that health workers almost take it for granted. In efforts to catch up, they have become inured to patients waiting in clinics and to short and unsatisfactory encounters with them. In one community, where a special project made possible a considerable increase in public health nursing staff, one nurse reported that it was the first time in her professional life she had been able to give patients the time they needed.

Many health workers are able to achieve mutually confident relationships with some poor people, and it is they who are most acutely aware of the futility of piecemeal attempts to relieve the burdens of poverty. The doctor in a chest clinic may be able to inspire the loyalty of his patients and keep them coming regularly until their treatment is completed; but knowing the pressures of their lives and that it is their personal friendship for him rather than real understanding that keeps them following his recommendations, he cannot be confident that they will remain well when he discharges them. The public health nurse who climbs the tenement stairs to visit a mother with a new baby wonders how much of her counsel she can realistically expect will be followed by a woman with little education, meager income, and a view of life that does not reach beyond a day. Such professional people know that promotion of health may well depend on the cure of other ills of poverty.

Until recent years, improvements in health services for the indigent have been chiefly in projects dealing with a particular disease, a special population group, or even a type of service. Thus a community might have excellent clinic service for persons with tuberculosis, a high-quality public pediatric clinic, or outstanding home nursing service—but even the beginning of comprehensive care for people unable to pay for it has been almost nonexistent. In recent years, a number of communities have sought solutions to the problem through such arrangements as hospital-based centers providing outpatient care and home services, or the contract in New York City with a prepaid group prac-

tice plan. Even these, however, have chiefly been concerned either with patients with chronic disease or those in older age groups.

The national movement addressed to improving the circumstances of the poor, centered in the Office of Economic Opportunity, has provided a means of incorporating health service in community action programs with broad social aims. The Community Action Program for Child Development Centers, usually called Operation Head Start, is an example.[3] Aimed at interrupting the "cycle of poverty" in which children of poor parents ultimately become parents of poor children themselves, Head Start programs provide health, education, and welfare services for children of preschool age in neighborhood centers, with up to 90 per cent financing from federal funds.

In the Head Start program groups of children are small, so that individual attention is possible; warmth, sympathy, and understanding are considered essential qualities of staff. Children who receive health services in such a setting, sometimes for the first time, are helped to accept them as a part of normal living rather than something strange and frightening, and the same impression can be given to parents. The aim is to provide a medical evaluation for each child, with necessary screening and laboratory tests; a dental assessment; immunizations that have not been completed; a psychological evaluation; and arrangements for correction of defects found and necessary follow-up care. Whenever possible, parents' presence at evaluation is encouraged, health counsel is offered, and recommendations are discussed in detail.

Other health projects of the Community Action Program include neighborhood health centers in which all existing publicly financed health services are integrated and comprehensive outpatient services can be provided to all members of a family at a single, conveniently located building. Centers are staffed and operated by professional persons, but neighborhood residents are involved in such a way as to ensure response to needs of those using services.

---

[3] See Office of Economic Opportunity, HEAD START CHILD DEVELOPMENT PROGRAMS AND HEAD START GUIDES, NUMBERS 1 TO 9 (Washington: The Office, undated).

When highly specialized services or hospital services are necessary, the center arranges for them, and the patient's health center physician maintains continuity of care. Eligibility determinations are not made at the time of need or request for service. There is "specific and conscious emphasis on a continuous, personalized relationship between the responsible health personnel and the patient."[4] So far as feasible, the same physician treats all members of a family. The neighborhood health centers may very well provide patterns that can be used in planning similar services for people in the general population.

Other programs of the Office of Economic Opportunity have aspects directly concerned with health. Young people who apply for the Job Corps, many of whom have never been to a doctor or dentist before, receive medical examinations, and those accepted not only get medical and dental care but also have better meals than they have usually been accustomed to and participate in physical fitness programs aimed at improving their health and strength. Some of the Vista volunteers are engaged in health-related activities, from helping to improve rural sanitation to working with mental patients. Certainly whatever the poverty program can accomplish in overcoming the isolation of the poor and their belief that they cannot affect their own lives will contribute to their health and their responsiveness to health services.

The changes in federal support for medical care for the indigent under the Social Security Amendments of 1965, discussed in Chapter 14, will provide a financial basis for comprehensive services for the poor. In encouraging provision for the medically indigent, people with low incomes but not on assistance, this legislation also enables a simpler and less forbidding system than is now usual.

Changes in the situation generally prevailing for the poor will not be effected quickly. Estimates made by several different methods place the number of people living below the poverty line at nearly one-fifth of the population.[5] But the direction of present programs offers new hope for ultimate solution. As the 1964 *Annual Report of the Council of Economic Advisers* pointed out, it would be perfectly possible for the majority of people, by taxing themselves an amount less than 2 per cent of the Gross National Product, to supplement the incomes of the poor to bring them to the minimum for decent living.

But this "solution" would leave untouched most of the roots of poverty. Americans want to *earn* the American standard of living by their own efforts and contributions. It will be far better, even if more difficult, to equip and to permit the poor of the Nation to produce and to earn the additional $11 billion, and more. We can surely afford greater generosity in relief of distress. But the major thrust of our campaign must be against causes rather than symptoms. We can afford the cost of that campaign too.[6]

Aging

Today's major health problems strike older people more heavily than the young. People over 65, who now make up almost 10 per cent of our population, are twice as likely to have chronic conditions as those who are younger and more than twice as likely to be limited in their activities. They go to the hospital more often and average about twice as long a stay for each hospitalization. They make up most of the population of nursing homes. The rate of admission of this age group to mental hospitals is about two and one-half times that of the population under 65, and they account for about 30 per cent of resident patients in mental hospitals.

Obviously, old people need more health services than other people, especially more time, not only in hospitals but with health workers outside the hospital. In New York City, while providing medical care under Old Age Assistance and Medical Assistance to the Aged

---

[4] Office of Economic Opportunity, Community Action Program, Health Division, THE NEIGHBORHOOD HEALTH CENTER (Washington: The Office, 1966, mimeographed).

[5] Mollie Orshansky, "Counting the Poor: Another Look at the Poverty Profile," SOCIAL SECURITY BULLETIN, January, 1965, p. 11, Table 1.

[6] (Washington: Government Printing Office, 1964), pp. 77–78.

through a prepaid group plan which otherwise served employed people, it was found that:

> . . . it took longer to provide all types of assistance to these patients than to others. Faulty memories and language barriers sharply increased the time for history-taking, and the difficulties in dressing and undressing made the taking of chest X-rays, for example, far more time-consuming.[7]

The New York project also indicated another special need.

> Since they were not employed people, and usually without heavy family or household responsibilities, the visits to the medical centers became important events. They often came hours before appointments and remained to gossip with their friends.[8]

For an elderly person living alone or with a husband or wife who is also elderly, illness can be a catastrophe that disrupts his whole life. Even if the trouble is not permanently disabling, inability to get around and care for himself during the prolonged convalescence imposed by his age may very well mean that institutionalization is necessary—and too often it lasts the rest of his life. Sadly enough, many old people in dread of such an eventuality put off seeking care that might prevent it, in the hope that what they don't know won't hurt them. Medical care and services in hospitals, in extended care facilities, or in the home, all aimed at restoring function as far as possible, are needed to help old people keep as much independence as possible. Services and programs related to chronic disease, described in Chapter 11, have particular application to the elderly.

Although medical and other health services can do much to relieve health problems of old people and lessen disability, real prevention usually must begin before the fact of old age. However, the kind of health service in middle age that would prevent or minimize illness and the deterioration of health in old age is neither widely offered nor eagerly sought. In general both the public and the medical profession place greater value on the treatment of illness than on preventive care—an attitude that is a

continuing obstacle to the achievement of good health in older age groups.

For a group whose median income is about half that of the younger population, the economic burden imposed by increased health problems is great—and in the public mind the health problems of the elderly have come to be equated with economic problems. A series of federal actions, begun in 1935 with the Social Security Act, have been aimed at relieving the situation. The provisions of the Social Security Amendments of 1965 for financing medical care of the elderly, discussed in Chapter 14, will help significantly to resolve the problem.

The financial burden, important as it is, is only one of the social circumstances aggravating the health problems of old people. The loneliness that brought the New York patients to the clinic ahead of time is a very common feeling among the elderly; and although it may be compounded by illness, it is also experienced by many who are well. Older people who once lived active lives and would still be capable of doing so may find themselves with no significant role to play in the active world, and they feel useless and rejected. Low morale keeps them from feeling well, provokes exaggerated concern with receding strength or competence, and by discouraging activity may actually contribute to physical disability.

There is no doubt that, in support of adequate and understanding health care, elderly people also need interests and occupations to promote their physical and mental well-being. Full- or part-time employment would often be the best answer for those able to work, but present-day practices regarding hiring and retirement tend to hinder employment of people over 65. Volunteer work is stimulating and rewarding to many older people, and some of the community programs supported by the Office of Economic Opportunity offer new opportunities for the elderly to participate in community service. The Vista program, for instance, imposes no upper age limit for its full-time volunteers. Golden Age or senior citizens' centers operated in many communities under a variety of auspices offer companionship and activity as well as a place where old people can feel they belong.

---

[7] Edwin F. Daily, "The Health Insurance Plan—New York City Welfare Department Project," AMERICAN JOURNAL OF PUBLIC HEALTH, September, 1963, p. 1357.

[8] *Ibid.*

Good living arrangements for elderly people are vitally important to their health. But old people too often live in dilapidated, unsanitary houses or apartments, in boarding homes that provide little except food and shelter, and in nursing homes that are seriously inadequate. Changes in the pattern of American family life and increased urbanization have tended to minimize the role of grandparents and other elderly relatives as family members. Fewer old people now live with younger relatives, and many live alone.

The elderly are as individualistic in their tastes and desires as young people, if not more so, and a variety of approaches is needed to provide them with satisfactory housing and living arrangements. Some, prefer living in their own homes if possible. Others can be happy in apartments or housing projects, some of which either are planned especially for older people or include modified units to accommodating old people with physical incapacities. Homes for the aged, if they provide for needs beyond bed and board, are congenial settings for retirement. And for those whose physical or mental condition restricts their ability to care for themselves, nursing homes or personal care homes may be the solution.

When assisting local communities, a number of programs of the Department of Housing and Urban Development give priority to projects for the elderly and make special provisions for them. In public housing, construction and equipment cost ceilings are higher for units built especially for old people. Low-cost loans are available to nonprofit sponsors (church groups, labor unions, fraternal and civic clubs, and the like) of housing for older people with incomes too high for public housing but too low for the private housing market. Mortgage insurance can protect private loans for other housing for older people in a wider income range. Of course, old people who live in urban renewal areas are eligible for help in renovating their property and for adjustment payments if relocation is necessary.[9]

The Older Americans Act of 1965 established an Administration on Aging in the Department of Health, Education, and Welfare to serve as a clearinghouse for information, provide technical assistance to the states, and administer several grant programs. The Act authorized formula grants to the states for the purposes of community planning and coordination of programs for the aging, demonstrations, and training of personnel. Funds may also be used for establishing or expanding the programs of multipurpose centers for older persons, furnishing recreational and other leisure-time activities and informational, health, welfare, counseling, and referral services. Project grants for study, demonstration, and evaluation are also authorized as well as grants for training personnel to carry out programs for older people.[10]

A majority of the states have agencies concerned specifically with aging—either independent units or parts of state departments. Their budgets are generally low, however, and their activities limited. In addition, some state welfare departments have staff specialists on aging, and a number of gerontologists have been assigned to state or local health departments by the Public Health Service. There is general need for coordinated planning among the numerous agencies, both public and voluntary, whose activities affect elderly people.

Alcoholism

Although experts and workers in both health and social fields generally recognize alcoholism as a disease, the view of it as a form of willful misbehavior still persists to a certain extent in the eyes of the general public and the professions. However, there is no disagreement about the magnitude of the social problems associated with alcoholism—dependency, family disruption, accidents, and crime and delinquency.

CHARACTERISTICS

The World Health Organization defines alcoholism as follows:

---

[9] See PROGRAMS OF THE DEPARTMENT OF HOUSING AND URBAN DEVELOPMENT (Washington: Government Printing Office, 1965).

[10] See "Older Americans Act, P.L. 89–73," in HEALTH, EDUCATION, AND WELFARE INDICATORS, August, 1965, pp. 41–56.

. . . a chronic illness that manifests itself as a disorder of behavior. It is characterized by the repeated usage of alcoholic beverages to an extent that exceeds customary dietary use or compliance with social customs of the community and that interferes with the drinker's health or his economic or social functioning.

Definitions by other groups are similar, but the American Medical Association refers also to the alcoholic's degree of dependence on alcohol, and the National Council on Alcoholism to his powerlessness to stop drinking. Alcoholism is not simply a matter of the amount of alcohol consumed. Indeed, some people drink a great deal but do not become alcoholics. It involves inability to refrain from drinking and a progressive increase of the amount of alcohol consumed.

The cause of alcoholism is not known, although there is increasing belief among experts that, like other diseases, it has multiple causes. Some evidence implicates physiological factors such as defects of metabolism. Social conditions are thought to contribute to some cases, but psychological or emotional inadequacy is widely believed to be involved, and many methods of treating alcoholism are predicated upon this belief. Whether emotional disturbance is cause or effect, treatment for emotional problems often brings about remission of alcoholism.

The objective of treatment for alcoholism is to help patients achieve and maintain abstinence from drinking and return to normal living. This objective is accomplished in various ways according to individual cases. Sometimes it begins with emergency hospital care for acute intoxication. When a case has been evaluated, outpatient treatment may include medicines, psychotherapy, or membership in Alcoholics Anonymous. This group provides a form of treatment and rehabilitation, offering the patient association with and support from others who share and understand his situation. Social, and sometimes vocational, rehabilitation is necessary to help patients maintain their sobriety and live normally. People whose alcoholism is of long standing may need residential care in a special facility, such as a farm or halfway house, as a step toward return to community living;

for some, vocational rehabilitation requires a sheltered work situation. The majority of alcoholics who recognize their problem and seek treatment for it can succeed in remaining sober. Those who resist treatment or do not accept the idea that they must never drink are less likely to recover. Authorities on alcoholism recognize that some alcoholics may require a lifetime of sheltered living in order to maintain sobriety.

According to expert estimates, 5 million people in the United States are alcoholics, and 1 in 15 of those who drink becomes an alcoholic. Although both men and women become alcoholics, the rate among men is several times higher than among women. The problem is somewhat greater in cities but occurs in rural areas as well. The stereotype of the alcoholic as a skid-row bum is common, but actually such people make up only a small percentage of the total. Many alcoholics are employed full-time, although their rate of absence is high. Some 200 industries consider alcoholism a sufficiently important problem among their employees to include treatment and rehabilitation services for alcoholics in employee health programs.

In spite of the growing acceptance of alcoholism as a health problem, the most dramatic measurement of it as a community burden is still found in court statistics. About half the total arrests made by local police are for offenses related to drinking, and police are said to spend about three-fourths of their time dealing with people who have been drinking excessively.[11] Some of the programs aimed at control of alcoholism have been instituted by the courts.

APPROACHES TO CONTROL

Before alcoholism began to receive attention as a disease, the most common community facility for dealing with it was jail. (Unfortunately it remains so in many areas.) Some alcoholics or persons with brain disorders caused by alcohol were admitted to state and local mental hospitals, and for the wealthy there were private sanitariums that accepted patients with drinking

[11] Joan K. Jackson, "Alcohol and Crime," in Raymond G. McCarthy (ed.), ALCOHOL EDUCATION FOR CLASSROOM AND COMMUNITY, A SOURCE BOOK FOR EDUCATORS (New York: McGraw-Hill Book Company, 1964), p. 169.

problems. Most physicians did not consider alcoholism a medical problem, and general hospitals usually would not admit alcoholics, even for treatment of acute intoxication or delirium tremens.

Beginning in the 1930s (after the prohibition amendment was repealed), three new approaches to the problem dealt with alcoholism as a disease. The Yale Center of Alcohol Studies (now the Center of Alcohol Studies at Rutgers) began to examine the subject scientifically, demonstrating treatment techniques and carrying on research and training for laymen as well as professionals.

Alcoholics Anonymous, founded in 1935, is the alcoholics' approach to control of their disease through a fellowship whose purpose is to help themselves and each other to stay sober. There are now more than 6,000 AA groups in this country, many of which have associated Al-Anon groups made up of families and friends of alcoholics. Alcoholics Anonymous is highly respected for its success in helping to rehabilitate many thousands of alcoholics.

The third approach was by the National Council on Alcoholism, a voluntary health agency formed in 1944. Its purposes are similar to those of other voluntary agencies devoted to the control of one disease: information, education, research, and promotion of services. It represents the point of view of the interested public. In about 75 communities, local organizations affiliated with the Council have been established.

Today, research on alcoholism is carried on by a number of groups in addition to the Rutgers Center. The federal government conducts or supports research in the PHS, the Office of Vocational Rehabilitation, and other constituents of the Department of Health, Education, and Welfare, and a great many study or demonstration projects operate in local communities.

Treatment facilities are also more widely available, but progress is slow. Many chronic alcoholics are still arrested repeatedly, jailed for a few days, and go back to their drinking when released. In spite of the success of the few treatment programs in jails or prisons and of treatment substituted for sentencing by the courts in some areas, drunkenness is still dealt with as a

misdemeanor, rather than an illness, in most communities—with no effect on the chronic inebriate. A decision of the United States Court of Appeals for the Fourth Cirucit held that a chronic alcoholic suffers from a sickness and cannot be prosecuted for public drunkenness.[12] This decision can be expected to bring about new approaches to the problem in many communities.

In 1956 the American Medical Association issued an official statement to the effect that alcoholism is an illness and urged general hospitals to accept alcoholics for treatment; in 1957 the American Hospital Association took similar action. Although this guidance has not been accepted by all physicians and all general hospitals, it has significantly changed the potential for community action by providing, for example, support in opposition to zoning ordinances that prevent hospitals from accepting alcoholic patients.

The majority of states now have programs for the control of alcoholism, carried on by either independent agencies or units of other state agencies. Although relatively few local communities have comprehensive programs, a number are including alcoholism services as part of their Community Mental Health Centers. (See Chapter 11.)

Today, the prevention of alcoholism depends to a great extent on education about it, along with early diagnosis and prompt and effective treatment. All states require by law that alcohol education be provided in the public schools. Unfortunately, there is sometimes little direction given as to the nature of this education, and teaching is often more hit-or-miss than factual. In some states, departments of education are beginning to cooperate with health agencies, alcohol control agencies, and other organizations in planning improved programs of alcohol education designed to cultivate realistic attitudes and to encourage youngsters to make intelligent decisions about drinking.

A comprehensive alcoholism program requires cooperation from many different agencies and resources in the community. There must be

---

[12] *Driver* v. *Hinnant*, 356 F.2d 761 (4th Cir. 1966).

provision for hospital care and outpatient treatment, either in a clinic or doctor's office; psychotherapy; AA membership; social casework, and social and vocational rehabilitation. The courts and the police are inevitably involved, as well as industry, with regard both to alcoholism among its employees and to policies about hiring treated alcoholics. All the means of public information and education should be used to present the facts about alcohol and to reinforce public acceptance of alcoholism as a disease from which most sufferers can recover. Local schools must face the sometimes difficult task of providing factual information to school children. The clergy is important, as well as the Salvation Army and settlement houses.

Leadership for so complex an undertaking may be difficult to find among the disparate interests involved. The community then must itself find a way to relate its resources in combating this health problem that is also a serious social problem.

At the federal level, a coordinated program for prevention and control of alcoholism was initiated in the Department of Health, Education, and Welfare in October 1966. A National Advisory Committee on Alcoholism was appointed to advise and guide the Department, with representatives of medicine, social work, labor, industry, vocational rehabilitation, education, law, and civic organizations concerned with alcoholism. A National Center for the Prevention and Control of Alcoholism was established within the National Institute of Mental Health of the PHS. The center will conduct activities in both basic and clinical research, education and prevention, consultation and training, and support of local programs, and other constituents of the Department will also expand their activities related to alcoholism.

Drug Addiction and Abuse

Narcotic drugs are used in medical practice for the relief of pain. When such a drug is used habitually, it may result in both physical and psychological dependence upon it. Although a large number of drugs can produce this result, the use of heroin or morphine (opium deriva-

tives) is the most common form of narcotic addiction in this country.

Addiction may follow administration of drugs for medical reasons, but it results much more often from taking drugs for relief from the pressures of life, for thrill-seeking, as an outcome of social relationships with others who use drugs, or a combination of these reasons. A large proportion of narcotics addicts live in slums under conditions of severe social and economic deprivation.

Some authorities feel that the potential for becoming addicted exists only in certain people, and that others will not misuse narcotics even when given the opportunity. The reason is believed to be due to personality differences, susceptibility to drug addiction being sometimes a symptom of personality disorder.[13]

In addition to physical disorders and often physical debility, addiction causes anxiety about the availability of the next dose; this concern eventually supersedes everything else in the addict's life. Most crimes ascribed to addiction are committed to get drugs, and most of them are larceny or robbery rather than crimes of violence. (Antisocial people who take drugs may commit violent crimes, but these crimes are considered to be a part of a pattern of life established before they used drugs.) To support their habit, many addicts sell narcotics.

When a narcotics addict does not get the amount of drugs he needs—and this amount usually gradually increases—he suffers physical symptoms of withdrawal. It takes about a week or 10 days for him to lose most of his physical dependence on the drug. After that, he is restless and irritable for several months, and his psychological dependence continues. Prolonged rehabilitation, sometimes including psychotherapy, helps overcome psychological dependence. Unfortunately, however, addiction is difficult to cure permanently. A large proportion of patients, even those receiving proper medical care

---

[13] Nathan B. Eddy, et al., "Drug Dependence: Its Significance and Characteristics," BULLETIN OF THE WORLD HEALTH ORGANIZATION, 1965, pp. 721–33. See also U.S. Department of Health, Education, and Welfare, Public Health Service, NARCOTIC DRUG ADDICTION (Mental Health Monograph No. 2 [Washington: Government Printing Office, 1963]) , p. 5.

and rehabilitative services, relapse when they go back to normal life—or at least to the life that was normal for them before they were treated.

Both federal[14] and state laws regarding narcotics are strict. Addiction itself is not a crime; but the possession or sale of drugs by unauthorized persons is subject to severe sentence under both state and federal laws, and even physicians are supervised in prescribing addictive drugs. Under these circumstances, addiction is dealt with in local communities chiefly as a crime rather than as a health problem. There is considerable difference of opinion about the wisdom of such stringent measures and the severity with which they are applied. All opinion is in favor of strict laws dealing with the illegal sale of narcotics by persons not addicted, but there is feeling in both the medical and legal professions that criminal law is neither appropriate nor successful in combatting the addict's problem.[15]

Major resources for treatment of drug addiction have been, for many years, two federal hospitals operated for this purpose by the Public Health Service in Lexington, Kentucky, and Fort Worth, Texas. Addicts who are federal prisoners are treated there, as well as many persons who enter voluntarily. Several states now have hospital facilities for long-term treatment of addiction. In a number of the larger cities, where drug addiction is a problem of considerable proportion, clinics where treatment is voluntary and confidential have been established by health departments or hospitals. In order to discourage relapse, programs of aftercare are being set up, including clinics, halfway houses, and counseling and other social services.

The consequences of drug addiction are serious, often tragic. Treatment is difficult and often only temporarily successful. For these reasons, efforts toward prevention assume added importance. A Public Health Service Mental Health Monograph states the following:

Addiction can be prevented (a) through mental health programs to reduce the number of susceptible persons; (b) through continued efforts to reduce the availability of illegal drugs; (c) through treatment that reduces the number of addicted persons, since these bring the drug and the susceptible person together; (d) by improving the conditions in the deprived neighborhoods where addiction is most common.[16]

The need for joint social and health forces in preventive efforts is apparent.

The misuse of drugs other than heroin and morphine appears to be increasing and is the cause of considerable public concern. One such drug is marihuana, an intoxicant defined by federal law as a narcotic. People who use this drug, many of whom are young people who smoke it in social groups, do not develop tolerance to it or physical dependence on it; however, in unstable people its use may contribute to the development of psychosis or may lead to heroin addiction. Marihuana is under federal narcotic control, as is cocaine. Once a frequent drug of addiction, cocaine is rarely used today, either in medical practice or for hallucinatory experiences.

Barbiturate drugs are extensively used in medical practice for their sedative effect. Under a physician's direction, small amounts may be taken by patients, even regularly over a long period of time, without harm to the central nervous system. However, uncontrolled amounts taken at frequent intervals can produce addiction especially in persons with the personality disorders that make them ready subjects.

Next to opiates, barbiturates are the most common addicting drugs in this country. They produce intoxication, with symptoms similar to those of alcohol. Sudden withdrawal of barbiturates from an addict is exceedingly dangerous and may be fatal.

Another group of drugs, the amphetamines, are stimulants, sometimes prescribed in small doses for medicinal purposes. However, their use in excess, sometimes for the feeling of exhil-

---

[14] Federal laws regarding narcotics are administered by the Treasury Department, Bureau of Narcotics.

[15] See "Report of Joint American Medical Association —American Bar Association Narcotic Committee," in American Medical Association, NARCOTICS ADDICTION, OFFICIAL ACTIONS OF THE AMERICAN MEDICAL ASSOCIATION (Chicago: The Association, 1963).

---

[16] NARCOTIC DRUG ADDICTION, *op. cit.*, p. 21.

aration or excitement they produce, can bring on various physical symptoms, excessive nervousness, and even hallucinations—sometimes with tragic results. Although the amphetamines are not addictive in the sense that narcotics and barbiturates are, their use can become habitual. They are also sometimes used in combination with barbiturates, and true addiction to the latter follows.

Neither the amphetamines nor the barbiturates are controlled under federal narcotic laws, but the 1938 Federal Food, Drug, and Cosmetic Act required that they be sold only on a physician's prescription. Illegal traffic in these drugs became so extensive, however, that in 1965 about half the total nine billion doses manufactured were sold illegally. The 1965 Drug Abuse Control Act, administered by the Food and Drug Administration, requires strict accounting at each point of the production and distribution of these and other drugs; pharmacists are required to retain their purchase invoices and records of prescriptions filled. All such records must be made available to FDA inspectors on request.

Recently a great deal of public attention has been given to LSD, an hallucinogenic drug that is not legally available except as an "investigational new drug," even though it was first synthesized over 20 years ago. In spite of extensive experimentation, the effect of LSD is unpredictable, especially so when its potency and purity are unknown, as is often the case when produced illegally. Instances of suicide and prolonged psychosis following intake of LSD have been documented in the medical literature. Under the Food, Drug, and Cosmetic Act, LSD can be used only by qualified research investigators carrying on studies that have been reported to the Food and Drug Administration. All production and sale of the drug for other purposes is illegal and subject to action by the FDA.

The social components of the drug abuse problem are complex, and correction will require not only legal controls and education programs, but also continuing exploration of the individual motivations and group pressures leading to behavior that is antagonistic to personal and social health.

Necessary Community Health Services

Problems of poverty, aging, alcoholism, and drug addiction and abuse are related in the sense that they frequently affect the same populations. Their significance to communities, however, is greatest in the evidence they give to support the definition of health as not just the absence of illness but a state of total well-being. They illustrate the physical, environmental, social, psychological, and economic factors that combine to affect man's well-being throughout his life and thus undeniably affirm the need for comprehensive health services, not only for the populations considered here but for all people. Moreover, such problems call attention to the need for a broad definition of health services and for both physical and temporal organization that will complement and interact with other community activities influencing the well-being of people.

Health services *in* a community as well as those provided *by* a community are just one of many forms of intervention comprising man's progressive adjustment to life. Under whatever auspices they are offered, they are maximally effective as preventive, curative, and rehabilitative processes when they are planned, organized, and provided in concert with other activities. A principle or definitive guideline for concerted social intervention cannot be specified. Experimentation and innovation will be required until such time as a complete understanding of human development is attained—if that time ever comes. But at the very least, the time is past due for acknowledgement of the complex ramifications of health and for commitment to a comprehensive approach to man's betterment.

Part Four

Health Status Measurement
and Goal Setting

16

Health Records
and Statistics

In 1662 John Graunt of London published the first statistical analysis of health data in his observations on bills of mortality, or parish interment records. From this analysis of birth and death records, vital statistics evolved as the major method of assessing the health of populations. In the past few decades, death rates have declined in developed countries; social aspirations have demanded reduction of ill health as well as extension of life, so that measurements of the incidence and prevalence of disease and its resulting disabilities are becoming more important as one of the new devices continually sought for statistical assessment of health status.

At the same time, as in other fields of endeavor, records, reports, and statistics have become important tools of management in the health field. As health programs become more extensive and complex, these records also grow in number and in the uses made of them. New techniques of collecting and processing data have greatly added to the volume and utility of health information.

The three types of health records and statistics—vital statistics, morbidity data, and service records—are not mutually exclusive. Vital statistics are used for administrative purposes, and data from service records contribute to measurement of morbidity and other aspects of health status.

Vital Statistics

By modern definitions, vital records include certifications of birth, death (including fetal death), marriage, divorce, and such related legal actions as adoptions, changes of name, and marriage annulments. All vital records have legal status as permanent documents, but birth and death records are of special concern to the health professions. Marriages and divorces are related to family health, and records of them are now considered to be part of community health data.

In all states registration of birth and death is required by law. Procedures vary among the states, but in all except one the state health department, or a unit of it, is designated to administer and maintain vital records. (Some large city health departments are similarly designated.) [1] Local registrars are appointed in various areas of the state, with whom birth and death certificates are filed. The registrar makes sure that certificates are complete and accurate before forwarding them to the state. Registrars may be local health officers (or persons on health department staffs) but are sometimes other local officials or specially appointed individuals. When they are not directly connected with the health department, routine procedures must be devised so that the health department has current access to birth and death certificates.

---

[1] U.S. Department of Health, Education, and Welfare, Public Health Service, WHERE TO WRITE FOR BIRTH AND DEATH RECORDS, UNITED STATES AND OUTLYING AREAS (PHS Publication No. 630-A-1 [Washington: Government Printing Office, revised, 1965]).

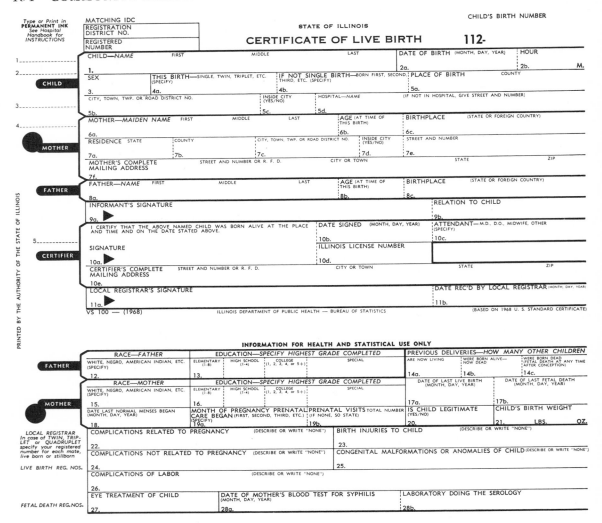

FIGURE 16. *Certificate of Live Birth, state of Illinois*

BIRTH RECORDS

The magnitude of work involved in administering birth records is increasing, not only because of population growth, but because the identifying information on birth certificates is needed for an increasing number of purposes by a larger proportion of people. Proof of age or citizenship is required by young people to obtain working papers or drivers' licenses, to register for the draft, sometimes to marry without parental permission, or to register the first time they vote. Parents may need such proof for their children when they enter school or if it becomes necessary to identify them as dependents or legal heirs. The increasing number of people who travel in foreign countries must have birth certificates to obtain passports.

Elderly people need such demonstration of eligibility by age for social security and other retirement provisions. Vital statistics offices had a sudden surge of business in 1965 and 1966 when thousands of people over 65 not receiving social security payments needed birth certificates to show their eligibility for Medicare. Staffing of vital statistics offices should be adequate to provide prompt service to the public; in large registration districts, it may be necessary to provide for temporary staff increases during certain times—in the spring, when plans for school and travel are being made, or in case of an event such as the beginning of Medicare.

Birth certificates are prepared and filed by either the attending physician or the hospital where the birth occurred. The form usually contains space for certain medical information that can be omitted in copies made for identification purposes. However, this information is especially important to health authorities, because it indicates such problems as prematurity (low birth weight), birth injury, congenital malformation, conditions present during pregnancy, conditions of labor, methods of delivery, and illegitimacy. In some areas, notation is made of the extent of prenatal care received by the mother and whether she was under public or private care.

On the basis of birth certificates, health departments can initiate action to provide services for mothers and children, especially those in need of special attention. In some communities, letters are sent routinely to all mothers of newborn babies, reminding them of the care their infants need and that they themselves should have. Public health nursing visits may be scheduled to all families of children born under public medical care or in all instances in which conditions of birth were abnormal for mother or child.

Periodic compilation of data from birth certificates provides measures of maternal and child health needs in the community and of progress in meeting them. It also can be used, with estimates of inward and outward migration in the community, for planning of schools.

DEATH RECORDS

As a legal document, a death certificate is needed first by the funeral director who has legal responsibility to file it in order to obtain a burial permit. Like birth certificates, death certificates contain specific identifying information that may be necessary to families in claiming insurance or other survivors' benefits or in settling estates. Such information is also used in some areas by various government agencies; for instance, by boards of elections or county clerks to remove names from voting rolls or jury lists, or by the state motor vehicle bureau, in order to discourage illegal traffic in drivers' licenses.

The health department is interested in the immediate cause of death as well as underlying causes and conditions that contribute to death. Such data should be entered by the physician who signs the certificate, in terms consistent with the International Statistical Classification of Diseases, Injuries, and Causes of Death.[2] This document provides standard terminology for description of diseases and causes of death, agreed upon by the signatory nations of the World Health Organization. Its use enables accurate compilation of statistics that would be impossible if diseases and causes of death were described differently by different physicians or in different areas.

Although health departments should have other means of obtaining information about communicable disease in the community or causes of death that they have responsibility to control, death certificates are sometimes their first notification and may call for prompt action. Fetal deaths (stillbirths, reported on special forms) and deaths of young infants are evidence, along with the medical information on live birth certificates, of need for special prenatal services. In many communities, deaths of mothers in childbirth are reviewed by the health department, in cooperation with maternal mortality committees representing the medical profession, as a means of improving maternal care before and during delivery.

Analysis of data from all death certificates is usually made monthly and summarized annually by the local health department. Such statistics provide one measure of community health status and help to pinpoint needs and trends by age, race, sex, and geography as well as by cause of death. Analysis made by the state health department, to which birth and death statistics are usually forwarded monthly, as well as the annual analysis made by the National Center for Health Statistics, serve similar purposes from a broader point of view.

---

[2] World Health Organization, INTERNATIONAL CLASSIFICATION OF DISEASES: MANUAL OF THE INTERNATIONAL STATISTICAL CLASSIFICATION OF DISEASES, INJURIES, AND CAUSES OF DEATH (Geneva, Switzerland: World Health Organization, 1957), 2 Vols.

Morbidity Data and Other Measures

The required reporting of cases of specified communicable disease[3] provides a rough measure of the amount of such illness occurring in the community. It is not an exact measure; some cases are relatively mild and do not come to the attention of physicians, and reporting of those that do is frequently incomplete. However, in most communities data on the incidence of reportable diseases are more nearly accurate than data on other causes of illness or disability, with the possible exception of conditions associated with childbirth.

Some of the communicable diseases that cause significant amounts of illness in the population are not reportable; influenza and the various respiratory conditions described as the common cold are examples. In order to be alert to the possibility of epidemics of such diseases, health officers often have an intelligence system that informs them when an unusual number of cases is occurring. Increased absence from schools and industries or extraordinary attendance at clinics or doctors' offices may be indications. Usually through informal relationships in the community the health officer is made aware of such trends and can estimate the effect on the population.

Information about the extent of chronic disease, accidents, and mental illness has become increasingly necessary for the administration of community health services, and considerable attention has been given to the problem of obtaining such information. Various methods have been used and tested. There are a number of useful sources of data in most areas, but each has certain limitations, so that none is a sufficient measure in itself.[4]

As health insurance coverage has been extended to large groups of the population, a great deal of information has become available on the nature of illness for which claims are made. It is confined, of course, to data on the experience of those covered and the conditions covered and may be further limited by the extent of coverage. With the advent of Medicare, in which almost all persons 65 years of age and older participate, communities will have an important new measure of the amount of illness in almost all members of an age group especially subject to chronic disease. Health insurance data, however, can give information on incidence and prevalence only of illness for which care is sought. With the exception of programs of health appraisal undertaken by some of the prepaid group insurance plans,[5] insurance records do not provide any index of undiagnosed or unattended illness.

Hospital admission or discharge records, if they can be related to a defined population served, also make an exceedingly important contribution to the overall picture of a community's health problems.

While hospitalized illness represents only a small fraction of all illness receiving medical care and there is undoubtedly great variation from one economic or social stratum to another in the types and severity of cases that are hospitalized, nevertheless, hospitalization rates by diagnosis, age, sex, and other characteristics of the population are much in demand for use in planning for facilities, services, and personnel.[6]

Records of the physical examinations given in some industries may provide estimates of the health status of the examined population, although they may omit reference to conditions not affecting ability to work. Usually they produce incidence rates for conditions that suggest the possibility of disease rather than rates of diagnosed cases. Selective Service examination data are sometimes used as measures of the health status of young men, but criteria are determined by the needs of the military and are not necessarily consistent among different boards or from one time to another. Health referral programs under way in many communities offering treatment or rehabilitation services to men rejected for the draft for medical reasons can increase knowledge in this area.

---

[3] See Chapter 7.

[4] See U.S. Department of Health, Education, and Welfare, Public Health Service, National Center for Health Statistics, ORIGIN, PROGRAM, AND OPERATION OF THE U.S. NATIONAL HEALTH SURVEY (PHS Publication No. 1000, Series 1, No. 1 [Washington: Government Printing Office, 1963]), pp. 28–31.

[5] See Chapter 14.

[6] ORIGIN, PROGRAM, AND OPERATION OF THE U.S. NATIONAL HEALTH SURVEY, *op. cit.*, pp. 29–30.

Screening programs for casefinding purposes are potentially a good measure of the prevalence of diseases for which tests are made if the programs include follow-up to diagnosis. Casefinding data reflect more nearly the actual prevalence of disease than do insurance or hospital admission data. Of course, no screening program reaches all the people toward whom it is directed, and there is no way to determine whether rates of disease among those not participating are comparable to those participating. Furthermore, the practicability of mass screening for any particular condition depends on an available test that is reasonably inexpensive and simple to apply and that neither has too many false positive results nor overlooks too many cases by false negatives. The number of diseases for which there is such a test is not extensive.

In attempts to find satisfactory measurements of illness and health and their effect on populations, household interview surveys have found many supporters. The broadest and best known of these is the interview survey of the National Center for Health Statistics in which information has been collected since 1957 from a sample of households statistically representative of the nation's civilian noninstitutional population. Data from the national survey cannot be assumed to be representative of localities smaller than major geographical areas. However, the experience accumulated by the National Center for Health Statistics in conducting the survey can be very useful to communities considering such programs locally.

There are many possibilities for variation or bias because of different interviewers, and the nature and arrangement of questions asked can also affect the validity of answers. Quality control procedures and continual adjustment and improvement of the survey design help overcome these problems as well as those related to the person interviewed—the length of time he can recall episodes of illness or disability and the difference in his ability to answer questions about himself and about others in the family. With these safeguards, the interview of household members can elicit information about "the circumstances of illness or injury and the resulting action taken by the person, such as going to bed or seeing a physician."[7] The diagnostic information obtained, however, depends on whether or not a physician was consulted and whether the respondent is able, or indeed willing, to report the physician's diagnosis. It is generally recognized that interview data will not provide dependable information about actual diagnoses, for which health examination procedures are necessary.

The National Health Survey also conducts health examinations on a limited sample of the population. Although their content is far from exhaustive and the procedures are expensive, they cover a wider population range and are generally more objective than industrial or Selective Service examinations. However, an examination given only once "cannot provide diagnoses of the many conditions which require repeated and continuous observation and tests before they can be identified."[8]

None of the presently developed techniques enables a single, feasible, valid measure of general morbidity in a community. The use of mortality rates will obviously no longer suffice; indeed, reduction of death rates may very well mean increase in the prevalence of chronic diseases or in rates of disability due to accidents. To determine the community's health status, systematic collection of data from many sources is necessary as well as the exercise of professional judgment in estimating their significance.

Service Records and Statistics

An efficient record system is as important for the planning, operation, and evaluation of health activities as it is for any other field. It must serve a number of necessary purposes with the least possible expenditure of scarce professional time, and it must be continually adapted to meet new requirements of growth and change.

---

[7] *Ibid.*, p. 17. See also Commission on Chronic Illness, CHRONIC ILLNESS IN THE UNITED STATES, VOL. IV, CHRONIC ILLNESS IN A LARGE CITY, THE BALTIMORE STUDY (Cambridge, Mass.: Harvard University Press, 1957), p. 15*ff*.

[8] *Ibid.*

The value of records to the planning and conduct of health activities is contingent upon such records being skillfully analyzed and used in decisionmaking. Programs engaged in record keeping should employ staff people with statistical skills and technique to adequately analyze the available data so that results can be incorporated in further planning.

According to a differentiation that is sometimes made, *administrative records* are considered to be those concerned with activities performed and are a means of supervision and cost analysis, whereas *service records* are concerned with the persons or conditions to which service is addressed. The nurse's daily activity sheet, where she accounts for the expenditure of her time, is thus an administrative record; but the "family folder," often maintained in public health nursing offices to record the services received by families as well as their health status and progress, is a service record.

Actually, in a thoughtfully constructed record system, administrative and service needs are often met by a single record. The sanitarian's report on a swimming pool inspection, for example, may record not only the procedures he followed and perhaps the time it took (although units of time are often obtained in special studies), but also the condition of the pool and whether it meets standards.

When an agency's records are analyzed, the resulting statistics must show not only the amount of effort and money expended, but also the results they produced. Thus, a health department should be able to say that in a given period of time in its food sanitation work, not only were so many inspections, laboratory tests, and other actions taken, but also, as a result, a particular increase came about in the number of proportion of various types of establishments complying with standards. Obviously, in order to do this, the program must have baseline data; in the example given, it must know what the rate of compliance was at the beginning. Baseline information is not always easy to determine in ongoing programs or even in new activities and is often especially difficult to obtain in personal service programs. It is not unusual to find service statistics given entirely in terms of the number of people served, without reference to the number service is intended for. However, not only are baseline data necessary for proper evaluation of program effectiveness, but they also provide one of the types of information needed in assessing community health status.

CASE REGISTER

One device commonly used in health departments that serves both administrative and service record purposes is the case register. It is most often concerned with tuberculosis services, although in some communities registers are kept for other purposes, such as crippled children's services. The register technique is especially appropriate in the administration of programs for the control of diseases or conditions requiring continuous services to patients over a long period of time. A record for each patient is entered in the register when his condition is diagnosed, and subsequent entries provide information on his current situation and on services needed and rendered until his record is closed. An efficient register can thus show at a given time the number of persons in the caseload according to their medical status and whether or not they are currently receiving recommended services; it can also produce action lists for nursing visits, clinic appointments, or other services and indicate when these are not met so that additional action can be taken.

A case register is truly effective only when it is a dynamic part of operations. If it is only a file that must be brought up to date on occasion for report purposes, it probably does not justify itself. The introduction of automation in the management of case registers holds considerable promise of increasing their usefulness. Because many areas do not have tuberculosis case-loads of sufficient size to justify automated registers, the PHS is developing a computerized central records service that will help local health departments to provide continuity of service and also enable continual assessment of the effectiveness of tuberculosis control efforts.

HOSPITAL RECORDS

Another area in which a continuing record of individual service is made is in the hospital. Individual patient records, initiated when the patients are admitted, are the responsibility of attending physicians. They describe history, diagnosis, results of tests, treatment prescribed, and continuing assessments of that patient's progress and condition. When the patient is discharged, the record goes to the medical records librarian, who checks it for completeness and abstracts from it the data needed for statistics on admissions, discharges, births, deaths, length of hospital stay, and other matters necessary for hospital reports. The records are also the basis for "medical audit," a process of evaluating the quality of medical care, and for utilization review and examination of the propriety of hospitalization and length of hospital stay. Both of these procedures are conducted by committees of the hospital staff.

In an effort to make routine medical audit and utilization review more efficient and effective, the Commission on Hospital and Professional Activities, sponsored by the American College of Physicians, American College of Surgeons, American Hospital Association, and the Southwestern Michigan Hospital Council, provides computerized statistical service to several hundred hospitals in many parts of the country. Abstracted case records on standardized forms are prepared by medical record librarians in the hospitals and forwarded to the Commission, where processing periodically produces a number of listings, analyses, indexes, and tabulations that facilitate evaluation.[8]

Increasing use of automation, although it is generally agreed not to reduce the expense of health records and statistics, can considerably extend their usefulness. If it is to do so, however, the records system—including every form and report from which data will be fed into the computer—must be carefully designed. The computer expert's quip, "Garbage in, garbage out," is true as well as witty. If a health program is not able to produce appropriate information for storage and analysis and to define useful measurements, the machine cannot be expected to create a meaningful product. This need for appropriate input is not unique to computerized systems, but the speed and

amount of the computer's output emphasizes failures of content to satisfy needs for data and statistics.

Records and the forms on which they are made exist in large variety in many health agencies. Because change in program is so continual, they frequently become outdated, and recording then becomes a routine chore inadequately related to operations. Information is often duplicated unnecessarily, and information about the same person or environment is accumulated in several uncoordinated sets of records. If reports are not a clearly understood aspect of current operations and are not planned in terms of stated objectives, the information required may have a negative effect on staff activities. For example, the worker required to account for the time spent on each activity may very well interpret this as placing a premium on speed, when actually thoroughness rather than speed is needed to accomplish program objectives. A good record system can help to instill a sense of direction in staff activities, but a poor one prevents effective channeling of efforts.

Records and statistics are sometimes disparaged as mere bookkeeping. If the simile is to be used, bookkeeping should be recognized as the means through which a business is controlled and current knowledge about profit and loss is maintained. Individual health agencies need adequate program bookkeeping in order to measure profit in the form of the effect their activities have. Communities urgently need some kind of interrelated system from which they can prepare a balance sheet that shows health status.

Health is obviously not the only aspect of the community's life about which an information system is needed. All the city's departments of government keep records and refer to them for information. City administration, urban renewal, and planning require a composite of information. As automation opened the way for not only speed but sophistication in record keeping and information production, there has been increasing exploration of the possibilities of systems to serve many community purposes in management and planning. The concept of the "data bank," where data are deposited,

9 PROFESSIONAL ACTIVITY STUDY, 1963–65 (Ann Arbor, Michigan: Commission on Hospital and Professional Activities, 1963).

stored, and can be withdrawn, and which also facilitates correlation of divers statistics, is receiving growing attention. Data banks are actually in operation in some communities, and the inclusion of information about health in the community system gives its products an extra dimension. Furthermore, the use by health officials of other community data in planning can increase the potential of setting and achieving realistic objectives. Thus health officials must join with other leaders in the search for ways to accumulate and make use of information from the many sources that exist in the community.

The question of the confidentiality of health records has presented a problem especially with regard to the collection and dissemination of health information. The legal and ethical requirements for confidentiality have never been clearly enunciated and are undoubtedly changing as a result of newer techniques of information handling. Although caution and concern for confidentiality are necessary in organizing and conducting a health information program, confidentiality should not be used to inhibit the utilization and purposes for which the data are collected.

17

Research

HEALTH RESEARCH is often casually equated with research in biology and symbolized by the picture of the white-coated scientist bending over a microscope, peering into a test tube, or inoculating a guinea pig. This limited impression of health research fails to include even the clinical investigations made by physicians in hospitals or the epidemiologic research that directs itself to populations and their environment. It disregards the important bearing of the physical sciences on biological problems.

To remedy the misconception, the term *biomedical science* has come into use to cover the several disciplines of biology, medicine, and biophysics that all contribute to health research. Only gradually, however, are the social sciences becoming accepted as an essential part of the whole. Epidemiology deals with populations and uses some of the techniques of social science, and its historical concern with biological phenomena is now being expanded. But it is still common for scientists engaged in the study of man as a biological being in a physical environment to have a very unscientific blind spot about the science of man as a social being in a social environment. The economist Kenneth Boulding has made the point:

In the natural and biological sciences we have largely eliminated rhetoric as a means of conflict resolution. The attempt on the part of the Victorian bishop, for instance, to resolve the conflicts around evolution by asking Mr. Huxley whether he was descended from the monkeys on his father's or mother's side, we now regard as a piece of impudent stupidity. The devices of the debator are wholly inappropriate in dealing with physical or even biological systems. We have not yet got to this point in social systems, partly because we still operate so largely in this area by folk knowledge, where the skills of the debator may be an important means of solving conflict. Over an ever increasing area of social life one hopes that rhetorical dispute is gradually being replaced by reality testing through improved means of perception of social systems.[1]

The delay in application of the scientific method to social phenomena has resulted in an unevenness of knowledge that interferes with the full use of the findings of biomedical research. The health professions find themselves with a great store of knowledge usable for promoting and maintaining human health, for curing illness or minimizing disability—but with far less than adequate understanding of how to put it to effect. A special subcommittee of the Public Health Service National Advisory Community Health Committee, in a report prepared on Congressional request, described the situation in 1964 in this way:

Forces both within and outside the health field have combined to produce a gap between the volume of scientific knowledge available to the health professions and the community, and the amount of that knowledge actually being used to save lives, prevent disability, and restore human productivity. The cost paid by the Nation for this imbalance is staggering in both humanitarian and economic terms. A major National effort is required, first to bridge the gap and eventually to eliminate it.[2]

[1] Kenneth Boulding, THE MEANING OF THE TWENTIETH CENTURY (New York: Harper and Row, 1964), pp. 72–73.

[2] RESEARCH IN COMMUNITY HEALTH, A REPORT TO THE SUBCOMMITTEE ON THE DEPARTMENTS OF LABOR AND HEALTH, EDUCATION, AND WELFARE AND RELATED AGENCIES OF THE COMMITTEE ON APPROPRIATIONS, UNITED STATES HOUSE OF REPRESENTATIVES (PHS Publication No. 1225 [Washington: Government Printing Office, 1964]), p. 11.

The subcommittee went on to say:

The fundamental elements upon which comprehensive services depend are improved knowledge of methods, manpower, facilities, organization of more effective services, and financing.

Scientific research can be carried out in relation to each of these fundamental elements. Indeed, the national effort to deliver the best in modern health services can succeed only if scientific methodology, which has been so brilliantly successful in developing biological and medical knowledge, is employed imaginatively to the solution of problems related to the institutions and individuals which provide and receive health services.

The Content of Community Health Research

Scientific research is often divided into three categories: (1) basic research, which extends the scope of science, affects its general laws, or changes them; (2) applied research, which provides knowledge needed to accomplish a particular goal; and (3) development, which produces the techniques for application of existing knowledge. The divisions are not clear-cut and have been the subject of much discussion and disagreement.[3] The scientist engaged in applied research sometimes produces basic findings; sometimes he develops techniques. None of the three types can be said to be more necessary, in terms of human benefit, than the others. Certainly basic knowledge is necessary to broaden the potential of science; on the other hand, some basic research has waited on the technical development of instruments—powerful microscopes, for instance, or computers. However, the three classifications suggest the necessary aspects of the production of knowledge for the positive benefit of mankind.

In community health, perhaps the most urgent needs are for applied research and development, building upon existing basic knowledge in the biomedical and social sciences and effecting increased interaction of the various concerned professions. Community health services must be seen as a part of the social system, and increased understanding must be sought in this context.

Examples of research studies now in progress illustrate the point.[4] In one area, a long-term continuous survey of a population is "a start toward systematic focus on the psychological, social, and economic variables in illness and their relationships to health status and use of health services." In another, a project is "investigating patients' views of what information they need to adhere to a medical regimen and the personal factors influencing these views." In order "to determine whether there is any relation between organizational structure and the performance of medical tasks," a project is studying "how medical and paramedical personnel are coordinated and used in the care of ambulatory patients." And another study is comparing the styles of decisionmaking on public health issues in 10 urban communities and constructing a model to show whether these issues are handled similarly to others such as urban renewal, education, or hospital construction.

Some research effort is directed to improvement of techniques. Under a contract with the PHS, a group of consultants representing a number of medical and social disciplines—neurology, psychology, audiology, opthalmology, and others—is evaluating the relative usefulness of various known techniques in arriving at definitive diagnoses of minimal brain damage in children who have learning problems at school.

Community health demonstrations are generally studies or experiments aimed directly at improving particular health services. Some of those supported by PHS community health project grants are directed to the community as a whole. For example, in one demonstration, monthly household interviews of a sample of

[3] See Fritz Machlup, THE PRODUCTION AND DISTRIBUTION OF KNOWLEDGE IN THE UNITED STATES (Princeton, New Jersey: Princeton University Press, 1962), pp. 145–50; Charles V. Kidd, "Basic Research—Description versus Definition," SCIENCE, February 13, 1959, pp. 368–71; and The President's Commission on Heart Disease, Cancer, and Stroke, REPORT TO THE PRESIDENT, NATIONAL PROGRAM TO CONQUER HEART DISEASE, CANCER, AND STROKE (Washington: Government Printing Office, 1965), Vol. II, pp. 143–45.

[4] U.S. Department of Health, Education, and Welfare, Public Health Service, RESEARCH OPPORTUNITIES IN COMMUNITY HEALTH SERVICES AND MEDICAL CARE ADMINISTRATION (PHS Publication No. 1225-D [Washington: Government Printing Office, 1965]).

the population are being used as a means of providing sensitive, up-to-date measures of morbidity, population characteristics, and health attitudes and information in the community. Data collected will be used for planning and evaluating health programs.

Another important subject for demonstration is service of a particular type or for a defined population group, especially various home health services for the chronically ill or aged. Current demonstrations in these fields range from modest extensions of home nursing service to quite complete home health services for a whole medical service area crossing traditional community boundaries. A number of communities are instituting information and referral centers; others are experimenting with the use of volunteers in aid of home care; in still others, innovations such as automated records systems or hospital day care rehabilitation programs are being evaluated.

Research and demonstration for the improvement of hospital care are often considered separately but contribute significantly to the total body of knowledge about community health services. Research on the use of computers as an aid to many procedures in the hospital has important implications for the future of patient care. Other projects deal with management problems, such as personnel needs or methods of measuring obsolescence, or with such technical subjects as bacterial contamination in surgical suites or fire and explosion hazards of static sparks in oxygen tents. Demonstrations in area-wide planning for hospital and related health facilities have had a significant effect on the coordinated development of hospital facilities and related services.

Programs for Heart Disease, Cancer, and Stroke

A new effort to close the gap between the production of scientific knowledge and its application is embodied in the Heart Disease, Cancer, and Stroke Amendments of 1965 to the Public Health Service Act. This legislation resulted from the studies and deliberations of a President's Commission established in 1964 to rec-

ommend measures to combat these diseases, which account for about 70 per cent of all deaths in this country. On the basis of the Commission's recommendations, the law provides for grants

. . . to encourage and assist in the establishment of regional cooperative arrangements among medical schools, research institutions, and hospitals for research and training (including continuing education) and for related demonstrations of patient care in the fields of heart disease, cancer, stroke, and related diseases.[5]

The stated intent is also to afford opportunities for physicians and medical institutions to make available to their patients the latest advances in treatment and diagnosis, and to improve health manpower and facilities generally, without interfering with patterns of patient care or professional practice, or with methods of financing. The program will not superimpose a new system of medical care but will provide for more effective cooperation of existing agencies.

Research in Environmental Health

The possible effects on human health of changes in the environment resulting from technological development and population growth, discussed in Chapters 5 and 6, have created an urgent need for extension of knowledge about the physical environment and man's interaction with it. The environmental health sciences include a variety of disciplines—biology, chemistry, physics, engineering, and medicine. Investigations in this area range from basic research on cell metabolism to technological development of devices for the disposal of refuse.

A number of federal agencies either conduct or sponsor environmental research that relates in some way to human health. However, the environmental programs of the PHS are focused entirely on health implications. In the general environmental health sciences, the PHS makes grants for research in five areas: (1) analysis and measurement of substances in the environment; (2) the fate of environmental agents—

[5] Public Law 80–239, 89th Congress, S. 596, October 6, 1965, Section 900 (a) .

how they get into the environment and how they move about and are changed in it; (3) the biological effects of the agents; (4) the epidemiology of environmental health hazards; and (5) the development of standards and control measures. The PHS also supports the establishment of university research and training institutes in the environmental sciences, where scientists in the several pertinent fields are brought together to study the relationship between men, plants, animals, and their environment.

In addition to such general studies, research in the categories of air pollution, radiation exposure, solid waste disposal, food protection, and occupational hazards is conducted or financed by the PHS.

Financing and Administration

Because health research is widely recognized as potentially benefiting all people, it is considered a suitable object of public support. Although industrial establishments such as pharmaceutical, medical supply, and medical electronics firms spend sizeable amounts of money for the purpose (estimated at $415 million in 1964), the major proportion of medical research and development is publicly financed.

Expenditures by governments and philanthropy (foundations, voluntary health agencies, and so on) for health and medical research grew from $117 million in 1950 to $1.3 billion in 1964,[6] more than an elevenfold increase. During the same period, overall expenditures for health purposes increased from $12.9 billion to $36.8 billion, less than threefold. In 1964, 3.6 per cent of the health dollar went for research, compared to less than 1 per cent in 1950.

As the data presented in Table 12 show, health research expenditures by the federal government, state and local governments, and philanthropy all increased significantly in the 15-year period. By 1964, however, the contribution of philanthropy had become a considerably

[6] Louis S. Reed and Ruth S. Hanft, "National Health Expenditures, 1950–1964," SOCIAL SECURITY BULLETIN, January, 1966, p. 10, Table 5.

Table 12

Publicly Financed Medical Research Expenditures, United States, 1950 and 1964

Source	1950 Amount (in millions)	%	1964 Amount (in millions)	%
Total.................	$117	100	$1,329	100
Total government.....	83	71	1,169	88
Federal............	79	68	1,117	84
State and local......	4	3	52	4
Philanthropy.........	34	29	160	12

Source: Louis S. Reed and Ruth S. Hanft, "National Health Expenditures, 1950–1964," SOCIAL SECURITY BULLETIN, January, 1966, Tables 5 and 13.

smaller proportion of the total; but the contribution of government had grown from 71 to 88 per cent. The largest increase was in federal support, which grew to 84 per cent of the whole. Although total expenditures of state and local government funds for all health purposes are slightly larger than those of the federal government, only about 1 per cent of that total is for research, whereas almost one-quarter of federal health expenditures is now devoted to research. As is usual with national averages of state expenditures, their aggregation does not reflect the expenditures of individual states. Some states spend a large amount for research but others spend practically nothing.

The reasons for the increasing role of the federal government in this area were discussed by a group of economists called together at the request of the President's Commission on Heart Disease, Cancer, and Stroke.

Not only are the States and municipalities short of revenues to discharge all their pressing obligations, but they lack compelling reasons for devoting their resources to medical research. Indeed, the high rate of mobility of the population of this country and the inability to localize the application of medical knowledge means that the benefits of research will not accrue exclusively to the residents of any small area who pay for it.[7]

[7] Herbert Klarman, "Source Paper, Conference on the Economics of Medical Research," in The President's Commission on Heart Disease, Cancer, and Stroke, *op. cit.,* p. 636.

A large proportion of the health research supported by the federal government is conducted in academic institutions and state or local agencies. The National Institutes of Health, for instance, spend only about one-sixth of their total research monies for intramural activities carried on by their own staff; but in fiscal 1965, they made over 15,000 grants totaling more than half a billion dollars to investigators in universities, hospitals, research institutes, health departments, and other organizations in the United States and more than 50 other countries.

In the PHS (both NIH and the other constituents), the most usual way of supporting extramural research is through a research project grant. When an application for such a grant is received, the Division of Research Grants assigns it to the institute or division it relates to and also to a study section for review.

Study sections are advisory groups made up of experts, chiefly from outside the government, in specific scientific specialties. Their function is to review projects for scientific merit and significance, the qualifications of investigators, the adequacy of research facilities, and the appropriateness of the budgets proposed.[8] They approve or disapprove applications, or defer them for further information, and give approved applications priority ratings. From the study section, the application and the study section's findings on it go to the public advisory council or committee serving the division or institute concerned with the project. The membership of these councils or committees represents both the scientific community and the interested public. Applications approved by such groups are forwarded to the designated official for final decision and action.

This detailed procedure, sometimes involving site visits by members of study sections or councils and PHS staff, helps to foster quality in supported research and to protect against bias in distribution of large sums for research. Although administration of other types of PHS research grants—for program projects, training,

or facilities—varies from the pattern for individual research projects, the principle of review by nonfederal experts is also followed.

In addition to research grants, some federal agencies administer grants for studies or demonstrations aimed at initiating improved methods of applying research findings. In the PHS, the several divisions administering demonstration grants carry more of the responsibility for project selection than they do for research grants, although applications are usually reviewed and approved or disapproved by committees with members from outside the PHS.

A third method of federal financing of research carried on by universities or state or local agencies is the contract mechanism, in which the federal agency in a sense purchases research or development services. A contract may be made with a single organization—a university or health department, for instance, or a commercial company—to carry out a particular study or develop a certain technique. Contracts are also the funding mechanism used in collaborative studies. In such studies the federal agency (often with advice from public committees) defines a problem and establishes protocol for its investigation, which is then carried out by a number of hospitals, health departments, or other agencies, under contract. One such venture in cooperative research is a series of community studies conducted by health departments and universities, under contract with the PHS, to assess the amount and nature of human exposure to pesticides and other contaminants and to investigate their possible long-term effects on human health.

Research in Health Departments

Research as an important element of public health programs has been urged vigorously by leading practitioners and teachers in the past decade. In 1960, an official statement on research policy of the American Public Health Association recognized research as "a fundamental activity of public health and a fundamental responsibility of public health agencies."[9]

[8] BIOMEDICAL SCIENCE AND ITS ADMINISTRATION, A STUDY OF THE NATIONAL INSTITUTES OF HEALTH, REPORT TO THE PRESIDENT (Washington: Government Printing Office, 1965), pp. 52–55, 192–98.

[9] AMERICAN JOURNAL OF PUBLIC HEALTH, December, 1961, p. 1907.

Hardy points out that "Public health was conceived and nurtured in an atmosphere of research,"[10] and he refers nostalgically to his early days in the field. "For me public health came to mean the opportunity for fascinating and productive field studies. Also it was the channel for stimulating contact with research scientists."[11] Beginning in the 1930s, however, the great need for extension of public health services—for which federal support became available under the Social Security Act of 1935—took the lion's share of health department attention. Rapidly increasing investigation of the emerging problems of chronic disease, whether supported by the PHS, foundations, or voluntary health agencies, was largely laboratory or clinical research and took place in universities, research centers, and hospitals, rather than in health departments. Most of the knowledge uncovered through these efforts was useful in the treatment, rather than the prevention of disease— an area in which health departments were not expected to function.

The controversy over the financing of medical care did not encourage public health officials to take aggressive action. Even though a report of a committee of the American Public Health Association concerned with medical care went so far as to state in 1954 that "The public health agencies—federal, state, and local —should carry major responsibilities in administering the health services of the future,"[12] many health departments continued to focus on traditional programs. By failing to concern themselves with what Mountin called "the great unsolved problem in public health,"[13] such health departments turned their backs on opportunities for research and accomplishment that could have been peculiarly their own. Epi-demiologic studies were carried on, but although some of these were exceedingly important to the control of communicable diseases, they were not aimed at what the public increasingly recognized as the main research targets and did little to enhance the scientific image of the health department, in the eyes of either the public or the increasingly research-oriented health professions. Research in the health department had none of the prestige of research in the laboratory or the hospital.

The predicament that health departments soon found themselves in was summed up by James in 1958.

Anyone who has discussed the career of a health officer with young medical graduates has noted the profound change which the last decade had brought to the challenges facing public health. While much remains to be done in every aspect of public health practice, it is becoming increasingly difficult to recruit the best physicians by stressing our need for continuation of familiar activities in tuberculosis control, child health, and general sanitation. Certainly we rate a poor second to the glamor of the cardiac surgeon, the neurophysiologist and the laboratory investigator. Our newer technics for chronic disease control offer promise, but effective public health programs based on them are still few, expensive, and untested. To the potential recruit the time of most health officers seems to be fully occupied with their more traditional commitments, leavened at intervals with "administrative" emergencies caused by poliomyelitis immunization, civil defense, or influenza.

This discussion deals with one activity of the modern health officer which can present our field as creative, challenging, and stimulating to the most ambitious and energetic of medical graduates. I am referring to the unique opportunities offered by public health research. What the laboratory bench is to the virologist, what the medical ward is to the clinical researcher, every single community can be to an inquiring health officer.[14]

The health department that proposes to undertake research today need not look far for problems to investigate. There are enormous gaps in knowledge of ways to determine a community's health status, to provide and systematize the services needed, to encourage and motivate people to use them, and to evaluate their success. These are community problems, as are

[10] Albert V. Hardy, "Research—or Stay Behind!" AMERICAN JOURNAL OF PUBLIC HEALTH, January, 1962, p. 1.

[11] Ibid., p. 2.

[12] "Preliminary Report on a National Program for Medical Care," presented to the Committee on Administrative Practice by a Subcommittee on Medical Care as a Statement of Principles, AMERICAN JOURNAL OF PUBLIC HEALTH, September, 1944, p. 986.

[13] Joseph W. Mountin, "Content and Administration of a Medical Care Program," in SELECTED PAPERS OF JOSEPH W. MOUNTIN, M.D. (Washington: The Joseph W. Mountin Memorial Committee, 1956), p. 85.

[14] George James, "Research by Local Health Departments—Problems, Methods, Results," AMERICAN JOURNAL OF PUBLIC HEALTH, March, 1958, p. 353.

many of the unsolved problems of environmental health, and they must be solved in the community. All of them are in areas where extension of knowledge is necessary.

The opinion that research should be conducted by health departments is shared by the great majority of health officers. However, a survey conducted by the Research Committee of the APHA Health Officers Section in 1963 found that only 168 of the 1,053 local health departments responding to a questionnaire were carrying on "planned and organized scientific efforts, carried out under controlled conditions and designed to obtain findings which will have wide application"—the APHA definition of research.[15] Among those reporting, there was general agreement that the major factors inhibiting research were lack of funds, personnel, and time.

Since this information was obtained, federal funds for research in community health have increased. In a number of states, the state health department provides financial assistance for research. Although there is probably never enough money available to health departments for all desirable programs, funds can usually be found for well-constructed research projects when motivation to conduct them is sufficient.

The lack of personnel capable in the area of public health research is a serious hindrance. Although it is true, as James said, that it is difficult to interest competent young professional people in public health without opportunities to do research, there is a limited number of people with research training, and they cannot always be found even when research opportunities are offered. The training of most practitioners in public health is oriented toward service. Such exposure as they have to research methodology is usually in the biological sciences. The methods of research in this field cannot always be readily adapted to social problems needing study. Mayes states:

Research in public health practice cannot be accomplished successfully merely by reassigning available people from other tasks to the key research positions. Moreover, the necessity for team research is demanded in public health practice as in few other fields, since the problems are so often multidisciplinary in dimension. Skills in community medicine and economics, social science skills, and administrative skills, as well as the more familiar epidemiological and biostatistical expertise, are all needed. During the past few years, there has been a slow but steady trickle of such research specialists into the ranks of health department workers. But they are still in extremely short supply.[16]

Undoubtedly increased training of new workers and research training opportunities for presently employed public health people are greatly needed, and efforts are being made throughout the country to provide them. Some health departments have been able to share in research activities through cooperation with academic institutions and thereby to acquaint their staff with research techniques. Whether service staff participate directly in research or not, its potential benefits to health department programs depend considerably on their understanding and acceptance of its place in the overall efforts.

Lack of time is as common in health departments as lack of money, but time would seem to be well spent in any operation in order to improve (and perhaps make less time consuming) the methods used and make them more productive.

If health departments are considered as agencies functioning for the benefit of communities, they have responsibility not only to provide service but to preserve and extend their ability to do so. For this purpose, research serves the health department as well as the hospital and has been defined as:

. . . the process whereby the system constantly renews itself; it prevents dogmatism; it fosters a questioning, self-critical attitude; and it constantly generates new information to stimulate the inquiring mind.[17]

[15] Leon J. Taubenhaus, "A Study of Research Activities by Local Health Departments in the United States," AMERICAN JOURNAL OF PUBLIC HEALTH, September, 1965, pp. 1443–50.

[16] William F. Mayes "Research Programs and Projects by Local Health Departments—General Policies and Practices," AMERICAN JOURNAL OF PUBLIC HEALTH, November, 1963, p. 1816.

[17] Edward Dempsey, "Report of the Subcommittee on Manpower," in The President's Commission on Heart Disease, Cancer, and Stroke, op. cit., p. 279.

18

Planning for Community Health

THE RAPID GROWTH and increasing complexity of economic and social enterprise in this country have necessitated the development of the modern art and science of planning. Activities requiring the interacting decisions and efforts of many people and affecting large segments of the population call for greater sophistication than the personal foresight based on observation and experience that sufficed for the individual entrepreneur in a simpler time. For many years now, American industry has been developing and using techniques for continual planning of operations and evaluation of their effectiveness and efficiency. In the public sector, similar techniques have been adapted for application to such essential national operations as the defense effort.

Planning of a different order, concerned with development policies and comprehensive approaches to social problems and growth, has received a good deal of international attention. In our country, increasing concentration of urban populations has evolved concepts of comprehensive city and regional planning as a governmental function aimed at "the comprehensive improvement of all aspects of the urban environment."[1]

Although the aims of city planning are to enhance the well-being of people, it has most commonly concerned itself with their well-being as it is affected by the physical environment. There is a growing body of opinion among urban planners that the scope of city planning should be broadened to include at least all the activities with which local government is concerned—services as well as facilities. Some take the position that "comprehensive planning involves all organized endeavors including governmental, voluntary, and private activities which may directly or indirectly influence health and welfare."[2] On the other hand, others suggest that, although this concept is a desirable ideal, it is impossible for any one agency to encompass all the skills and breadth of view and to be able to understand all the social, economic, and physical interactions included in this view of comprehensiveness.[3] In any event, there must be an appreciation of the interactions of various planning, service, and development activities and their total impact on the present and future status of communities, as well as a determined effort at cooperation among those engaged in planning and operations.

At a time when planning has become an accepted if not overused concept, there are many definitions of what it is or should be. Bertram Gross offers an interesting definition: "Planning is the process of developing commitments

[1] John T. Howard, "City Planning as a Social Movement, a Governmental Function, and a Technical Profession," in Harvey S. Perloff (ed.), PLANNING AND THE URBAN COMMUNITY (Pittsburgh: University of Pittsburgh Press, 1961), p. 152.

[2] L. S. Goerke, "The Relationship of Health Agencies and Planning Agencies," AMERICAN JOURNAL OF PUBLIC HEALTH, May, 1964, p. 713.

[3] Howard, op. cit., p. 168.

to some pattern of objectives."[4] Noteworthy in this definition is the emphasis on commitment. For those who are overenthusiastic about our growing technical competence and who seek, through planning, "the one best answer," this is a reminder that planning is first and foremost the gaining of acceptance and consensus. It suggests that guidelines for the organization and conduct of planning should stress broad participation in the formulation of objectives by those who will be affected by actions. It implies that the exact nature of objectives may be less important than the process of gaining commitment.

This definition applies equally well to the various types of planning that occur in any community. For present purposes, three types that contribute to the orderly and effective development of health programs can be distinguished: health program planning, comprehensive health planning, and comprehensive community planning. The third type of planning tries to coordinate the total development efforts of communities. All employ similar techniques of analysis, program development, and implementation, but they differ in scope of concern and in organizational means for accomplishing their purposes.

Program planning generally deals with the organization of activities of a single agency whose goals are discrete and relatively limited and whose resources are largely internal. Comprehensive health planning is aimed at more broadly defined goals and the establishment of priorities among the programs of many agencies. It involves the organization of resources that exist throughout a community and consequently has a broad base of participation in planning. Although both voluntary and governmental agencies often assert their responsibility for comprehensiveness, it can fairly be said that comprehensive planning for health (in which a continuing dynamic process of need determination, goal setting, program development, and evaluation is applied to the interrelated activities of private, voluntary, and

public health agencies) does not exist for practical purposes in any community.

Benefits of Health Planning

In industry, the rationale for planning is economic; planning helps to ensure proper return for expenditure, prevent waste, and improve efficiency. Although many health professionals are reluctant to evaluate their activities in economic terms, all health agencies are obliged to keep expenditures within the limits of their budgets. There is also growing recognition that the size of expenditures made in the nation for health purposes necessitates assurance that they are economically sound. No community has enough resources to be able to spend them without considering cost, and health service is only one of the benefits people desire. Furthermore, the overall supply of at least the trained manpower required for health service has definite limits and must be used efficiently.

Planning also helps to maintain and improve the quality of health services. When examination of individual programs in terms of effectiveness is built in, opportunity for correction of deficiency and innovation to increase effectiveness is also built in. At levels above the individual program, the objective processes of planning encourage the use of resources where their impact on community well-being can be greatest.

Whether health activities are carried on under governmental, voluntary, or private auspices, they must be accounted for and their financial support justified. Planning enables an organization to describe the effects and requirements of its programs and activities, thereby justifying them to legislative bodies, boards of voluntary agencies, or owners of private enterprises. At the community level enlistment of public support for new or expanded services is facilitated by planning.

As an administrative tool, planning makes it possible for the executive to guide operations rationally. It helps him to anticipate difficulties, so that his time is not unduly occupied with emergencies; it points up weaknesses and unproductive activities, as well as strengths and

---

[4] Bertram M. Gross, "What Are Your Organization's Objectives?" HUMAN RELATIONS, Vol. 8, No. 3, 1965, p. 212.

areas where effort is productive. For the staff of an agency, planning provides a clear idea of objectives as well as a basis for judgment in their own work. It discourages complacence, thereby promoting creative discontent to overcome the inertia of routine and tradition.

If it is to serve such purposes, planning must represent the participation and commitment of the operators, so that it is their plan, rather than something imposed on them. Some workers resent or feel threatened by planning, for it connotes control. Some do not wish to state objectives explicitly and especially do not want objectives stated for them, because standards would then be formed by which others could judge their adequacy. Viewed in another light, if planning is properly organized and conducted, the controls inherent in it extend the authority of those responsible for programs.

A city's health officer is the government's chief health official as well as its chief health planner. His actions are necessarily subject to review, and his decisions are subject to modification by the legislative and executive leaders of the government, whose considerations of available resources and extent of need cover a wider range of programs than those concerned specifically with health. But his ability to communicate with these leaders is increased by his having developed a plan. A plan including statements of needs and objectives expressed clearly alerts all to the consequences of action and pinpoints responsibility for the consequences of decisions. A health officer who justifies his budget recommendations for new programs merely on the grounds that they contribute to better health should not be surprised if a council fails to agree with the importance he attaches to his "plans."

Similarly, the interprogram decisions made by a health officer are facilitated and the responsibilities of his program chiefs are clarified through their preparation of good plans. This suggests that planning should be formalized at all organizational levels, not merely at the level of a central planning unit. The District of Columbia Health Department has recognized this necessity through the assignment of planners to major operating units as well as to central planning sections. Individual program planners are responsible to the operating heads of their programs but deal frequently with the central unit in developing a consistent pattern of programs for general presentation.

Processes of Program Planning

Although some techniques will vary according to the nature of program content, all program planning proceeds by certain steps: (1) definition of the problem and resources; (2) formulation of a practical objective; (3) selection and implementation of a course of action; and (4) evaluation. These steps are necessary for each level of program and, in multipurpose agencies, for each program area. The steps must be continually related and adjusted within and among different levels or program areas.

DEFINING THE PROBLEM AND RESOURCES

The problem a health agency is concerned with may be a particular disease or condition that causes illness and death, or it may be an area of need, such as hospital care, rehabilitation, or nursing service. Health departments are concerned with the general problem of ill health and premature death, but often the problems their programs focus on are specified, at least to some extent, by law, custom, and community expectations.

For purposes of program planning, an agency must delineate its problems specifically, in quantitative terms. Such measures as rates or numbers of cases and deaths due to certain causes may be used, or the degree of need for a service or the extent of a condition potentially threatening to health. Data should be related to specific population groups or geographic areas and should show trends if possible.

In defining a city's tuberculosis problem for instance, the fact that 120 active cases had been reported in the city during the previous year, at a rate of 30 per 100,000, would be less significant than the distribution of new cases, showing half of them occurring in a low-income area with 10 per cent of the population where the rate was 150 per 100,000. Further examination might show that the case rate in the rest of the community had been moving steadily downward, whereas there had been little change in the high-incidence area. Examination of case register data could further illuminate the situation if it were analyzed by place of residence:

	City	High-incidence Area
Total cases on Register 12–31	800	450
With active disease	250	175
In hospital or under current treatment	168	101
Overdue or lost	82	74
With inactive disease needing treatment	475	215
Examined in past 6 months	306	97
Overdue or lost	169	118
With activity undetermined or unknown	75	60

These data show that the high-incidence area has 56 per cent of all cases; 70 per cent of active cases but 90 per cent of those overdue for or lost to treatment; 45 per cent of inactive cases but 70 per cent of those overdue for examination or lost; and 80 per cent of those whose disease status is undetermined or unknown. This and similar information not only show the nature and extent of the tuberculosis problem but provide baseline data on which objectives can be set and measurements determined for evaluation.

Data on many health problems are not as readily available as on tuberculosis, which is a reportable disease on which case registers have been kept for some time in most sizable communities. Estimates rather than quantitative analyses may then have to be made on the basis of other data. For instance, a Visiting Nurse Association might measure the extent of need for home nursing service under Medicare in this way: Of the 400,000 people in the community, the latest population estimates show 10 per cent, or 40,000, to be 65 years of age or older. It is estimated that about 7 per cent of the elderly will need home nursing service, or a total of 2,800. The Association provided 22,500 home nursing visits to the 1,500 elderly patients on its caseload in the past year, or an average of 15 visits per patient. The need under Medicare, therefore, can be calculated at 42,000 visits (15 × 2,800) per year. Other data from the agency's records, such as average time required per visit, can further refine the estimate of need.

In defining resources for program planning, funds available for each program area should be included, as well as the time of trained professional and nonprofessional workers, facilities, and equipment. Care should be taken that in multipurpose agencies available staff time is not counted more than once. For example, in a health department with a generalized nursing service of 60 staff members, each program requiring nursing cannot consider the time of 60 nurses as its own resource. However, if resources are determined to be available from other agencies, they should be included.

FORMULATION OF A PRACTICAL OBJECTIVE

Goals of health programs are sometimes expressed in terms of ideals or general purposes of organizations—better health for all the people, prevention of a disease, or even its eradication. Although expression of such theoretical aims is useful in keeping a program focused on its ultimate goal and in discouraging the pursuit of activities for their own sake, objectives must be more specifically limited to be useful in program planning.

Program objectives should define the following clearly: (1) the condition that is to be attained or maintained; (2) the degree of change required; (3) the affected population group or aspect of environment; and (4) the period of time needed for accomplishing the objective. For instance, an immunization program objective might be a 75 per cent level of immunization, increased from a present level of 40 per cent, among children first entering school in a specified low-income area, achieved during a calendar year.

Programs may have more than one related objective; that is, in order to accomplish an overall objective, several others may need to be achieved simultaneously. The final spelling out of all objectives will depend on the specific activities undertaken, each having its own objectives, sometimes called subobjectives. The time period for accomplishing the overall objective may have to be adjusted in terms of time required for various activities. In the technique called PERT (Program Evaluation and Review Technique), a graphic design is made of activities involved in accomplishing an objective,

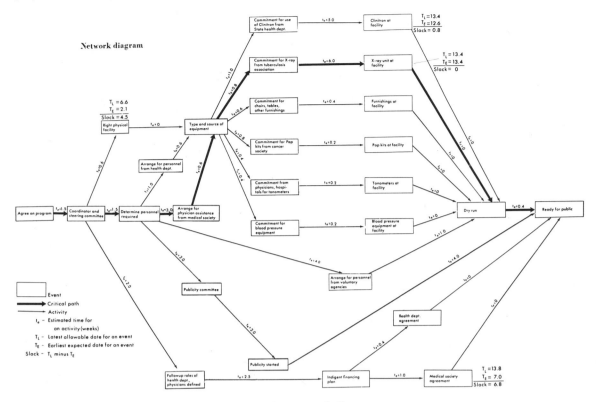

FIGURE 17. *Network diagram*

with time periods estimated for each. The longest period of time required for successive activities, called the critical path, then determines the time required to accomplish the program objective.[5]

Formulation of objectives is conditioned by potential availability of resources and alternative courses of action. But the way in which objectives are stated can encourage imagination in designing alternatives or utilizing resources. It can also influence responses to bring support to the program within and outside the agency.

An example of an inadequately considered objective causing loss of interest and routinization of activity is seen in the all too frequent reports of health departments indicating the number of restaurants inspected. The purpose of inspection is not to visit restaurants, but to ensure certain conditions vital to good health. A program objective stated as 1,000 restaurant inspections provides neither an inspiring goal for a city manager nor a criterion by which to evaluate programs. Year after year the "planned" number of inspections may be made, so that the objective is accomplished even if the rate of poor conditions found remains high. If the objective were stated as a decrease in the rate of violations found, without regard to the number of visits, the program operators might more clearly see the alternatives available to them. Perhaps inspection is not the way to ensure sanitary conditions, but an increased effort in training food handlers is what is needed—an alternative that would not even be considered when the objective is stated in terms of visits.

The more clearly objectives are stated, the easier it is to communicate health goals to other agencies, and the easier it is for other agencies to accommodate them. For example, many communities, through outmoded zoning ordinances, inhibit the decentralization of hospitals and other health facilities, a locational pattern increasingly recognized by health professionals

[5] Walter Merten, "PERT and Planning for Health Programs," PUBLIC HEALTH REPORTS, May, 1966, pp. 449–54.

as necessary to adequate service. Unless a clear description of the need for bringing services closer to the people is presented, it may be difficult to accommodate this objective within the land-use plans of the community planning agency and to generate support from the public.

SELECTION AND IMPLEMENTATION

Very few community health objectives can be achieved through only one course of action. Planning must include careful study of all the possible courses and selection of the most suitable in terms of effectiveness, efficiency, and acceptability to the particular population concerned. Evaluation of previously conducted activities contributes importantly to the selection process.

A multipurpose agency, such as a health department, must establish priorities among the various programs competing for resources. Health departments have certain responsibilities prescribed by law that must be high on the list. Communicable disease control, vital statistics services, and food protection services are examples. Because of these legal prescriptions, the health department may have on its staff professional expertise not available elsewhere in the community. The availability of such staff may in itself warrant undertaking such related activities as epidemiologic study of disease incidence and many aspects of environmental sanitation that might not stand high in a simple calculation of priorities.

Other considerations combined in weighing objectives and activities are the proportion of the community affected by the problem, severity of the problem, relative effectiveness of possible measures, and cost in money and time. For example, dental caries is widespread among children, and fluoridation of the water supply can reduce its incidence in children by nearly two-thirds at a relatively low annual cost and without adding staff. It is an obvious example of a high-priority program. Indeed, extensive efforts invested in gaining community acceptance are probably warranted in light of the anticipated return.

Programs aimed at most of the growing present-day health problems, such as chronic diseases, are much more difficult and costly in money and staff. Their priority must be high, however, because of their serious effects on a large proportion of the population. Efforts in such areas may have to displace some established activities of lesser urgency.

All objectives do not require completely separate programs but can be accomplished by adding activities to staff functions. Family planning services may be added to postpartum clinic service for mothers of newborn babies, accomplishing the objective of increased use of family planning services as well as a special program would. (The possibility should not be overlooked, however, that the added activities can take significant amounts of time and necessitate increasing staff.) Sometimes, too, an activity pays a bonus beyond its immediate objective. Offering family planning advice, for instance, has been found to double the proportion of mothers who return for postpartum examination and even to increase the early use of prenatal clinics.[6]

Although the objectives of health departments are more diverse than those of other health agencies, even single-purpose agencies usually have more than one objective; and in determining programs within the limits of their available resources, they, too, must often be guided by legal requirements, special staff competence, the potential impact of activities, and the relative severity of problems. All agencies must be alert to opportunities for more return for their investment in services and for accomplishment through cooperative arrangements.

If a community had both the tuberculosis problem described earlier in this chapter and the need to increase home nursing service under Medicare, for instance, a change of health department policy, making home nursing visits to tuberculosis patients selective instead of routine and placing greater emphasis on tuberculosis clinic service (perhaps in a clinic located in the high-incidence area), would release time spent on tuberculosis by VNA nurses for use in Medicare visits. At the same time, the tuberculosis association might

---

[6] Frederick S. Jaffe, "Family Planning, Public Policy and Intervention Strategy," JOURNAL OF SOCIAL ISSUES, October, 1967, p. 158.

arrange with the local Community Action Program supported by the Office of Economic Opportunity to tie in a special tuberculosis case-finding effort with a project in the low-income area, and the health department might take advantage of the Headstart project in that area to tuberculin-test youngsters in a search of sources of tuberculous infection.

EVALUATION

Evaluation can be viewed as an independent check on the adequacy of planning. On the other hand, evaluation contributes to the other planning steps in clarifying problems, resources, and objectives, and in rational determination of courses of action. It is an essential part of the dynamic process of planning.

Evaluation is the process of determining the extent to which stated program objectives are met through program activities. It requires a detailed description of program, in which all activities are set down with the subobjectives of each, leading toward the stated overall program objective. Measurements must then be selected to indicate the extent to which each objective is accomplished. They should assess conditions, not activities—the proportion of the city's restaurants that comply with sanitary regulations, for instance, rather than the number of inspections made. Sometimes, but not always, the measurement is implicit in the objective. In the immunization program objective already suggested, for instance, the measurement would be the proportion immunized among children in the specified area entering school for the first time. When the objective does not suggest a measurement, it is important to select one that will accurately assess progress made.

Evaluation measurements may be built into service records or may be obtained through special procedures. In either case, they are most satisfactory when they cost little—in either money or time.

When measurements have been made, the evaluation process requires determination of the extent to which results can be attributed to program activities. In operating programs, the use of control groups typical of research programs is not usually practical. However, failure to consider to what extent the objective might have been accomplished without the program obviates the purpose of program planning. External events or conditions can either obstruct or accelerate progress, and productive programming must take such events into consideration.

Examination of evaluation results will show not only the effectiveness of efforts at each level in accomplishing the objectives, but also the validity of the assumptions on which objectives or activities were based. That is, if an activity does not result in attaining the desired objective, the assumption that it would may be false. Or if subobjectives are attained but do not result in achievement of overall program objectives, the assumption that they would may be false. It is in this examination that evaluation provides guidance to program planning, by indicating where the problems lie when objectives are not being met.

Comprehensive Health Planning

As health services have grown in number and variety, coordination of effort between agencies carrying on related activities has increased. Coordinated functional planning began at the project level. Several agencies would form an *ad hoc* committee to plan a community screening program, for instance. Such planning, however, is more often for the purpose of enlisting support for an activity already chosen than for a joint examination of a problem and resources, formulation of objectives, and choice among alternative courses of action.

In recent years, the pattern of functional planning by all or most of the agencies in a community engaged in a particular category of health activity has emerged as a step toward comprehensive planning. Planning for mental retardation centers and regional medical complexes, for instance, has stimulated those providing service to get together and has increased communication between them and the recipient public.

As useful as such categorical planning is, it falls short in several ways of meeting overall community health needs. Instead of closing the gaps in services, categorical planning too often tends to make them more distinct. For example, in many communities now, adequate attention is being concentrated on hospitals, but the growing need for out-of-hospital service is often almost ignored. Categorical planning tends to isolate areas of service instead of creating working relationships among them, and it does not provide for distribution of limited resources of manpower, costly equipment, and money to the best advantage of the whole community.

Increasing recognition of the need for comprehensive planning for health led to the enactment by Congress of the Comprehensive Health Planning and Public Health Services Amendments of 1966.[7] This legislation authorized grants to the states for comprehensive health planning, administered by a single state agency established or designated by the state, and with the advice of a health planning council including "respresentatives of state and local agencies and nongovernmental organizations and groups concerned with health, and consumers of health services. . . ." Project grants to public or nonprofit private agencies for aid in developing "comprehensive regional, metropolitan area, or other local area plans for coordination of existing and planned health services" were also authorized. The Act specifically acknowledges that attainment of the nation's health goals "depends on an effective partnership, involving close intergovernmental collaboration, official and voluntary efforts, and participation of individuals and organizations. . . ."

Comprehensive health planning includes procedures similar to those of program planning. It must define community needs and resources in a health profile continually adjusted to changes; set long-range goals reflecting the community's health aspirations; consider alternative policies, select the most realistic, and translate the policy into operating-level action; and reexamine the validity of policies and plans.

Health Profiles

The first step of comprehensive community health planning has been taken in a number of communities using the detailed *Self-Study Guide for Community Health Action Planning*

developed by the American Public Health Association.[8] Under the auspices of the National Commission on Community Health Services, formed in 1962, 21 communities undertook similar self-examination with regard to health.[9] Bringing together many agencies and individuals in each community, these studies were an initial step in action programs to improve health services.

A health profile for planning purposes includes descriptions of all community characteristics pertinent to health. Information should be measurable; the measurement should be quantitative if possible, although if proper standards are devised, judgments can be given numerical ratings. Most items in the profile should provide recurring data so that change in and effect of actions can be measured, but occasionally single items could be incorporated.

The content of the profile should include the following: (1) ecological characteristics—physical conditions, economic functions, and the density, age distribution, income, occupation, education, race, nativity, and housing of the population; (2) health resource characteristics—numbers of public, private, and voluntary facilities and personnel, types of activities, and available funds; (3) health utilization characteristics—cost of servicing various illnesses and conditions, utilization of health facilities and personnel by different population groups, occupancy and service ratios of facilities and institutions, and, if possible, a matching of utilization against need; and (4) health condition characteristics—mortality and morbidity data from various sources, supplemented by periodic household sampling if possible, as well as specific environmental conditions related to health.

The benefit of a health profile of such detail is in enabling the presentation of a community picture that can be matched *over time* with other community profiles and can serve as a basis for epidemiologic research that correlates various conditions, indicates areas of multiple

---

[7] Public Law 89–749.

[8] (New York: The Association, 1960).

[9] HEALTH IS A COMMUNITY AFFAIR, REPORT OF THE NATIONAL COMMISSION ON COMMUNITY HEALTH SERVICES (Cambridge, Mass.: Harvard University Press, 1966), p. 168.

problems, and pinpoints changing physical distributions of conditions, problems, and resources. It must be organized spatially in such a way as to fit with other planning activities and to point to the "communities of solution" that the National Commission on Community Health Services found to be a necessary basis for planning, organizing, and delivering health services.[10] As the Commission pointed out, the problem-sheds for environmental health services and the health marketing areas for personal health services often do not coincide with each other or with existing health jurisdictions. The health profile can delineate these problem-sheds and health marketing areas, as a basis for comprehensive health planning.

LONG-RANGE GOALS

The process of establishing long-range goals must include projection of probable changes in the community that would affect the identified problems. It is important that goals and programs of resource agencies be considered and community goals developed in terms of the magnitude of identified problems, present knowledge that can be applied to their solution, and the community's technological and economic ability to apply such knowledge. The values and attitudes toward health of various socioeconomic groups should be identified and weighed.

As in program planning, goals should not be considered as final and unalterable. They should always be subject to modification when new information or changes in judgments make it desirable.

ALTERNATIVE POLICIES AND PLANS

The policies and plans considered should take into consideration the techniques to be used and the distribution of resources to reach each goal, as well as methods for developing additional resources. There should be a time schedule for program and resource development, an operating responsibility for each health service provider, and an estimate of costs involved in achieving objectives. The supporting relationship of each program to all others should be ex-

plained. The prospective effectiveness of the plan and its potential for further program development should be analyzed.

From among the several alternatives, the policy and plan selected should be the most realistic. The decision must be based on the community's economic situation, the aims and programs of resource agencies, and the probability of successful implementation.

Putting the plan into action will take not only persuasion but technical expertise, the use of sanctions, and the leverage of dollars. Community support is essential. Many of the agencies whose resources may be rearranged by the plan will be in sympathy through involvement in the planning process. However, there must be an opportunity provided for the resolution of disagreements.

EVALUATION

If the health profile is suitably designed, it will provide the means of assessing the effectiveness of the chosen plan in attaining desired goals. Comprehensive planning should be as continuous a process as program planning, with evaluation used as a guide to adjustment and change in program.

At the present time, complete information systems on which community health profiles could be based do not generally exist, and evaluation is limited by their absence. Although emphasis must be given to the establishment of such systems, comprehensive planning can proceed on the basis of present knowledge and understanding of community health problems. Attention should be directed to existing facilities, services, and manpower, to encourage their maximum utilization toward the solution of the problems identified through professional judgment. Both coordination of resources within the health service system and promotion of interrelationships with other community planning systems are urgent.

The Health Planning Agency

A number of the organizations described in Chapters 2 and 3 have participated in or conducted planning activities related to certain

[10] *Ibid.*, pp. 2–4.

areas of health services. However, because comprehensive health planning is in the earliest stage of development, the relative effectiveness of different types of agencies operating in this area has not been assessed. Undoubtedly, community differences will be reflected in health planning agencies as well as in plans. However, a number of essential qualities can be identified.

The planning region with which the agency is concerned may not be coterminous with a political jurisdiction or even with several. In most urban areas, neither problems nor service resources are contained within city or even county boundaries. The differing environmental health problem-sheds and personal health marketing areas will affect the patterns of health planning regions, which should be based on communities of solution.

All health interests of the community must be represented in the planning system, and the

agency cannot limit itself to government, private, or voluntary providers of service, nor to any group or class of consumers of service. If it is to be recognized as responsible for health planning—also indispensable—there must be no faction that considers itself outside the agency's purview.

The agency must be designed to provide for coordinated decisionmaking, brought about through continous exchange of knowledge and opinion, and information and techniques among health agencies and forces in the community. Furthermore, it must participate actively in overall community planning, not limiting its role to commenting on the health aspects of proposals, but advocating policies, programs, and projects.

HEALTH PLANNING SKILLS

The need for training resources for health planning was recognized by the National Commission on Community Health Services, which recommended that:

> Schools of social work, public health, and hospital administration, and graduate schools of social and political science and public administration should initiate or expand short-term and long-term health-planning courses to provide opportunities for public health personnel, social welfare personnel, and hospital planners to be trained together with the broadest possible professional orientation and communitywide perspective.[11]

It also recommended the development of academic programs that would qualify students to conduct community self-studies.[12] Although these long-term actions will be necessary to build up a cadre of professionally trained health planners, to meet immediate needs communities will have to consider the talents of current health personnel and perhaps develop provisions for inservice training in health planning.

Comprehensive health planning obviously requires a variety of skills. The epidemiologist and statistician are indispensable to analyze data and determine health problems and changes in health status. Public relations talents must be applied to interpret planning to

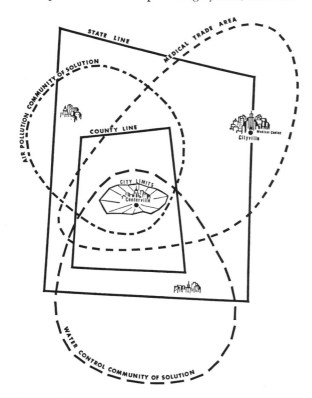

FIGURE 18. *One city's communities of solution (Political boundaries, shown in solid lines, often bear small relation to a community's problem-sheds or its medical trade area. From* Health Is a Community Affair, *p. 3.)*

[11] *Ibid.*, p. 222, Recommendation N-6.
[12] *Ibid.*, p. 213, Recommendation J-7.

the many professional groups whose participation will be necessary for implementation, as well as to community leadership and the general public.

Blending of plans and programs of separate health agencies or categorical groups into comprehensive health planning requires a particular type of skill in community organization, as does relating health planning to the total life and aims of the community.

All agencies responsible for health programs should themselves continually seek to blend their activities with those of other health agencies, and the comprehensive health planning agency should blend with total community development planning activities. The real potential of viewing health and all the factors that affect it can be put to full advantage only if the community has a focus for its many health programs, problems, and services. A comprehensive health planning agency should provide this focus.

Health planning skills also include an awareness of what is going on in other areas of community development and ability to relate health goals and actions with those of other planners. Knowledge is needed of what other planning agencies are doing that might affect health, and what they are doing in the way of data gathering and community organization, for instance, which need not be duplicated. Health departments and the special skills of their demographic analysts are often called upon by planning and economic development agencies to project populations and age distribution. Health planning agencies should similarly call upon transportation, land-use, and economic planning agencies, as well as other social agencies, for aid in anticipating where population will be spatially distributed and what kinds of transportation networks are likely to develop—both of which are vital considerations in locating new hospitals and other health facilities as well as in anticipating other changes that might affect aspects of the health profile. Economic projections not only indicate potential needs correlated with various economic levels, but also provide economic knowledge for forecasting potential financial and manpower resources applicable to health programs. Such cooperation should cover not only forecasting, but also joint programming and phasing of construction and service programs.

In such ways truly comprehensive community planning is advanced. As bridges between the various health interests represented in comprehensive health planning and the governmental planning programs of other agencies, the health officer and city manager are in key positions to encourage and arrange for such cooperative endeavors. In doing so, not only are they fulfilling their responsibilities as public officials to total community progress, but they are specifically bettering health planning as well.

Part Five

Health Department Management

Introduction

THE LOCAL health department's role as leader in developing, supporting, and assuring the availability of a full range of community health services has become a precept of the public health professions. In an official statement, the American Public Health Association defines the fundamental responsibility of the local health department as follows:

. . . to determine the health status and health needs of the people within its jurisdiction, to determine to what extent these needs are being met by effective measures currently available, and to take steps to see that the unmet needs are satisfied.[1]

It is in the spirit of this definition that health departments are broadening their programs to deal with emerging problems—conducting screening programs to identify early chronic disease, providing home nursing service for the chronically ill and aged, engaging in education campaigns to discourage cigarette smoking.

Most importantly in the exercise of community leadership for health, the health department's role extends beyond the development of its own programs to a concern for all community activities influencing the health of its citizens. Indeed, it might be said that a health department's effectiveness is more appropriately measured in terms of its effect on the adequacy of total community health efforts than in terms of the extent of its own programs.

The way in which community health services have developed historically makes the health department's leadership both more necessary and more difficult than it would have been if they had grown up in a unified structure. Because earlier definitions of health department functions were narrow, and also because of the limitations and peculiarities of systems of local government in the states, even governmental health functions are dispersed among a bewildering array of agencies in most areas. And that characteristic American expression of humanitarian interests, the voluntary agency, has been added in even greater number to community resources for health. As the only public agency representing the public interest in all aspects of health, the health department is obliged to lead the complex into common effort toward community health goals.

When most health departments were formed, the most urgent problem and the one most subject to remedy was that of environmental sanitation; it received the most health department attention until the beginning of this century. In succeeding decades, improved knowledge of communicable disease and demand for improvement of the condition of mothers and children resulted in the establishment of new programs in health departments. These programs were usually added as separate services, built around professional specialization. As Mountin pointed out in 1952:

It was, in fact, out of this period that our current ideas of public health services evolved—concepts that included a "categorical" approach to disease, specific control techniques, and specialized, even compartmentalized services. As another result, public health workers began to give thought to the organizational structure for conveying services to the people. We began, thus, to acquire rather firm ideas about "basic" responsibilities and services, and about minimum standards of personnel and organization. And these concepts, once highly

---

[1] "The Local Health Department—Services and Responsibilities," AMERICAN JOURNAL OF PUBLIC HEALTH, January, 1964, p. 133.

appropriate, still cling to our consciousness in the face of changing conditions and altered needs.[2]

In the past two decades, health departments have been redefining their role in the community. It is viewed increasingly as that of participator in all community health services in a co-ordinating and organizing capacity, rather than simply direct provider of "basic" or even additional specialized public health services.

Legal Responsibilities

As governmental agencies, local health departments operate within a legal framework more specific than that of private agencies. Its nature depends in part on the nature of the delegation of authority from the state. For instance, a county health department may act simply as agent for the state in administering and enforcing the state health code. On the other hand, the health department of a municipality that has either home rule or broad delegation of powers under its charter will operate under local ordinances and local regulations, which must be generally consistent with state law but usually go beyond it. In either case, the health officer has the legal obligation as a public official to enforce the law, although he is given considerable discretion about the method he will use to do so.

The laws that health departments must enforce deal as a rule with the traditional areas of public health—vital statistics, communicable disease control, environmental sanitation, and licensure—and although today's health needs extend into other areas, these areas are all necessary functions that only government can appropriately conduct. Although more challenging opportunities may seem to exist in other areas, continued attention to and improvement in its "basic" services are a significant contribution to community health in addition to being a legal obligation. Vital and health statistics are needed more than ever as a dynamic force in the planning and administration of all community health services.

Communicable disease is to a very large extent preventable with modern methods. If past success has lessened the drama and challenge in communicable disease control, continued vigilance is still required, and newer opportunities constantly emerge from laboratory and community research. Such prevention determines in good share the possibility of preventing the chronic diseases and disabilities that are important as modern problems. The environment of today's cities has added new threats to human well-being, and efforts to make it more healthful belong to the advance guard in public health. Licensure, properly administered, is one of the health department's most effective tools of prevention. The broadening scope of the health department surely begins with a reaffirmation of its traditional legal responsibilities.

In addition to what a health department is required to do by law, all its activities must be allowed by law. In some states, laws are sufficiently permissive to allow a local jurisdiction to carry out health programs as it sees fit. In others, statutes enacted and precedents set in a different time on the basis of a more limited understanding of health and disease may restrict public health functions unduly in the light of today's knowledge and needs. Instead of seeing the health department as without recourse in such a situation, Grad states:

The public health officer has a positive duty—which, to be sure, may be unexpressed in the statutory description of his powers and functions—to advance the course of public health by active participation in program development, and this includes legislative development of public health law generally.[3]

Participation is a key word, and Grad goes on to say:

An examination of the major developments in the field of public health proves that only through the cooperation between the many professional and technical specialists active in the field and the specialists in the use of legal techniques, lawyers or legislative draftsmen, has there been progress

[2] Joseph W. Mountin, "The Health Department's Dilemma," in SELECTED PAPERS OF JOSEPH W. MOUNTIN (Washington: The Joseph W. Mountin Memorial Committee, 1956), p. 61.

[3] Frank P. Grad, PUBLIC HEALTH LAW MANUAL, A HANDBOOK ON THE LEGAL ASPECTS OF PUBLIC HEALTH ADMINISTRATION AND ENFORCEMENT (New York: American Public Health Association, 1965), p. 209.

from a limited epidemiologic and environmental sanitation focus to the broad areas of present concern.

The health department's position in regard to legislative action should represent the community's health interests as a whole, with regard both to enactments immediately affecting health programs and to those concerning other areas of municipal policy with only implied or less evident impact upon the community's health. As a member of a municipality's governing team, the health officer must concern himself with these other areas, and other executives must be led to seek his advice and reaction in regard to matters not readily recognized as within his sphere of interest. A city manager who brings his health officer into all deliberations will further this kind of mutuality of interest.

The Health Department Jurisdiction

The health problems of a community are not confined to the areas of the health department's jurisdiction, and, as was pointed out in Chapter 18, communities of solution cross jurisdictional lines. The multiplicity of local governments providing health services in many areas necessitates cooperative arrangements on the part of each health department with the state and with neighboring local health departments.

The Health Department as an Organization

Although the structure and programs of health departments vary, they have in common certain characteristics that set them off from most other agencies of government and must be especially considered in their administration. These characteristics have to do with the professional skills involved and the nature of the agency's activities.

THE PROFESSIONAL COMBINATION

The necessity for teamwork of the various professions in public health has been so vigorously urged for so long as to become a truism. However, it cannot be taken for granted, as teamwork among persons with dissimilar academic

training and points of view does not happen easily. A health department has a variety of objectives and carries on an assortment of activities related to a general health goal but often difficult to relate to one another. Moreover, different programs may be directed by members of different professions, and any one program often requires the combined efforts of persons with various skills, who inevitably have different points of view.

Professionalism and multidirected programs are not unique to health departments. However, there are few public health activities that do not require cooperative effort of experts in several disciplines, and some of the new programs will create the need for adding skills of other professions. Leadership in the health department has no more important task than that of welding the team together, imbuing the various professionals with a common sense of mission, fostering through example a mutual respect for expertise and qualifications, and resolving fairly the unavoidable differences that emerge.

A well-organized planning program can forestall quarrels by allowing the entire professional staff to share in establishing objectives and measuring progress, and by setting a pattern of policy decision through staff participation rather than administrative fiat. Arrangements in daily operations that bring staff members together emphasize their common purpose. Professional meetings and inservice training not only help the professional to keep his skills up to date, but increasingly stress that health needs demand interdisciplinary services. The need for greater mutual understanding applies not only to relations among the health professions but also to those with other professions and agencies. A training program within the health department that concentrates on upgrading health skills and interactions is not meeting its full potential unless it also brings health people together with other municipal departments and gives them a sense of the larger system in which they operate.

THE HEALTH DEPARTMENT'S ACTIVITIES

In broad terms, the health department's activities are enforcement of laws and regulations, direct and supportive services, and research and education. Historically, services and education were begun in order to accomplish the enforcement of laws and regulations. As the professional fields of public health developed, however, and as the positive values of health services and education became evident, they acquired their own reason for being. Today, most members of health department staffs conceive their mission to be in the area of service and education rather than law enforcement.

The two types of duties are in a sense incompatible. The success of service and education programs depends to a great extent on the ability of the health department staff to inspire the confidence of the people to whom their efforts are directed. But enforcement procedures must often be carried on in an atmosphere of disagreement or resentment not conducive to confidence. Ideally, perhaps, service and education might be so effective that resorting to legal action would not be necessary—and this is an ideal that health departments must earnestly strive for. However, to assume that recourse to the law would never be necessary would be utopian, and to avoid the use of force or litigation when reasonable efforts of service, education, and persuasion have failed would be irresponsible and discriminatory.

Many service programs of a modern health department are related less to the exercise of police power than to the promotion of general welfare—chronic disease services, dental health, rehabilitation, even the traditional maternal and child health services, for instance. Paradoxically, these programs may be obstructed by the health department's alliance with law enforcement, when, for example, the very people it is trying to encourage to use diagnostic or clinic services are at the same time being cited for noncompliance with sanitary or housing codes. Tact in conducting enforcement programs, emphasizing services and benefits, and information campaigns prior to enforcement activities will encourage cooperation and at the same time heighten the potential of other health department programs.

The health department must teach individuals and groups the facts about their personal health problems and about sanitation and communicable disease, thereby motivating them to act for their own and the community's protection. But it must also interpret its own mission in such a way as to encourage both the support of health department services and their utilization.

The educational function of the health department, however, is not limited by the nature of its own services. In providing community health leadership, it has the task of providing information about and interpretation of the community's health status, health resources and their adequacy, and health needs. It is the health department that must make the community aware of the economic and social value of health to the whole population, promote positive health, and build public support for its own and other community activities.

Although the health department's leadership functions and the degree to which it coordinates and stimulates action by other agencies are as important as the extent of its own program activities, there is a risk of carrying the concept too far. Unless a department has an adequate, rigorous, imaginative, and competent staff, carrying major responsibilities for health, it cannot perform its irreplaceable leadership function.

Practice by New Definitions

The limitations of legal status, the complexity of jurisdictions, and the multiplicity of responsibilities do not keep health departments from moving toward fulfilling their fundamental responsibilities in today's terms. The professional journals of public health produce many varied examples.

In Brookline, Massachusetts, the health department addressed itself to the problem of improving the quality of nursing home service. Recognizing that isolation of nursing homes from other health resources stands in the way of continuity of long-term patient care, the health department enlisted the cooperation of a hospital, from which had come a complaint about nursing homes and a request for enforcement of higher standards, in an improvement program. A report of the program's accomplishments emphasizes the particular need for health department participation in the resolution of community problems:

The complexities of urban facilities where several hospitals and numerous nursing homes serve the same population group are additional barriers to close hospital–nursing home relations. So is the mutual distrust of each agency for the other. The health department is an organization that can bridge this communications gap, and as it has done in this case, can serve as a catalyst to initiate action.[4]

Montgomery County, Maryland, is a suburban area with thousands of private water supplies and septic tanks for sewage disposal.

At the health department's suggestion a subdivision review committee consisting of representatives from the health, planning, public works, sewer and water, and education agencies has been formed to give a concerted approach and review to rapid expansion of housing without public water and sewer systems.[5]

Health departments in many areas of the country are working with antipoverty agencies in different ways. The Monroe County Health Department in Rochester, New York, is committed to provide preventive, treatment, and referral services in multipurpose centers sponsored by Action for a Better Community; employment, welfare, recreation, social service, and education programs are also offered.

We have an opportunity before us which must not be wasted. We are now coming to grips with the problem of providing more adequately for the continuum of preventive, diagnostic, treatment, and rehabilitative services plus health information and guidance [for less privileged groups] and we will be doing this for as many years to come as any of us can see ahead.[6]

In discussing experience with health department involvement in a Community Renewal Program, the Commissioner of Public Health of Springfield, Massachusetts, presents this very contemporary question:

Planning department pieties notwithstanding, what immediate and eventful profits can a city health department expect to receive for involving itself in controversies lapping about CRP and planning department activities? Is it worth the involvement? After all, the health department has enough inevitable controversies of its own without encroaching on unfamiliar and perilous bureaucratic territory.[7]

His summarized answer:

In balance, however, a city health department receives positive professional gains from involvement in a community renewal program in facilitating additional communication of public health data to community decision makers, in forecasting far in advance what public health services will be needed and where they should be located, in establishing a housing data bank, and in giving opportunities for research in the effects of urban housing environment.[8]

In such varied ways local health departments evidence their capacity to keep up with the times and to contribute constructively to the identification and resolution of health and other community problems.

---

[4] Leon J. Tabenhaus, James E. C. Walker, and John G. McCormick, "A Public Health Approach to Nursing Home Care," AMERICAN JOURNAL OF PUBLIC HEALTH, January, 1964, pp. 53–58.

[5] William J. Peeples, "The Local Health Department's Responsibility for Environmental Health Programs," AMERICAN JOURNAL OF PUBLIC HEALTH, April, 1964, p. 633.

[6] Wendell R. Ames, "Redirection of Health Department Services in Rochester, N.Y.," AMERICAN JOURNAL OF PUBLIC HEALTH, April, 1966, p. 602.

[7] Lowell E. Bellin, "Health and Planning Department Efforts in a Community Renewal Program," PUBLIC HEALTH REPORTS, April, 1966, p. 326.

[8] Ibid., p. 328.

19

Organization and Staffing

Because the tradition of local autonomy in health matters has always been strong in this country, local health departments vary greatly in the way they fit into local government, in the nature of their internal organization as well as in their staffing patterns. It is impossible either to describe all kinds of local health departments or to designate an ideal that would suit all situations. Even in the matter of minimum size of population served, there is room for variation. For some time it has been generally agreed that a population of 50,000 is required to support an effective health department, but there is a considerable body of opinion that this figure should be higher if today's health needs are to be met and the problems of increasing concentration of population solved. However, when communities are physically isolated, or when populations are spread over a large area, the logistics of delivering service may demand that the department serve a smaller population.

The Health Department in Local Government

Local governments themselves vary considerably, and health departments fit into them in any of a number of ways. The health department may be a department of municipal government and directly responsible to the city manager, mayor or commissioner, or to a city board of health. But more than half of cities with over 50,000 population, and almost two-thirds of cities of that size with the council-manager form of government, are served by county health departments (see Table 13).

About 60 per cent of all local health departments in the United States are county health departments.[1]

Inasmuch as most counties do not have an executive, the county health department is usually accountable to the county board of supervisors or to one of its committees, sometimes through a board of health. In some states, county health departments are directly under the control of the state health department.

When a city is served by a county department, it may have a contract with the county, or, as in some California counties, health service may be provided to all or some municipalities in the county as a function of county government. Another type of city-county arrangement is one in which a division of labor is agreed upon and both governments provide certain services county wide; for instance, the county may provide health services and the city provide police protection. When this is the case, the health department may be considered either a county or a local district health department. Other local district departments are supported by two or more governments—cities or counties or both—and are responsible to a board representing the cooperating governments.

An interesting arrangement exists in Albuquerque and Bernalillo County, New Mexico, where a city department of environmental health now extends these services throughout the county under contract, while a state health

---

[1] U.S. Department of Health, Education, and Welfare, Public Health Service, DIRECTORY OF LOCAL HEALTH UNITS 1966 (PHS Publication No. 118 [Washington: Government Printing Office, 1966 Revision]), p. 75.

district covering Bernalillo County provides other health services.

In many states, areas that are not heavily populated and do not have their own local health departments receive service from state health districts. However, in Hawaii, all local public health services are provided by four state districts, and in Rhode Island and Vermont the state health departments serve the entire state.

HEALTH DEPARTMENTS IN METROPOLITAN AREAS

The practice of several governments' cooperating to support a single health department is more common in sparsely populated areas than in metropolitan areas. In the metropolitan areas that are comprised of single counties, a county health department often serves the entire metropolitan population. In larger metropolitan areas, there are various combinations of perhaps several county health departments, from one to more than 30 municipal health departments, a local district, or part of a state district. The legal responsibilities of these departments may vary considerably, and their staffs and resources almost certainly do, but each has status and obligation under law for public health services within its own jurisdiction.

Most metropolitan areas have a large number of special districts, independent of other local government, set up for health purposes. There may be from one to several hundred school districts alone, as well as districts that run hospitals, provide water supply or sewerage or both, administer housing or urban renewal programs, and supervise cemeteries.[2] These are in addition to the other departments of county or city government whose functions touch on those of the health department.

The profusion of local governments providing health services in some metropolitan areas is obviously inappropriate for the purpose of supplying even traditional health services in a metropolitan area and can seriously hamper expansion of programs to meet growing needs. Reformers in the field of metropolitan govern-

[2] U.S. Department of Commerce, Bureau of the Census, Census of Governments 1962, Vol. I, GOVERNMENTAL ORGANIZATION (Washington: Government Printing Office, 1963), Tables 12 and 15.

Table 13

Sponsorship of Health Departments Serving Cities with over 50,000 Population (1965)

Type of Sponsorship	All Cities		Council Manager Cities	
	Number	%	Number	%
City	148	39.8	49	29.7
County	189	50.8	105	63.6
State (health district)	20	5.4	2	1.2
Local (health district)	15	4.0	9	5.5
Total	372	100.0	165	100.0

Sources: THE MUNICIPAL YEAR BOOK 1965 (Chicago: The International City Managers' Association, 1965), pp. 122–128; United States Department of Health, Education, and Welfare, Public Health Service, DIRECTORY OF HEALTH UNITS 1966 (PHS Publication 118 [Washington: Government Printing Office, 1966]).

ment have long urged the establishment and financing of metropolitan health departments with powers, responsibilities, and resources to serve as single health jurisdictions. This has been accomplished most dramatically in Rhode Island where local health departments have been dissolved in favor of direct state service, but the proposal has not been popular in most of the complicated metropolitan areas.

A number of approaches can help to resolve the problem of providing more nearly uniform public health services for the whole area than would be possible if each health department operated independently. Under contracts for services, one health department may serve the whole area in certain programs, and sharing of personnel among several jurisdictions can allow each to have a broader program even though it cannot afford a full range of expertise on its own staff. Some of the new regional programs, such as the construction and programming of community mental health centers and mental retardation facilities, also offer opportunities for local communities to participate in programs of high quality without changing the structure of metropolitan health organization.

Arrangements such as these enable small health departments to extend services within limited means. However, they cannot be a satisfactory substitute in any health jurisdiction for a full-time, qualified health officer who has public health responsibility.

BOARDS OF HEALTH

Many city health departments were established when civic reformers were attempting to take government out of politics. A device often used for that purpose was the bipartisan or nonpartisan board or commission essentially independent of city government, set up to carry out a function such as public health. Eventually, however, the trend away from partisan politics in city government and the disadvantages of a board rather than a single executive for the administration of an agency have removed much of the board of health's original reason for being. Yet, in the City of Los Angeles, until its health department consolidated with that of Los Angeles County in 1965, a five-member, part-time, unpaid board of health commissioners, appointed by the mayor with City Council approval, had authority stated in the city charter to supervise, control, regulate, and manage the health department. Many cities still have boards of health, and they are required by law in some states; but in most instances their roles have changed and they are advisory or policy-making groups rather than administrative.

The American Public Health Association considers a board of health "essential to the operation of many departments"[3] and suggests that it should have 5 to 11 members interested in health but should not be dominated by a single profession. Although it should not conduct day-to-day operations of the health department, the APHA recommends that it have the power to appoint or recommend the health officer and to adopt policies, rules, and regulations of the health department, as well as to conduct hearings.

If a board of health is representative of the community, and not just health professions, it can guide policies so that they will be acceptable to the public. The members of the board can help to interpret department policies and

actions to the community and can spend more time on health matters and advising the department from community perspectives than is possible for a legislative body.

The effectiveness of the board of health depends on the ability of its members and on their perception of their roles. If they see themselves, or are seen by the health officer, as a means of sheltering the department from the forces influencing other government agencies, they may separate the department from the mainstream of community action. Or if they consider their task to be maintaining the status quo, they may prevent the department from adjusting its programs to meet changing problems. On the other hand, an effective board of health provides the means of bringing the health department into the total complex of government and helps it to move forward in terms of community aspirations in health.

Internal Organization of Health Departments

A small health department, in which the health officer and a staff of 10 to 20 people conduct all activities with, perhaps, some paid help from local physicians and other professionals, has few problems of organization. Most of the professional staff are nurses and sanitarians, and they give generalized services; that is, they direct their efforts toward families and places rather than to specific diseases or environmental conditions. In a larger department, there is a greater degree of specialization. Almost universally the staff nurses give generalized services, so that an infant, a tuberculosis patient, and an elderly diabetic, all in the same family, for example, will not have three nurses calling on them. However, the larger department may have consultant nurses on its staff, specialists in maternal and child health, tuberculosis, or chronic disease or even specifically diabetes, who provide guidance in these areas to staff nurses. This is likely to be the case even if field nursing service is provided by a visiting nurse society. In larger departments, sanitarians are more likely to be specialized, even in their field assignments.

[3] Policy statement, "The Local Health Department—Services and Responsibilities," AMERICAN JOURNAL OF PUBLIC HEALTH, January, 1964, p. 137.

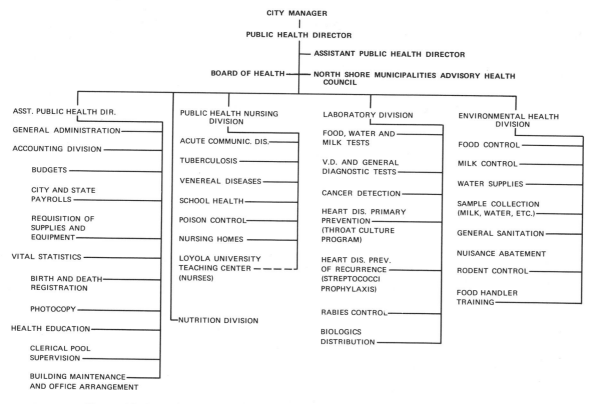

FIGURE 19. *Organization chart—Evanston (Ill.) North Shore Health Department*

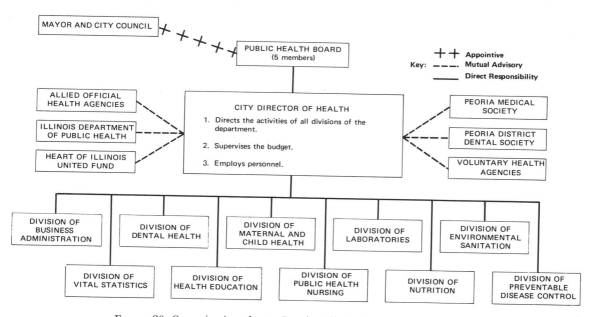

FIGURE 20. *Organization chart—Peoria (Ill.) City Health Department*

Organization of public health services in the larger health departments is almost always according to both processes and program areas, and it is usual for professional units to serve program units.

The Evarston–North Shore Health Department in Illinois, serving a suburban population of over 110,000, had a staff in 1965 of about 30, including two physicians, seven nurses, and three sanitarians. Its major units are organized by processes, such as nursing. In this department's jurisdiction, maternal and child health services and a considerable share of public health nursing service are provided by voluntary agencies, and health services in the public schools by the school districts; assistance in VD control is available from the county health department, and the suburban Cook County Tuberculosis Sanitarium District has major responsibility for tuberculosis control.

Although the Peoria City Health Department, also in Illinois, serves a similar sized population of 125,000, it had some 55 employees in 1964, including five physicians (two part-time), 21 nurses, and eight sanitarians. Unlike Evanston–North Shore, this department is responsible for maternal and child health and for health services in both public and parochial schools, and conducts a dental public health program. It has 10 divisions chiefly organized by processes, but also by program.

The Dade County (Miami) Department of Public Health in Florida provides services for a population of 1.2 million and had nearly 400 employees in 1964. Except for laboratory services, provided by a regional laboratory of the state health department, the Dade County department conducts a full range of public health activities, including those concerned with mental health. It is organized into 13 divisions and operates seven centers distributed throughout the county.

The Los Angeles County Health Department is one of the largest in the country, with a staff in 1965 of more than 1,500, serving a population of nearly 7 million. It is the product of a consolidation with the Los Angeles City Health Department effected in 1965. In contrast to the Dade County department with its 13 divisions all directly responsible to the health officer and his assistant, the Los Angeles County department has three directors subordinate to the health officer and his deputy, with responsibility respectively for seven program and process bureaus, administrative services, and 23 health district operations. In this way, the need for coordination and communication in this large agency is recognized.

The form of organization of a health department may depend on such factors as size of staff, nature and extent of program, and state requirements. The workability of a particular form in a given situation, however, may very well depend on the personalities of the health officer and key members of his staff. For instance, some people would find the direct rela-

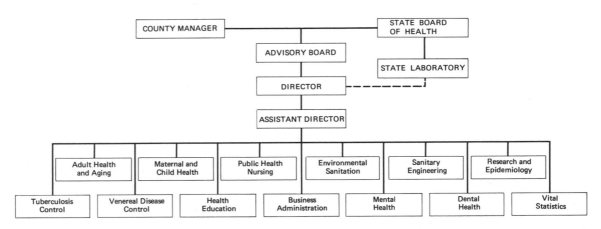

FIGURE 21. *Organization chart—Dade County (Fla.) Health Department*

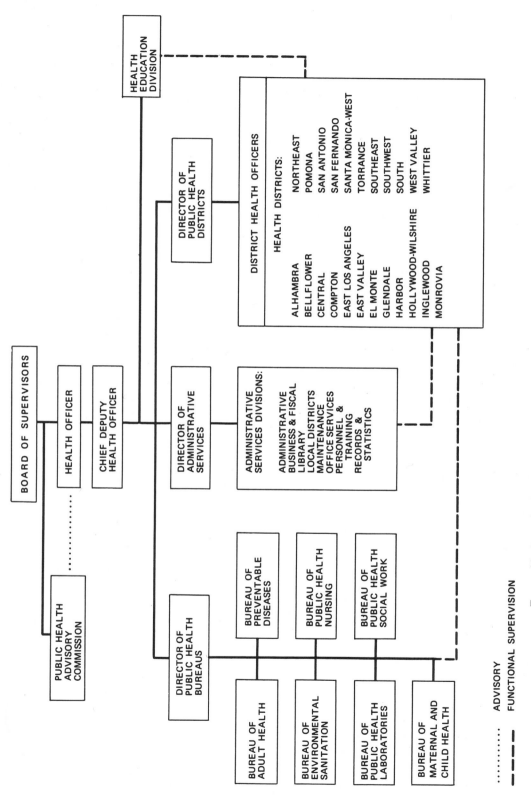

FIGURE 22. *Organization chart—Los Angeles County (Calif.) Health Department*

tionships of the executive with 13 divisions in Dade County exceedingly difficult and would prefer to deal with three directors as in Los Angeles. Others would consider the increased levels of supervision in Los Angeles a disadvantage and prefer direct supervision of divisions by the health officer.

In a department that serves a large, well-populated area, some sort of decentralization of health activities is a necessity. The manner in which it is accomplished may be through centers providing facilities for operations conducted by headquarters staff or actual decentralized organizations of staff—separate branch health departments—receiving technical guidance in program operations and policies from headquarters divisions. The latter form has the advantage of offering opportunities for tailoring total programs to the needs of specific neighborhoods; but as Kaufman's 1959 report on *The New York City Health Centers*[4] indicated, it requires especially talented administration to effect coordination of headquarters programs with district operations. Roles and areas of responsibility for both headquarters and district staff must be clearly defined and channels of communication designated.

The Health Department Staff

To serve its functions, defined by the American Public Health Association as "1. Promotion of personal and community health; 2. Maintenance of a healthful environment; and 3. An aggressive attack on disease and disability,"[5] a health department needs staff with expertise in a number of professional and technical areas, with practical judgment, and with skill in human relationships and community organization. Public health practice requires knowledge of subject matter that continually changes, and it also demands ability to apply knowledge creatively and to adapt it to situations that vary and change.

THE HEALTH OFFICER

To head the enterprise, the health officer should have medical and public health training so that he can diagnose the community's health problems and prescribe treatment for them. (In a small health department, he may have to practice some clinical medicine.) He should be a skilled administrator, able to plan programs and supervise their execution, evaluate results, and adjust program content accordingly. He must have qualities of leadership useful both within the organization and outside with groups and individuals in the community; he must often be able to "sell" public health programs. He should understand the principles of business and financial management in government and in some instances be able to carry this responsibility himself.

Medical education and special training in public health are essential in the health officer's background, and he needs a working knowledge of health agency administration. His personal qualifications should include objectivity, the ability to establish rapport with many kinds of persons and groups, imagination, belief in his chosen field of endeavor, and a high level of intellectual competence.

THE STAFF

In the past it was customary to set forth minimum staffing requirements for health departments providing basic public health services, as follows:

one public health physician for every 50,000 people;
one public health nurse for every 5,000 people if duties are limited to health supervision. If care for the ill is provided, one public health nurse for every 2,500 people;
one sanitary engineer or sanitarian for every 15,000 people;
one clerk for every 15,000 people.[6]

Such ratios, however, must be adjusted to the differences among communities in the public health services provided by voluntary agencies, availability of private care, environmental

[4] Herbert Kaufman ("The Inter-University Case Series," No. 9 [University, Alabama: University of Alabama Press, 1959]).

[5] AMERICAN JOURNAL OF PUBLIC HEALTH, *op. cit.*, p. 135.

[6] John J. Hanlon, PRINCIPLES OF PUBLIC HEALTH ADMINISTRATION (St. Louis, Missouri: The C. V. Mosby Company, 4th ed., 1964), p. 260.

threats to health, and even the amount of time field staff must spend in travel.

The number and kind of staff members needed in any health department must be determined in terms of the budgeted program. Essentially all health departments employ at least one physician plus public health nurses, sanitarians, and clerks. Large departments may also have health educators, statisticians, administrative officers, and other types of workers. The APHA has established qualifications for more than 15 types of public health positions, which are revised from time to time to adapt to changing programs and concepts. Although the APHA lists more exacting qualifications than many communities can require of all staff members, they do provide standards to aim for.

Recruiting and Maintaining Staff

Trained and otherwise qualified health workers are in short supply throughout the country, and health departments must compete for them not only with other health departments but with other health agencies. A number of important factors operate to place a department in a position to compete for staff, not the least of which is salaries.

In recent years, many health departments have increased salaries, but they still tend to lag behind those of peers employed elsewhere. The median annual salary of health officers in municipalities of 50,000 or more was less than half the median annual income of self-employed physicians.[7] The meagerness of the median salary for health officers perhaps overstates the situation in terms of remuneration for professional services, inasmuch as some health officers work in the health department only part time. However, it does reflect the amounts communities are paying for what should be a full-time responsibility. And other professional staff of health departments are also paid less than their full-time colleagues in other employment. In 1965, the median salary of staff nurses employed by boards of education was $6,639, more than $1,000 over the median of $5,603 paid to staff nurses in local health units.[8]

As the data in Table 14 show, salaries of health department staff tend to be higher in larger jurisdictions. However, there is also a considerable difference in median salaries for various geographical regions, as shown in Table 15. Although competition within a given region is important to a health department, in the present health professions shortage it may be necessary for departments to bid for employees outside their own area.

Adequate pay is of crucial importance in staffing the health department, but job satisfaction is also a determining factor. A basic requirement in this regard is employment under a merit system that ensures selection and advancement on the basis of ability, protects employees from arbitrary discharge, and provides equal compensation for equal work. Most health department employees work under merit systems that meet federal merit system standards as a requirement for receipt of federal funds.

Another factor in job satisfaction, perhaps equally important, is a working situation that allows the fullest exercise of professional skill. The department that has broad staff participation in program planning and evaluation, so that all staff members understand and identify with department objectives, provides a more attractive working milieu than one where members have assigned tasks without occasion to relate them to the total program. It goes without saying that the department's program must be of high quality if staff members of high quality are to be attracted. Opportunities to increase and improve professional skill through inservice training, attendance at professional meetings, and sometimes training courses or educational leave are another important asset in job satisfaction. If government policies reduce such opportunities, as they frequently do, the health department has difficulty in recruiting and keeping the mature health professional who recognizes that continuing education is necessary to maintain and increase his competence.

Like other workers, health department staff

[7] Georgie B. Druzina and Earl E. Phillips, "Salary Trends for State and City Health Officers, 1953–1965," American Journal of Public Health, June, 1966, p. 911.

[8] American Nurses' Association, Facts About Nursing (New York: The Association, 1966), p. 139.

Table 14

Median Minimum and Maximum Salaries Reported for Selected Positions in Local Health Departments by Size of Jurisdiction and Type of Position, December 1965[1]

Type of Position	Population					
	Under 250,000		250,000–500,000		500,000 and over	
Health officer	$15,230	$18,512	$17,585	$20,556	$19,554	$22,500
Medical program chief (M.D.)	14,400	16,440	14,340	17,628	15,204	17,500
Director of public health nursing	7,320	8,940	7,726	9,744	8,784	11,026
Public health staff nurse	4,776	6,000	4,800	6,000	5,229	6,347
Graduate nurse	4,368	5,503	4,320	5,520	4,818	5,990
Sanitarian	5,340	6,909	5,244	6,930	6,364	7,728
Health educator	6,303	7,560	6,771	8,448	7,072	8,748
Statistician	6,468	7,764	6,270	7,620	7,134	8,637
Director of administration	7,705	9,420	7,634	9,582	10,674	12,612
Director of laboratories	7,200	9,000	8,664	10,302	9,834	11,232

Source: Salary information for selected health department positions with comparable specifications, submitted to The Association of Management in Public Health and processed by the Division of Community Health Services, Public Health Service, U.S. Department of Health, Education, and Welfare.

[1] Health departments, exclusive of state health districts, with 30 or more full time noninstitutional positions included.

Table 15

Median Maximum Salaries for Selected Positions in Local Health Departments,[1] by Type of Position and Public Health Service Regions,[2] December 1965

Type of Position	Region								
	I	II	III	IV	V	VI	VII	VIII	IX
Health officer	$15,500	$19,680	$20,594	$20,900	$20,000	$20,020	$16,800	$ —	$20,400
Medical program chief (M.D.)	—	16,605	18,146	16,440	17,875	15,225	—	—	17,628
Director of public health nursing	7,945	10,000	10,224	8,544	9,540	9,456	8,916	9,834	10,776
Public health staff nurse	5,569	6,160	6,636	6,000	6,000	6,095	5,616	6,051	6,672
Graduate nurse	5,533	5,700	5,880	5,100	5,553	5,454	5,256	5,874	6,162
Sanitarian	6,511	7,497	7,464	6,300	6,900	6,597	6,240	6,600	7,788
Health educator	—	7,770	8,436	6,900	8,031	7,461	7,320	—	8,904
Statistician	—	7,107	—	—	9,012	—	—	—	8,724
Director of administration	—	12,225	—	8,700	12,000	9,384	—	—	13,512
Director of laboratories	—	15,041	11,232	—	10,452	11,886	9,732	—	10,368

Source: Salary information for selected health department positions with comparable specifications, submitted to The Association of Management in Public Health and processed by the Division of Community Health Services, Public Health Service, U.S. Department of Health, Education, and Welfare.

[1] Health departments, exclusive of state health districts, with 30 or more full time noninstitutional positions included; where fewer than four health departments in a region reported on a given position no salary figure is given.

[2] States included in Public Health Service Regions:
    I. Connecticut, Maine, Massachusetts, New Hampshire, Rhode Island, Vermont (regional office: Boston);
    II. Delaware, New Jersey, New York, Pennsylvania (regional office: New York City);
    III. District of Columbia, Kentucky, Maryland, North Carolina, Virginia, West Virginia, Puerto Rico, Virgin Islands (regional office: Charlottesville);
    IV. Alabama, Florida, Georgia, Mississippi, South Carolina, Tennessee (regional office: Atlanta);
    V. Illinois, Indiana, Michigan, Ohio, Wisconsin (regional office: Chicago);
    VI. Iowa, Kansas, Minnesota, Missouri, Nebraska, North Dakota, South Dakota (regional office: Kansas City);
    VII. Arkansas, Louisiana, New Mexico, Oklahoma, Texas (regional office: Dallas);
    VIII. Colorado, Idaho, Montana, Utah, Wyoming (regional office: Denver);
    IX. Alaska, Arizona, California, Hawaii, Nevada, Oregon, Washington, Guam, American Samoa (regional office: San Francisco).

members value such fringe benefits as paid vacations and sick leave, health and other insurance, and retirement plans. They are as much affected by their physical surroundings as anyone else and appreciate pleasant, light, well-ventilated, appropriately furnished offices. Although health departments are not as commonly located in the basement of the city hall or county courthouse as they once were, many still have unsuitable space for an agreeable working environment. Other things being equal, physical comfort can be a deciding factor in taking or staying in a job.

The success of the health department in reaching its objectives calls for positive personnel management, in which the best possible staff is assembled and its combined potentials are realized to the fullest. Recognizing and accepting the particular nature of individual competences, motivations, and personal orientations, the skillful administrator fits together complementary talents and characteristics in such a way as to enhance work satisfaction and encourage creativity. He must guard against damping the enthusiasm or deflating the confidence of young staff members, but at the same time he must insure productive application of more mature talents. In short, positive personnel management requires acceptance of staff members as individuals rather than simply professionally trained personnel.

STRETCHING THE PROFESSIONAL STAFF

When a professional health function is to be carried out by one person, he must of course be professionally trained. However, if additional staff can be added, it is often as satisfactory if some of them are nonprofessionals. Thus, in many health departments, in addition to administrative and clerical staff, nonprofessional workers contribute to health programs. Their various functions have been discussed in Chapter 4 and will not be repeated here. However, it should be emphasized that imaginative use of technical and nonprofessional staff is an important part of health department management.

20

Community Relations

THE WORK of the health department is technical and requires special professional skill in a number of health sciences. Inasmuch as the work is done with people, supported by them, and carried on in their interest, the department needs proficiency in human relations in addition to technical skill.

Public relations is a composite of relationships, both human and institutional, for all persons involved in local government. It is concerned with opinions, attitudes, information, impressions, context, and images. It is circular, interacting, and composite. It is perceived by the general public in terms of public information—news releases, radio and television programs, press conferences, and the like. It is not so well known or appreciated as a process of interaction in which facets of both program performance and public relations are inextricably involved.[1]

The health department shares in the public relations of the government. That is, attitudes and opinions about the government as a whole apply to the health department, and those about the health department reflect on the government. However, like other departments, it has its particularized sets of relationships that can be characterized as dealing with (1) government, (2) special interests, and (3) its clientele. Because it is an agency of government, it interacts with government officials, other government agencies, and the legislative body. Its special area of competence involves interaction with groups and organizations that share, participate in, or are affected by the goals and operations of the health department. And because

it is a service agency, it interacts with population groups and individuals receiving service.

Thus, the local health department has three major types of public. They are not mutually exclusive; one person may at different times belong to all three. However, they do represent three sets of attitudes, opinions, and perceptions about the health department, and they represent different areas of power within the community that are usually dissimilar and sometimes in actual conflict. The anthroplogist, Goodenough, has said:

To accomplish its mission, an agency must be able to mediate successfully among the several publics in such a way as to get its technical job done in a spirit that does not violate human dignity or trample cherished values. Such mediation obviously calls for great political and social skill.[2]

The Three Publics[3]

Communities in this country are highly differentiated, and the characteristics of their populations cannot be adequately described in general terms.

GOVERNMENT

When the health department is a unit of municipal government directly under supervision of the city executive, concepts of the health

---

[1] Desmond L. Anderson (ed.), MUNICIPAL PUBLIC RELATIONS (Chicago: International City Managers' Association, 1966), Preface.

[2] Ward H. Goodenough, "Agency Structure as a Major Source of Human Problems in the Conduct of Public Health Programs," AMERICAN JOURNAL OF PUBLIC HEALTH, July, 1965, p. 1068.

[3] For a discussion of "The Multitudinous Publics," see Anderson, op. cit., Chapter 5.

officer's role determine the manner in which he participates with the executive and other department heads in managing city affairs, as well as the extent of the advice and support he receives from them. If the health officer sees his role as limited to direction of the department's technical operations, he may not consider that active participation in total policy development for city government is part of his job. On the other hand, the city executive, as well as other department heads, may fail to recognize the public health agency's role in this regard and may expect it to be separate and unconcerned with matters outside its defined program.

Constructive relationships between health departments and related governments require conscious and continual communications, not limited to official reports and budget presentations. Conversation that helps the city executive become familiar with department activities and their goals increases the support he gives them. For instance, discussion in advance of enforcement actions that could produce repercussions makes it easier for the city manager or mayor to back up the health department should the matter come up in the city council or the press. And if the executive holds regular meetings of all his department heads, he provides a setting in which the health officer's technical advice can be applied to community problems and the counsel of others is made available in consideration of health department problems.

Coordination of health functions of various city agencies is furthered through the broadened perspectives of department heads that result as interchange reveals roles, expectations, and attitudes in an atmosphere of common purpose. In some cities, interdepartmental committees concerned with health have been formalized, and regularly scheduled meetings with prepared agenda serve as a continuing forum for cooperation and a sounding board where potential disagreements can be aired and presented to the executive for resolution.

In most county systems of government and in some cities, the health officer is responsible to a council or board of supervisors or commissioners, rather than to a city or county executive. The manner of operation of these bodies differs from place to place, and the health officer must familiarize himself with his own situation. The governmental body's acceptance and support of the health department's program may depend entirely on his ability to present it in terms that make sense to them, although he may have a board of health that could be helpful in this regard. Coordinating efforts with other governmental agencies and exercise of his function as health advisor usually will come about only on his own initiative.

When a county or district health department serves one or more municipalities, the need for established and frequent communication is great. The health department must plan its program to meet the public health needs of all people in its jurisdiction as adequately as it can with available resources. Health problems are not equally distributed throughout an area, and therefore a rationally planned public health program will place greater emphasis in some locations than in others. It is incumbent on the health officer and his staff to explain public health needs in such a way as to assure municipal officials that intensification of services in some areas benefits all.

It is generally accepted that control of communicable disease or of such environmental hazards as mosquitoes or air pollution in one area protects people in surrounding areas. It is less usually recognized that concentrated health services in a slum area may help to relieve frustration and resentment leading to violence that can spill over into other neighborhoods, or that preventing dependency due to disease or injury can in the long run affect tax rates. Furthermore, city executives need to be well informed about the health field to judge whether services received are adequate in terms of those provided in the entire health jurisdiction, and it is to the advantage of county or district health officers to facilitate relationships by helping them to acquire such information. County and district health departments, by reason of serving large jurisdictions, have the potential for providing more and better services than are possible in smaller operations. If that potential is to be realized, there must be objective professional judgments on the part of the health departments, reasonable demands for service by municipalities, and mutual respect and understanding between the two.

Physicians, even those with public health training, are sometimes reluctant to enter into the processes of government beyond their own sphere of direct responsibility. Although it is wise for health officials to avoid partisan political activity, the best interests of community health can be served only when the health department is an active partner in community government.

SPECIAL INTEREST GROUPS

In the normal course of its activities, the health department comes into frequent contact with professional societies, voluntary agencies, business or industrial groups, and the press, all having interests in common with the department but often different points of view. Constructive relationships with these groups are so important that they deserve the particular attention of the health officer and his staff.

Professional Organizations. A large proportion of the health department staff is drawn from the various health professions. Staff members therefore not only have common ground with professional organizations but are often active members of local societies. In many communities there is official cooperation of the department and professional organizations in educational programs and recruitment of young people to the health field.

Inasmuch as many health department programs and functions involve or are concerned in some way with medical care, there is continual need for good working relationships with medical practitioners and with the local medical society representing them. Health officers are frequently able to establish rapport with medical societies through their own active membership, which provides them with opportunities to emphasize areas of agreement and to discuss objectively the points of difference between public health and private practice. The health officer who is not a physician has a distinct disadvantage in this essential aspect of community relations.

Voluntary Health Agencies. In the many voluntary health agencies existing in most communities, the health department has potential allies, whose support it must enlist in the interests of comprehensive community health services. Some of them, notably the visiting nurse societies, provide certain public health services; and when their efforts are coordinated with those of the health department, they extend the coverage and adequacy of health services in the community.

Voluntary agencies concerned with specific diseases or health problems, in carrying out their function of informing the public, may strongly influence public opinion. They also constitute pressure groups, seeking to affect the decisions of legislative bodies and city officials, as well as the health officer. Recognizing the sincerity and validity of the special interests of voluntary agencies, the health department must try for a balance among them that will represent the total public interest[4] and must accomplish it without estranging any group. If a community has a device for comprehensive health planning, it provides an arena in which such a balance can be achieved through deliberations of all concerned. Whether this is the case or not, the health officer's responsibility for community leadership in health requires that he create an atmosphere in which the interests of these groups can be discussed objectively and mutual understanding effected.

Economic Interests. Other special interest groups in the community may be those representing industrial or business interests, such as trade associations or unions. Although the health concerns of these groups must be assumed to be in their own and not necessarily the public interest, the health department, as a governmental agency, has an obligation to consider their point of view. It is important for the health officer to be sensitive to the community's economic interests; and if it is sometimes necessary to oppose such interests to protect community health, health officials must be prepared to provide documentation in support of their opposition.

The Press. Representatives of the press and other news media are especially concerned with obtaining information to interest the public. Press relations have been extensively discussed

[4] *Ibid.,* p. 58.

in both public health and city management texts[5] and will not be treated in detail here. It is important to emphasize, however, that the opportunity provided by news media to disseminate information to the public is so important to health department programs as to justify considerable effort in understanding them and cooperating with them.

The health department must have a clear understanding of the responsibility of the press with regard to government, summarized by MacDonald as follows:

> In part that responsibility of the press is (1) to report, explain, and make understandable to the people their government wherever possible; (2) to protect the general public against shenanigans either by special interest groups or by public officials; (3) to support by explanation and news coverage such officials, programs, and causes as—in the best judgment of the reporter and his editors—are necessary for the general public; and (4) to give the citizen the information he needs to decide if his government is working satisfactorily, on the theory that our type of government is best for the individual.
>
> But in a more basic sense, that responsibility is twofold: (1) to help government officials make a public accounting of their administration and (2) to make certain that government at all levels operates in the public eye.[6]

THE PUBLICS SERVED

Although the health department is concerned with the health of all, it accomplishes its mission in large part through services and enforcement activities directed specifically to certain groups. Health department relationships with all citizens should foster positive attitudes toward the government generally and the department in particular. However, relationships with what have been called target groups[7] often decide the success or failure of programs.

As several preceding chapters have emphasized, values and perceptions about health generally shared by health professionls may be very different from those of persons whom they judge to need health services. Rapport of physicians, nurses, and other professional workers with health department clientele requires knowledge and sometimes acceptance of clients' attitudes and values even when they are counter to professional judgments. Such acceptance helps to bridge the cultural distance that separates professionals from people they seek to serve, and thus enhances communication with them.

When the health department takes action against householders, business men, or industries, to enforce sanitary regulations, it must consider the economic effect of compliance in determining and selecting reasonable courses of enforcement. Serious and definite threats to health must of course be removed at any cost, but in the case of less harmful conditions, the expense of correction can well determine alternative methods of seeking compliances. In enforcement, the health department should first be sure that its requirements are necessary and then be prepared to advise as to the most satisfactory and economical ways of effecting corrections. Needless to say, all enforcement actions must be made impartially. To excuse some violations because compliance would work a hardship is discriminatory and will damage the department's relationships in the community.

Techniques To Foster Good Relationships

The basis for a health department's effective relationships in the community is a rationally planned program. When the planning process has included consideration of the needs and points of view of the various publics, and when the background for selection of courses of action is understood by the staff, interpretation easily becomes part of implementation. The health officer has solid ground for his presentations to colleagues and superiors in government and to the special interest groups with whom he must work. Professional staff can confidently explain health department activities to their peers and approach the department's target populations with awareness of the need for mutual understanding.

---

[5] See for example, John J. Hanlon, PRINCIPLES OF PUBLIC HEALTH ADMINISTRATION (St. Louis: The C. V. Mosby Company, 4th ed., 1964), pp. 326–29; and Anderson, op. cit., Chapters 10 and 11.

[6] James C. MacDonald, PRESS RELATIONS FOR LOCAL OFFICIALS (Ann Arbor: Institute of Public Administration, University of Michigan, 1956), p. 3.

[7] Goodenough, op. cit., p. 1068.

STAFF RESPONSIBILITIES

It is apparent from the foregoing discussion that all members of the staff share responsibility for community relationships. Indeed, it has been said that *"An agency's public relations is a composite of relationships for all persons in the agency."*[8] This is a point for consideration in recruiting both professional and administrative staff. Ease and adaptability in relationships with people are just as important in public health nurses and sanitarians as in telephone clerks and receptionists in clinics. Discussion of attitudes and of response to service has a place in daily supervision as well as in staff conferences and inservice training aimed at improving staff skill.

In addition to setting the tone for all health department public relations, the health officer carries major responsibility for the department's relationships with government and many special interest groups. He has less contact with target groups as a rule, and his awareness of their interests and demands depends on the flow of information he receives from his staff. On the other hand, staff awareness of attitudes of government and special interests often depends on the health officer's interpretations. For a total program that truly considers the points of view of all publics, the health department must have an established means of continual internal communication, through staff meetings, reports, and informal conferences.

To perform particular functions in community relations, a health department may have staff members with special training and skills, serving under the direct supervision of the health officer. One such function is gathering information about attitudes and opinions of the various publics and interpreting this intelligence in terms of department functions. Only the largest health departments have staff members concerned solely with this aspect of public relations. In most departments, various members of the staff take responsibility for it, with contributions from other government agencies and sometimes from special studies made by college or university social scientists.

Another special function is preparation of communication materials, such as leaflets and exhibits, and speeches and reports. Few local health departments employ full-time writers or artists, but some use part-time or contractual services for this purpose.[9]

A third function is working directly with special interest groups and target populations in a variety of ways to enlist and channel interest in health programs and motivate response to them. This is the province of health educators, who are trained specifically for such work. They also develop techniques of presenting information in terms acceptable to the various publics. In many health departments, health educators have responsibility for all three aforementioned special functions. Health educators often provide consultation and staff services to other professionals.

A great many health departments have no staff members in any of the specialties of community relations. In 1964, fewer than 225 of the 1,641 local health departments had health educators on their staffs. A number of others had positions budgeted but vacant.

Assistance in some of the functions is often available from other agencies. All state health departments have health educators on their staffs, and some have sufficient numbers to be able to participate in local activities to a considerable extent. Voluntary health agencies are often able to give health education service in connection with various campaigns. In some cities, public relations officers on the city executive's staff can consult with or assist the departments. Information materials on health subjects are available from many agencies, at low cost or free, and can be adapted for use in local situations. In view of the key importance of its communications and community relations, however, health departments are unwise to depend entirely on others for special expertise in such fields. Plans and budgets should provide for these as well as for professional health skills.

---

[8] Anderson, *op. cit.*, p. 15.

[9] The National Public Relations Council of Health and Welfare Services (257 Park Avenue South, New York, N.Y. 10010) has a number of services for its subscribers, useful to local health agencies—how-to-do-it manuals, loan library, consultation on request, and a bi-weekly publication, CHANNELS.

SPECIAL QUALIFICATIONS

As in other human relationships, perceptiveness and imagination are essential tools in the health department's community relationships. If the health officer observes and understands the pressures and complexities of the city executive's job, he can find a way to communicate his own concerns in terms that will be understood. The public health nurse who sees that a mother's failure to follow recommendations for her child is because they conflict with customs of her culture will find a way to get her point across other than simple repetition. And the clinic receptionist who recognizes the patient's surliness as defense against strangeness will try to make the clinic a less threatening place.

Perceptiveness and imagination about other people is more natural to some people than to others, but ability in both can be fostered and improved. The social sciences provide insight into human behavior. Consideration of the social environment that helps to form personality, recognition of different cultures and subcultures and their attitudes and values, and study of how opinions are formed and decisions made all contribute to skill in relationships. All professional staff of the health department should have some indoctrination in the social sciences.

Some of the important implements of good public relations for all the staff are such everyday virtues as courtesy, patience, and neatness. They are most likely to be habitual when every staff member identifies with the service objectives of the department. Clerks who feel part of a health department serving the public have good reason to be helpful and pleasant on the telephone.

COMMUNICATION SKILLS

Effective relationships often depend on the skillful use of language and other communications techniques. Fluency and vocabulary are not enough. Fitting content and presentation to the audience's interests is equally important, whether the form of communication is a speech, publication, budget presentation, television appearance, or exhibit.

In order to produce the desired effect, communications require special preparation, which always includes organization of the points and ideas to be communicated, consideration of the audience, and selection of the language for the subject matter so it can have the most meaning to the audience. However simple or complex the communication is to be, it requires these steps. The preparation need not always be written, but it requires thought.

Many health professionals, whose training has not especially emphasized the use of language, go through such preparation in the course of their daily work without realizing they are performing the basic processes for effective communication. But the selection of ways to express their ideas may be influenced more by their professional knowledge than by the interests and circumstances of the people with whom they wish to communicate. Technical words or jargon of the health professions, and elaborate detail that confuses rather than clarifies a point for the uninitiated, lose the listener's attention before the presentation is well begun. Training in communication skills not only betters community relationships but increases the effectiveness of professional skill.

In health department publications, tailoring to fit specific audiences is especially important. The annual report of the department, for example, should be made interesting to legislative bodies and other community leaders. Important as it may be to health professionals, a stark listing of health statistics will not be of great interest to even knowledgeable laymen, but a narrative description of the community's health status and of health department activities to improve it can influence or reinforce opinion. Needs and inadequacies, as well as achievements, should be discussed. If they are not, the impression given may be that no improvements are needed or that the health department does not see what is needed. Such an impression will not result in enthusiastic support.

Publications for the target publics also require careful preparation. Some must be worded in simple language to be intelligible to people with little reading ability, or translated to another language so that those whose English is limited are not neglected; extensive illustration may be needed. But the content, as well as the technique of presentation, must be thoughtfully planned. A flyer urging immunization, for instance, might have no effect in a Negro slum, not because the written material is too difficult but because the illustrations show middle-class white children with whom the intended audience cannot identify. Such material, furthermore, would not strengthen the target public's respect for the health department nor its friendliness toward the city government. If a health department uses publications produced by other organizations, as most do, it must be careful to avoid those that would be inappropriate.

Budget Justification

Interpretation of the department's budget proposals is an important communication responsibility of the health officer. Preparation for it begins long before any formal presentation, in discussions with the city executive and other officials providing opportunities to introduce health program needs and objectives and to become informed about other government programs with health implications.

Throughout program planning for the health department, factors in decisionmaking must include the possibility of tying in activities with those of other government agencies, as well as the effect on the department's work of other government operations. For the year a new public housing project will be ready for occupancy, for instance, the health department might see the opportunity to locate a health center there. If the Parks and Recreation Department plans great extension of its swimming pool facilities, the health department must add to the time spent for swimming pool inspection. When such coordination is included in budget submissions, the health department is giving evidence of its concern with the city as a whole. If after consideration the department decides not to include some items, deliberation about them has provided the health officer with reasonable answers to questions about the omissions.

Another important aspect of budget justification is the effect of health department programs on the economy of the city. An increase requested for extended home health services, for example, could be shown to decrease the need for expensive hospital care. Control of air pollution could be supported in terms of its effect on property values. This, too, is evidence of the health department's concern for the total well-being of the city.

When the health officer is called on to defend his budget before a budget committee or the governing council, he can anticipate some questions by familiarizing himself with the particular interests of members of the reviewing group and with the kinds of issues they are identified with. It is a useful exercise in community relationships to go over the budget presentation in an effort to foresee how council members will react to it, and to prepare answers that will satisfy doubts and elicit support.

Consulting the Publics

As evidence that it considers the interests of its various publics, the health department is wise to make occasions for them to express their points of view. The health officer who goes to a meeting of the medical society and announces that a screening program will be conducted almost invites opposition. But if he first calls on a group of physicians, perhaps a committee of the society, to discuss the proposed project, he will not only have the benefit of their opinions but will enlist their support.

In connection with many department activities, especially enforcement actions, that may adversely affect various groups in the community, similar consultation should be sought. Even if the reaction of the consulted group is negative, the opportunity to be informed in advance and to state objections usually moderates opposition. If not, such a meeting can still prevent public controversy or the necessity for public retreat from a position. When the response is positive, the discussion brings about identification with the health department and support for its activities. In either case, these occasions are a means of gaining insight into the points of view of various publics and of enlarging the scope of intelligence about the community. They help the department to make wise decisions and often prevent unwise courses of action.

21

Fiscal Management

IN THE MODERN HEALTH DEPARTMENT, as in other agencies of local government, financial management is closely intertwined with program direction. Financial management began as a means of preventing fraud or other misuse of public monies, and was later developed to promote efficiency and economy. Historically, it included budgeting, accounting, purchasing, treasury management, and auditing. Financial management has now been further refined to become a major tool of program management and overall government decision-making. Whatever help the health officer has from specialists on his own staff or from a central finance department, he must play the leading role himself in the financial management of the department as an obligation of his position.

In approaching the subject of financial management, the health department should begin with the patterns and practices of its parent government. The legal basis for budgeting and accounting procedures and legal stipulations about the use of funds must be understood, as well as the administrative regulations established. It is obviously necessary to know where financial responsibility rests in the structure of government. In most cities, the mayor or city manager has administrative responsibility for budget formulation and administration and for accounting, and the council makes final determinations on the content of the budget, appropriates funds, determines revenues, and sponsors an audit of all municipal financial transactions. However, in many counties and some cities where there is no single executive, the legislative body itself or one of its committees performs the managerial functions. In either situation the health officer should have a clear understanding of the direction and service his department receives in financial adminstration. In the cities with centralized fiscal management, the officer must know the roles of the finance department and its constituent units for budgeting, accounting, and purchasing.

Within the health department itself, staffing for financial management will depend upon its size as well as the degree of centralization of financial functions in the parent government. In the increasing number of local governments with centralized, often automated, accounting systems, even large departments are relieved of much of the accounting work formerly necessary. Centralized purchasing also reduces the amount of departmental staff time required. In a large health department a member of the health officer's staff may have major responsibility in budgeting, although this is a function that can be delegated only in part.

As with the city and county government in general, the health department is concerned with almost every aspect of municipal or local government finance, either directly or indirectly. The health department relies on revenues, including local government appropriations and state and federal grants. Accounting and financial reporting are important legal requirements and also are indispensable for effective control. The health department, to the extent it collects and maintains custody over fees, has important treasury management responsibilities. The health department is also involved in purchasing and storing, property inventory and control, time keeping and payrolls, insurance, and other aspects of finance administration.

One of the most important fiscal responsibilities of the health officer, however, is budgeting, and the bulk of this chapter will be devoted to that subject.

Nature of the Budget

The municipal or county budget, essentially work accomplishments and forecasts expressed in financial terms, is the major control exercised by the city council or county board over the chief administrator and, in turn, over departmental and agency programs. It often is the most important decision made by the local legislative body during the fiscal year and is, for policy purposes, subordinate only to overriding decisions made directly and indirectly by the policies of other governments—local as well as state and federal.

An understanding of the governmental process is mandatory for good budgeting. The chief administrator is responsible for developing and evaluating a great deal of local government policy and for recommending it to the city council (or county board) for approval, modification, or rejection. The city council (or county board), in turn, is responsible for local government policy adopted, no matter where originated and formulated. The health program may of course be administered by a special district government; or a local board of health may have significant quasi-legislative and administrative powers such as those represented by adoption and enforcement of a sanitary code.

Regardless of formal governmental structure, it is the interaction of all elements of the community, public and private, as part of the governmental process that results in policy formulation. It is here that the budget takes its place as the principal means for policy formulation. When conceived this way, budgeting is a process that is dynamic, never-ending, and extremely influential.

In addition to its preeminent legal authority, the municipal (or county) budget can be viewed from several other perspectives.[1]

The budget can be conceived of as a political document in the sense that it is the product of community groups and associations, both private and public. It is the resolution of conflicting claims and competing interests for shares of a fixed amount of resources. The budget in this sense can be seen vividly every year as congressional committees and subcommittees consider departmental requests prior to adoption of the federal budget. The competitive forces in local government are just as real, though often not as visible.

From a "rational" point of view budgeting is a way of allocating available resources among competing uses, balancing relative needs against community goals. Budgetary decisions are increasingly derived from cost-benefit analysis to provide the most efficient economic use of resources. Efficiency, rationality, and optimum return in relation to investment are primary considerations.

A further conception is the budget as a major focus for organizational decision-making. The budgetary process, from its initiation to the final adoption by the legislative body, involves a number of points where decisions must be made by division heads, department heads, budget analysts, the chief administrator, and the city council. Considerations are given to points of conflict, relevant information, sources of information, and strategy and tactics for influencing others.

In presenting the budget the mayor or city manager has an unparalleled opportunity to explain programs and policy considerations to the city council. He can point to the many decisions made in the development of recommendations and to decisions that are still required from the city council.

For the health officer, the budgetary process furnishes his primary opportunity to review and evaluate programs and subprograms on a comparative basis and to work closely with key people in a fundamental review of objectives and the means of obtaining those objectives.

The purpose of these differing perceptions of the budget is not to say that one is better than

---

[1] The following comments are drawn from James Jernberg, "Financial Administration," Chapter 14, in the forthcoming sixth edition of THE TECHNIQUE OF MUNICIPAL ADMINISTRATION (Washington, D.C.: The International City Managers' Association, 1969).

another but, rather, to emphasize the ways in which different people will view the budget. The chief administrator understandably thinks in terms of program planning and control, and many health officers undoubtedly think of budgeting this way also. The economist is likely to give primary emphasis to the rationality of cost-benefit analysis and optimal use of resources.

The Budget Process

The organization for budgetary decision-making can be compared to a circular process from individual workers through sections and units to divisions and department heads, on to the chief administrator, then to the committee of the city council or county board, and finally to the full council or board. Figure 23 shows the circular nature of the budgetary process. Sequential steps in the formal decision-making process are part of the circle, whereas outside or indirect influences are shown in boxes as forces that can impinge on the budgetary process at any stage.

Most health officers are well aware of the fact that the budgetary process is also intergovernmental, more so in health than in most other

local government activities. Committed and hoped-for state and federal grants are an indispensable part of budgetary planning and estimating. The health department is affected, for example, by the school health program when it is under the jurisdiction of the schools, the direct services, if any, provided by the state health department, the proposed location for a new expressway (which, in turn, may determine the location of a proposed public health clinic), and many other plans and decisions made by school districts, counties, sanitation districts, and state and federal government agencies.

The budgetary process also can be viewed as a public-private continuum of services that uses the resources of private practitioners, private health and welfare agencies, and other public and private resources and facilities. This conception of public health has been the primary focus of this book.

The city manager, public health director, and other administrators in local government should not be intimidated by the foregoing relatively complex description of the budgetary process because, in practice, the work can be divided up. The health officer can draw on his professional resources to provide the expertise that is essential for program and budget construction. The city manager can draw on his

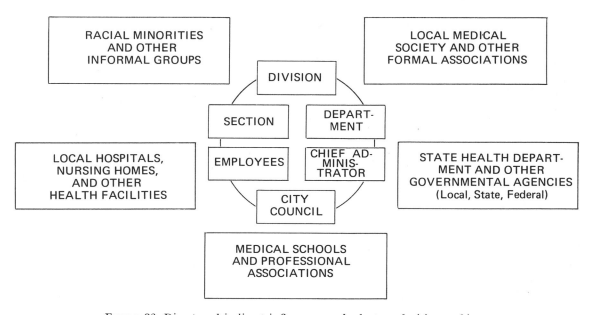

FIGURE 23. *Direct and indirect influences on budgetary decision-making*

generalist background to review the array of departmental proposals with the assistance of administrative assistants, budget analysts, and other staff. The city council can bring its special perspective which often is particularly alert to community needs and desires that sometimes seem "irrational" to the chief administrator and health officer. More attitudes, opinions, and information are fed into the budgetary process with specialization.

FORMULATING THE BUDGET REQUEST

The department's own budget request is developed in the process of program planning described in Chapter 18. Cost estimates are one of the considerations in selecting from among alternate courses of action to accomplish each objective and subobjective and are also a consideration in determining which objectives will be programmed and budgeted in the next year. Evaluation of on-going activities in terms of cost and effectiveness is also an aid to decision-making, and it helps in identifying activities that are not sufficiently productive in reaching objectives to justify their expense.

Program planning and evaluation are year-round activities, not limited to the period of budget preparation. They should be conducted with frequent counsel from the city executive or a budget officer who represents him. In this way, the processes that preceded the final budget request will be understood when it is considered with those of other departments, and the request will be consistent with the policies of the administration.

When the budget estimate for the health department is completed, program by program, it is usually necessary to organize the data in several ways. The program budget itself will be arranged by program objectives, sometimes with a short explanatory text for each, and with a cost estimate usually divided into salaries (with man-years or service units indicated) and other expenses.

Cost estimates must include pro rata shares of cost for services and other operating expenses of the department that will contribute to meeting the objective. For instance, a share of nursing supervision expense should be added to the cost of nursing time or visits made in the interest of

maternal and child health, as should Social Security or other retirement benefit costs unless these are covered in a single appropriation for the city. Costs of training that may be necessary to accomplish an objective should also be included. If activities are on-going, actual expenditures for the last completed fiscal year and a corrected estimate for the current year are itemized in parallel columns.

Requirements differ among governments, but in many cities a form showing detail of expenditures by object classification, such as personal services, contractual services, and supplies, must be compiled for the entire department from the program budget. This form must also show comparative expenditures for other years, data that are provided by the finance department in governments where this service is centralized. It is supplemented by a detailed salary estimate and a detailed estimate of other expenses.

In some budget systems, funds for new or expanded activities or for special, nonrecurring activities are requested on separate forms to highlight new and expanded program proposals and to simplify the review of budget by the city executive and the legislative body. These items are often submitted as separate budget requests, in contrast to "basic" budgets for continuing operations. Requests for capital outlays are usually handled through special procedures and a completely separate capital budget.

When the health department's budget request is completed, it should reflect the health officer's best professional estimate of the next year's expenditures for department programs. It will represent his selection from among various possible programs and activities, made on the basis of their relative importance to the public health, their effectiveness, and their cost. If the rapport between the city executive and the health officer is effective, the programs for which financing is requested will be in accord with administration policies and positions; the request will not be inflated on the assumption that allowances are always reduced.

ROLE OF DIVISION AND SECTION HEADS

In developing program, manpower, and expenditure estimates, the health officer in the smaller jurisdiction, where the department consists of perhaps a dozen employees, will probably do most of the budget work himself on the basis of informal consultations with his employees, with a budget analyst in the city finance or county department, and with the mayor or city manager. In larger health departments, the health officer should provide for meaningful involvement of division and section heads within the department, not just for such pleasing generalities as staff morale and group interaction, but for drawing on the talents, ideas, and resources of his people.

Division and section heads responsible for programs and specific areas within programs should be held responsible for preparing budget estimates and correlative justifications. These employees are often the best prepared to recommend improvements or modifications in the work they are responsible for. The more employees participate the more they have at stake in the overall effectiveness of their programs. Participation encourages employees to realize that all management levels share in making budget decisions.

In a large health department this kind of decentralization can significantly increase the number of persons who help prepare budget estimates and justifications. Consequently, training programs might be necessary to help these people understand not only the procedures for developing estimates but also how their work fits into the budgetary process. They need to know, for example, that work programs precede realistic estimates of cost, that new activities mesh with other activities of the department, and in turn, with activities of other city departments. In the larger cities and counties, the health officer should make every effort to obtain help from the finance department or the budget agency to supplement his own efforts.

When division and section heads have gained sufficient understanding of the budgetary process, they can be asked to provide detailed information on activities under their supervision, covering such items as the following:

1. A statement of objectives in terms of end results.

2. What would happen if the activity were increased, decreased, or eliminated.

3. Outside factors that are beyond the control of the health department (wage agreements for hospital maintenance personnel, for example).

4. Time factors, including continuous or periodic operation, peak loads, and work schedules.

5. Manpower needs, by man year and job classification.

6. Clinics and other facilities required.

7. Equipment and major tools required.

8. Samples of printed forms and periodic reports concerning the activity.

9. Authoritative cost data to the extent that such data can be obtained from accounting and other records.

10. Clientele served by the activity.

The amount and kinds of work, as measured by programs, activities, and tasks, are the basis for building budget estimates. (The effect on improvement of health status is an ideal, though often unrealizable, measurement of program effectiveness.) A number of methods are used to provide work load analysis, including general and cost accounting reports, budgets for prior years as compared with actual expenditures, work units accomplished, known demographic factors such as population influx, and health department personnel as measured by man-hours. Perhaps the simplest and most useful measure for most health departments is man-hours. One reason is that payroll expenditures account for such a large porportion of the typical health department budget. Another reason is that man-hours are easily and accurately recorded by work activity. A third reason is that man-hour data can, if desired, be brought into the accounting system.

Essentially the man-hour approach to estimating requirements based on work load differs from the cost accounting approach only in that personnel requirements rather than all costs factors are computed on this basis. One of the major advantages of the man-hour basis is that an extensive accounting installation is not required and attention is focused only on the major cost element, which can be recorded at much less expense than the recording of all cost elements.[2]

2 International City Managers' Association, MUNICIPAL FINANCE ADMINISTRATION (Washington, D.C.: The Association, 6th ed., 1962), pp. 151–52.

EXECUTIVE AND LEGISLATIVE ACTION

The function of the city executive and the legislative body in their review and modification of departmental budgets should be understood by the health officer. Although the following quotation refers to national government decision-making, its point applies to local government decisions as well.

The task of making the necessary compromises among various objectives is the function of planning, programming, and budgeting. To make those compromises it is necessary that the various government activities be expressed in terms of a common denominator, and the only common denominator is money. It is difficult to compare the relative merits of an additional military division and an additional university. It is often more feasible to compare the relative merits of spending an additional billion dollars in one direction or the other. But to make that comparison it is necessary to know how much an additional billion dollars will add to military strength and how much to university education. While defense and education cannot be measured in simple quantitative terms, quantitative information can throw light on the consequences of spending money in various directions.[3]

The health officer who has this concept of government decision-making can put his budget request in terms that will emphasize the effect of programs, and can be prepared for executive and legislative discussions of the consequences of money spent for health.

When the city's budget has been approved by the council (or the county's by the county board) and an appropriation ordinance passed, the funds appropriated must be spent for the purposes and activities specified. In some cases, the appropriations are made in detail according to the object classifications contained in the budget document, and funds cannot be transferred. However, they often provide a lump sum to each municipal department, and transfers can be made between objects of expenditure within each appropriation by the city executive or with his authorization. Such flexibility allows for changes in programs to meet emergencies and a variation in methods of conducting programs without delay when this is

advantageous. When the health department faces an emergency, and action cannot be financed through adjustment of its appropriation, it may be necessary for the executive to go back to the city council or county board for authority to transfer funds from other appropriations. In some cities, contingent funds are appropriated, from which the executive can make allotments to meet emergencies.

If less money is appropriated than was requested, the health officer must adjust his program so that it can be financed within the appropriation. If he is consulted when reductions are made in the budget, not only is he able to make suitable alterations, but his advice is available in determining where reductions can be made with least damage to the overall program of the department.

FUNDS FROM OTHER SOURCES

Some health departments collect fees for certain services. If the health officer is the local registrar for birth and death certificates, for instance, he will receive fees for providing copies. When the health department renders a direct service, such as home nursing or home care, it may charge for services to those who can afford it.

Many health departments collect fees for the issuance of licenses or permits that serve as a means of regulation, with all or part of the cost of regulatory activity charged to those regulated. However, such license or permit fees have often been used as a means of raising additional revenue. They then have no relationship to the cost of inspective or regulatory actions, and thus they become a series of nuisance taxes. A department and a municipality should regularly examine the licensing and permit structure and fee scale, if for no other reason than to weed out charter and ordinance anachronisms.

License and permit fees should not be collected by the person responsible for inspecting the facility, but should be paid directly to the city or county treasury through some other mechanism.

In any such operation, ordinances should either set fees or stipulate that they will be determined by the city administration on the basis of cost. In either case, the procedure recom-

---

[3] Arthur Smithies, "Conceptual Framework for the Program Budget," in David Novick, ed., PROGRAM BUDGETING (Washington: Government Printing Office, 1965), p. 3.

mended generally is to deposit the amounts collected in the general fund of the government. If this is not done, the amounts collected from these sources should be shown in the health department's budget estimate as funds available.

Another important source of financial support for health department programs is grants from state or federal governments or from foundations or voluntary agencies. Such grants are usually made for specific purposes, and it is important that these fit into overall departmental objectives. Programs supported from grant funds should be included in the budget statement, and the amount of the grant indicated as available income. It is usually necessary for the health department to have authorization from the governing body to accept grants.

Although the health department's budget request is for local government funds, it can neither indicate to the executive and council the needs and objectives of the health department nor serve as a tool of department administration if it does not show the complete program under support from all sources. Furthermore, if program planning and budgeting are too strongly influenced by the availability of special-purpose funds from outside sources, rational assignment of program priorities is all but impossible. The 1966 amendments to the Public Health Service Act, described in Chapter 3, by changing the structure of federal public health grants to the states, will contribute to planning and budgeting in terms of local needs rather than categories of available assistance.

Accounting

An accounting system to be used by a particular health department is usually determined by the laws or regulations of its parent government. In cities which have centralized fiscal accounting, the health department itself need not carry out many of the procedures required by the central government.

If fiscal management is to be a working tool of health department administration, however, accounting must be designed accordingly. When the central system does not produce the information needed for planning, conducting, and reporting health programs, the department must devise a modified or separate system for internal management.

In the foregoing discussion of constructing a budget based on program planning, it was apparent that identification of the costs of the activities undertaken to accomplish each objective is essential. In public health work, it is not feasible to organize staff entirely around individual objectives. Thus an accounting system related to organizational structure will not produce the cost data needed for planning and evaluating objective-directed programs.

The recommended accounting system is one that records and reports expenditures by object in terms of stated objectives. For instance, the health department might have an objective in communicable disease control, and it might have an organizational unit assigned full time to this program; but the objectives would also require efforts of the staff of other divisions—nursing, laboratory, and records and statistics, perhaps. The cost of this program, therefore, would be considerably more than the cost of the communicable disease control unit.

This type of accounting requires administrative records, such as daily time reports, that will assign expenses to appropriate program objectives. In its *Guide to Public Health Program Accounting*, however, the Committee on Program Budgeting and Accounting of the Association of Business Management in Public Health warned that "If carried to its ultimate conclusion, the dividing of costs into program segments could lead to a degree of refinement bordering on the absurd."[4] Experienced judgment is required to determine how cost allocations should be handled to provide adequate information without too much expenditure of staff time in record-keeping and analysis. Because health departments are increasingly expected to provide nursing service for which they are reimbursed, their need to determine costs has been urgent. A publication by Marion Ferguson, *How To Determine Nursing Expenditures in Small Health Agencies,* is addressed to the problem, and contains guidance that can be

---

[4] (Atlanta: The Association, 1958), p. 23.

adapted to other health department activities as well as to nursing.[5]

SINGLE FUND ACCOUNTING

As indicated previously, financial administration that separates elements of program according to sources of supporting funds is not in the interest of overall program effectiveness, and further complicates the accounting system. Single fund accounting, in which all expenditures are charged to a single account and adjustments made periodically to charge sources of income, has been found to be feasible for health departments. Funds from grants and other outside sources usually come with certain stipulations about both activities and types of expenditures to be supported. Program accounting can provide information about both points that enables adjustments so that expenditures can be charged to grants from which they can be paid for.

[5] PHS Publication No. 902 (Washington: Government Printing Office, 1966).

Bibliographic Epilogue

Concern about health on the part of the American public is continually growing. It is enthusiastic about scientific research and believes in its capacities to find new ways to improve man's lot. It is increasingly impatient, however, with the lag between discovery and application for the general benefit. The demand for improvement in the extent to which people's health is served by our vast and accumulating knowledge reflects this impatience. The public is aware of the costs involved, is willing to pay them, but at the same time insists on getting its money's worth.

People in communities throughout the country are asking and considering basic questions. What do we mean by the "health" we demand? What will we settle for? What will it cost—in money and effort? How can we get what we really want without giving up too much? How much must we give up, as individuals and communities? What frills can we cut out? How can we tell that they are indeed just polish and not the oil that makes the machinery run?

In response to the interests and demands of the people, governments at every level are taking action. At the federal level alone, more than 35 laws in health and related fields were enacted in 1965 and 1966. In recognition of the people's desire to seek rational answers to their questions about health services, the Congress passed the Comprehensive Health Planning and Public Health Services Amendments of 1966 (Public Law 89–749), providing federal support for state and local planning for health.

Official agencies, private and voluntary organizations, the health professions, and society itself is reassessing needs, approaches, and roles to bettering individual and community health. At such a time, guiding the reader to sources of timely and accurate information presents problems. This book represents some of the inaccuracy of generalization. Its descriptions of the way things are undoubtedly understate both the best and the worst at the time they were written and probably do not apply broadly in any particular place. To find out the situation in any one community, the reader must ask questions in that community. If this book helps him to formulate his questions, it will serve its purpose.

The reader who would pursue general or specific points is referred to the state health department and other governmental and voluntary agencies concerned with health in his state. At the national level, he may wish to ask for information from the Public Health Service (Public Inquiries) of the U.S. Department of Health, Education, and Welfare. The American Public Health Association and other professional organizations are also useful sources of information for specific inquiries.

Throughout the book, citations have been made to sources of detailed information on the various subjects discussed. Those who wish to pursue some subjects further may wish to look to these technical sources, as well as to the journals and nonperiodic manuals, guides, and program recommendations published by the many national and state organizations mentioned throughout the text.

For current information and discussion about general issues and new developments in health fields, the following periodicals will be useful:

American Journal of Public Health. Monthly. Published by the American Public Health Association.

Journal of the American Medical Association. Weekly.

Health Services Research. Quarterly. Published by the Hospital Research and Educational Trust.

Hospitals. Monthly. Published by the American Hospital Association. The August Guide Issue contains a directory of hospitals as well as data and analyses.

Medical Care. Six times a year. Sponsored by the Medical Care Section of the American Public Health Association. Published by J. B. Lippincott Company.

Medical Care Review. Monthly. Published by University of Michigan.

Trans-action. Ten times a year. Published by Washington University.

Periodical publications of the U.S. Department of Health, Education, and Welfare:

Children. Six times a year. Published by the Children's Bureau.

Health, Education, and Welfare Trends. Annually.

Public Health Reports. Monthly. Published by the Public Health Service.

Social Security Bulletin. Monthly. Published by the Social Security Administration.

Welfare in Review. Ten times a year. Published by the Social and Rehabilitation Service.